NATURAL SCIENCE
IN GERMAN ROMANTICISM

———

NUMBER ELEVEN OF THE
COLUMBIA UNIVERSITY GERMANIC STUDIES
EDITED BY ROBERT HERNDON FIFE

NEW SERIES

NATURAL SCIENCE
IN
GERMAN ROMANTICISM

BY

ALEXANDER GODE–VON AESCH

IN LITTERIS
LIBERTAS
1754·1893

NEW YORK: MORNINGSIDE HEIGHTS
COLUMBIA UNIVERSITY PRESS
1941

IN MEMORY OF MY MOTHER

TO MY WIFE

AND BOTH MY DAUGHTERS

UND ES IST DAS EWIG EINE,
DAS SICH VIELFACH OFFENBART.
GOETHE

PREFACE

THE PRESENT STUDY evolved from thoughts and materials gathered in the course of many years. Its earliest inception cannot be traced to a definite event, and while I am fully aware of the many obligations which determined its slow growth, it is impossible now to give a clear account of their importance. I must be content with a summary expression of my indebtedness to friends and former teachers.

In its later stages, however, the study benefited substantially from the helpful interest with which it met on all sides. Most of the preliminary research was done at the libraries of Columbia University and the University of Chicago, at the Preußische Staatsbibliothek and the Stadtbibliothek in Bremen. The unfailing courtesy and expert advice of members of the staffs of these libraries, given at times under trying circumstances, has been of considerable help.

The earliest drafts of the manuscript were read by several friends. I wish to thank all of them for their constructive criticism, but I must make particular mention of Dr. Thijs Jolles of the University of Chicago and of Dr. Hans Speier of the New School for Social Research in New York City. The benefit which my study and which I myself derived from discussions with these scholars was very significant.

The publication of this book was made possible by the liberality of the Henry Janssen Foundation of Reading, Pa. A grant from this organization was accepted in sincere gratitude and full awareness of the great honor it represents.

Finally I should try to state how deeply I feel indebted to Professor Fife of Columbia University for his interest in the progress of my investigations, for his scholarly advice and for his practical help. I can only say that this book would not have been completed if Professor Fife had not befriended it and if he had not been a never failing source of encouragement for its author.

A.G.-v.A.

CONTENTS

sufficiency of purely mechanistic conceptions—Insufficiency of
all views in which God remains an extramundane power—
Wieland's *Natur der Dinge* as representing an intermediate
stage between deistic and entheistic conceptions—Analysis of
Wieland's poem—Wieland's self-criticism and Herder's criterion
of Lucretian poetry—The problems suggested by Wieland's
poem as an outline of the major problems of the age of classic-
romantic idealism.

Romantic awareness of the gap between man and beast—The
post-Renaissance disintegration of the conception of man as the
Lord of Creation—Man's rehabilitation on the basis of his
complete animalization—The anatomical identity of man and
beast—Animal souls—Georg Friedrich Meier's evolutionism—
Ontogenetic and phylogenetic evolution—Bonnet's ideas on
palingenetic perfectibility—Man a *primus inter pares* in the
animal realm—Materialization of the soul—Eighteenth-century
spiritualism—Hardenberg's spiritualization of the senses—
Later materialistic spiritualism—The world of spirits and the
world of spectres.

Eighteenth-century evolutionism and the principle of descent—
The problem of time in evolutionistic thought—Temporal
versus spatial thinking—Romantic biocentrism as an heir to
the temporal thought of Greece—Life and time—The transformation of time into eternity—The temporal dimension and
the conception that stages develop from each other—Capacity
for temporal thought, a criterion of the rank in the order of
things—Romantic evolutionism: only that can become which
is—Herder's conception of history and August Wilhelm
Schlegel's conception of the origin of language.

The idea that man anticipates God—This idea as the climax
of a wave of epistemological optimism—The motif of the veil
of the goddess at Sais—The idea that the universe must be

understood on the basis of the human soul—The motif of
gnothi seauton—"Everything is so familiar," a literary "mannerism" of Hardenberg's—Romantic anthropocentrism and
Herder—Romantic anthropocentrism as the basis of all bio-
genetic thought—Romantic formulations of the basic law of
biogenetics.

"Romanticism" an attempt to conquer infinity—The emotional
significance of the relation of macro- and microcosm when the
former is held to be infinite—The idea of a plurality of worlds—
Sensual experience of infinity—The literary motif of the starry
heavens.

The post-Renaissance spread of the idea of infinity—The
romantic paradox of a finite representation of the infinite—
Phenomenal reality of the romantic idea of infinity—Robinet
and the idea of infinite continuity in phenomenal nature—
Robinet and Bonnet—The prototype in Robinet and Goethe—
Organic nature as a representation of infinity—The importance
of the organic idea illustrated by an analysis of Friedrich
Schlegel's conception of romanticism—*Athenäums-Fragment*
116—Related ideas of Hardenberg—Concluding excursus on
the opposing idea of a universal mechanism.

Mind and matter as variations of one electric protophenomenon—Mesmer a forerunner of Mesmerism—Mesmer's magnetic fluid and the Prussian Commission on Animal Magnetism
of 1816—Animal magnetism conceived as the living potency of
one universal essence—Discussions about superiority or inferiority of the magnetic powers in comparison with those
dominating man's normal consciousness—Troxler, Hufeland,
Carus—The romantic longing for a dissolution of individual
consciousness in the universal unconscious—This dissolution as
a conscious process—Man's redeeming influence on nature—
Hardenberg's hierarchy of messianic mediation—Hemsterhuis'
organe moral as an organ of loving cognition—Common sense,
Gemeingefühl, Vernunft, All-Sinn, sense of universal cognition

as variants of the *organe moral*—Somnambulism and universal cognition—Hardenberg's *creatio rationalis*—Hardenberg's biocentrism.

Reichenbach's *Od* a universal fluid responsible for universal animation—The assumption of a material agent of vitality is not romantic—The eighteenth-century background of the discussion of a special vital force—Brunonianism—Galvanism—Alexander von Humboldt's conception of a superimposed vital force—Herder's conception of organic laws as higher variations of inorganic laws—Humboldt's later views—Vital force and formative urge—The problem of a material medium for the manifestation of a vital force—Reil's *Lebenskraft*—Reil's homogeneous hierarchy from crystal to man.

Summary of previous references to the romantic conception of universal order—The emotional importance of the experience of this order—Carus and Kleist—Carus as the final clarifier of the romantic world view—Review of the series Oken, Steffens, Schelling, Reil, Herder, Wieland—Carus' hierarchy of organic life as outlined in his *Comparative Psychology*—Carus and Goethe—Carus a classical romanticist—Carus' biocentrism a system of philosophical physiognomics.

The misconception of physiognomic parallels—Symbolism and expressionism—Hardenberg's magic idealism an attempt to "speak nature"—The symbolic significance of individual form—Lavater's system of allegorical physiognomics contrasted with Herder's allusions to a possible system of symbolic physiognomics—Carus' symbolistic views anticipated by Aemilius Huschke—Huschke and the idea of organic *consensus*—Excursus on the importance of this idea for certain types of poetic imagery—Huschke's physiognomics—Huschke's physiognomics as an expression of romantic symbolism—Universal physiognomics and the idea of a new mythology of nature.

Didactic poetry of Lucretian ambitions in the later Eighteenth

CONTENTS xiii

Century—Chénier's *Hermès* as an instance of metaphoric representation—The universal principle of love conceived as more fruitful than metaphoric totalism—The mythological conception of the earth as an animal—The concept of infinity and its importance for mythical personifications of nature—Love as the world soul—Hölderlin's ether myth—The impossibility of a "discursive" mythology in an infinite world—Infinity represented in an infinite series of organic symbols: the infinite development of romantic poetry—Goethe's and Schelling's plan of a universal poem—The later history of the problem of a universal poem—Hardenberg—Romantic fragments, nature's fragments—Each fragment tends to represent the infinite whole.

NATURAL SCIENCE
IN
GERMAN ROMANTICISM

I

INTRODUCTION: GENERAL PRINCIPLES

GOETHE'S DOCTRINE of metamorphosis attained its greatest clarity as an hypothesis of botany. Its importance, however, is not thus limited. It is of generally biotic significance and represents the key to all of Goethe's thought. An understanding of the meta-morphic idea as a principle of natural science is the prerequisite which enables us to conceive of Goethe as a living totality with manifestations in a multiplicity of domains.[1] "Goethe teaches metamorphosis," said Fritz Cassirer;[2] and if there is a golden road leading into Goethe's world of thought, it is pointed out by this remark. The essence of Goethe's significance for us can be summarized best in a concept which must be interpreted primarily as a concept of the natural sciences. Goethe himself expressed the opinion that the character of nations and ages is often represented by outstanding individuals, just as the traits and peculiarities of an entire family are at times concentrated in one scion of a late generation.[3] It is in this sense that Goethe spoke of the century of Winckelmann,[4] and that we today have become accustomed to speak of the age of Goethe.[5] We do so because we conceive of him as the summary and fullest representative of his entire era. This means by implication that a basic assertion found to be valid with respect to the individual Goethe cannot be entirely devoid of meaning when applied to the age to which he gave his name. If it is true that Goethe's scientific work can supply the key to all

[1] Cf., e.g., Ewald Augustus Boucke, [Introduction to] *Goethes Werke,* kleine Ausgabe (Leipzig: Bibliographisches Institut, n.d.), I, 162: "Goethe wandte der Ballade besondere Aufmerksamkeit zu, weil sie ihm nach Analogie seiner morpholo-gischen Anschauungen gleichsam als die Urpflanze im Garten der Dichtung erschien."

[2] Fritz Cassirer, *Beethoven und die Gestalt* (Stuttgart, Berlin, Leipzig, 1925), p. IX.

[3] Cf. Goethe, [Notes to] "Rameau's Neffe," *Sämmtliche Werke* (Stuttgart and Augsburg: Cotta, 1858), XXIX, 363.

[4] Goethe, "Winckelmann und sein Jahrhundert," *Werke,* herausgegeben im Auftrage der Großherzogin Sophie von Sachsen (Weimar: Böhlau, 1887-1919), XLVI, 1-101.

[5] Especially since the publication of Hermann August Korff, *Geist der Goethezeit,* 2 vols., Leipzig: J. J. Weber, 1923 and 1930.

of his thought, then it follows that the problems of his age can be profitably approached from the standpoint of the natural sciences. This is briefly the task of the present essay.

The age of Goethe, which covers the periods traditionally called Storm-and-Stress, Classicism, and Romanticism, has been characterized by reference to its achievement of an "organic-religious synthesis of cosmic scope."[6] It may be viewed as a dramatic development in which the Storm-and-Stress functions as protasis while the age of classic-romantic idealism represents the dramatic conflict and its solution. However, a fully conscious understanding of an "organic-religious synthesis" as the major task of the entire period seems to have been attained with full clarity only by the poets and thinkers of the generation reaching creative maturity at the end of the Eighteenth Century. This is the reason why the following investigation of ideas of science in literature will concentrate its attention on the early Romanticists. It will concentrate on this group of writers, but it will not be limited to a definite era. It will include authors from an extensive period preceding and following the years commonly designated as the age of Early Romanticism. This independence of chronological limitations is dictated by the peculiar character of the concept of romanticism.

The present study is neither concerned with formulating a new definition of Romanticism nor bound by any of the old ones. It bases on the conviction that conceptual clarity is not necessarily logical, that it may also be psychological. This holds true for all the concepts which have been called "synchytic" concepts[7] because they are determined by the coincidence of various associations from a variety of logical planes. Romanticism is such a concept. Its associations in one single logical plane may well be covered by a rational description, but this results in a working agreement of only limited usefulness and not at all in a generally acceptable definition. The number of such agreements is obviously unlimited. They represent a welter of contradictory statements,

[6] Walther Linden, *Aufgaben einer nationalen Literaturwissenschaft* (Munich 1935), p. 54.
[7] For a discussion of synchytic concepts, cf. Karl Bühler, *Sprachtheorie* (Jena, 1934), pp. 221ff., 356f., 361, and 365. Bühler refers to J. von Kries, *Logik*, 1916.

none of which, however, can prove that its opposite must be wrong. Romanticism is "a chaos from which a new certainty . . . must necessarily develop."[8] "Romanticism is basically nothing but the ever recurring attempt to fulfill in poetry the great task of Christianity to mediate between the eternal and the secular."[9] Romanticism is "the love of change for its own sake."[10] "That many-sided thing called Romanticism may not inaccurately be described as a conviction that the world is an *englischer Garten* on a grand scale."[11] "The zest of Romanticism consists in taking what you know is an independent and ancient world as if it were material for your private emotions."[12] Romanticism is all of this and considerably more; and yet, it cannot be identified with the sum total of all the partial definitions of its individual aspects. It is the configurational synchysis of all its constituents, which cannot be stabilized in rational finality because each one remains exposed to the transforming influence of all the others. In other words, romanticism is an evolving concept which defies static definition.

The idea that romanticism is a living process rather than a static achievement has its origin with the Romanticists themselves. "Life," said Hardenberg,[13] "is like colors, sounds, force, etc., and the romanticist studies life as the painter, musician, mechanic studies color, sound, or force. The careful study of life makes the romanticist." Mme. de Staël summarized the ideas which she had learned in the Schlegel school by defining romantic literature as "rooted in native tradition," in contrast to classicism with its "dependence on classical antiquity . . . Romantic literature," she continued,[14] "is the only literature still susceptible of being perfected, for, having its roots in our own soil, it is the only

[8] Ludwig Tieck to Friedrich Schlegel, March, 1801. Cf. Willi August Koch, *Briefe deutscher Romantiker* (Leipzig: Dieterich, 1938), p. 149.

[9] Joseph von Eichendorff, *Geschichte der poetischen Literatur Deutschlands,* Paderborn, 1861.

[10] Agnes Addison, *Romanticism and the Gothic Revival* (Philadelphia, 1938), p. 5.

[11] Arthur O. Lovejoy, *The Great Chain of Being* (Cambridge, Mass., 1936), p. 16.

[12] George Santayana, *Three Philosophical Poets* (Cambridge, Mass., 1910), pp. 144 and 199.

[13] *Novalis Schriften,* edited by Paul Kluckhohn (Leipzig: Bibliographisches Institut, n.d.), III, 263.

[14] Mme. de Staël, *de l'Allemagne* (Paris, 1818⁵), I, 266. Cf. p. 151, n. 67.

one that can grow and come to life again." Insistence on the evolutionary character of romanticism seems to be also the only aspect which all the modern investigations of it have in common. With an amazing sensitivity for subterranean continuities, Nadler finds in German Romanticism the culmination of East Elbian colonization. Germanization of the soil and its people preceded, and Romanticism appears then as the final Germanization of soul and thought. If Classicism, with Nadler, is the highest flowering of the culture of the older tribes, i.e., a final maturity of the West Roman spirit in German blood, then Romanticism might be defined as the classicism of the German East, i.e., a final maturity of the Western spirit in East Elbian blood.[15] A less impressive variation of Nadler's methods leads Werner Deubel to the conclusion that Romanticism is the first modern victory of those spiritual forces whose continuity can be traced from their manifestation in Heraclitus and the pre-Socratic thinkers in general through many centuries of struggle on the part of the racial heritage of the Teutons against the Judaic-Christian or Graeco-Judaic invasion led by Socrates, Plato, Paul, and finally Kant, the antiromanticist *par excellence*.[16] Josef Körner identifies Romanticism as the

highest peak and decisive pivot in that development of centuries from the breakdown of medieval civilization through humanism and reformation to its revival and deification, to an extreme renascence of antiquity followed immediately by an equally extreme and radical rejection.[17]

The conception of Romanticism as a cultural process of coming of age is significant in several respects. First of all it determines our attitude toward the productions of the romantic spirit. What Mme. de Staël said about all German literature is particularly true of German Romanticism and perhaps of Romanticism in

[15] Josef Nadler, *Die Berliner Romantik 1800-1814,* Berlin, 1921. These thoughts were used as guiding principles for a vaster construction in Nadler's *Literaturgeschichte der deutschen Stämme und Landschaften,* 4 vols., Regensburg, 1923ff.[2], revised in a third edition as *Literaturgeschichte des Deutschen Volkes,* Berlin, 1938ff.

[16] Werner Deubel, "Gräkogermanisch-Gräkojudaisch," *Völkische Kultur,* October, 1934.

[17] Josef Körner, "Krisenjahre der Frühromantik," *Forschungen und Fortschritte,* XII (1936), 406f.

general:[18] "One should seek in it energies to further the formation of one's own self rather than finished works which might be transported elsewhere." Indeed, the modern interest in the age of Romanticism is not an objective interest at all. The great romantic works look insignificant when we detach them from the environment, where they appear as manifestations of cultural trends rather than as values in themselves. Furthermore, the interest in these trends can be inspired only by subjective participation. It is a prejudiced interest and depends on the possibility of viewing the problems of romantic history consciously or unconsciously as problems of contemporary life.[19] These assertions find support in the fact that the modern scholarly interest in Romanticism is not only contemporaneous with a neoromantic movement in literature but also that it is an interest in the romantic process[20] rather than in romantic achievements.

It is obvious that the problems of all the historical sciences and more specifically, all the problems of the historical science of literature can be studied genetically. It seems, however, that the genetic preoccupation in modern historiography was inspired by the study of romantic problems. A convenient slogan labels romantic thought as "biocentrically oriented" and contrasts it with the "logocentrism" of traditional epistemology.[21] This implies

[18] Mme. de Staël, de l'Allemagne, II, 315.

[19] The remarkable affinity between the present age and that of Romanticism is generally recognized. Cf. Julius Petersen, Die Wesensbestimmung der deutschen Romantik (Leipzig, 1926), and, especially, E. Aurich, Historische Zeitschrift, CLIII, 304: "Die ganze Romantik ist eine ungeheure Tat, ohne die wir nicht wären. Sie ist der Aufbruch unserer Epoche . . . Deshalb ist es eine Pflicht für die lebendige deutsche Geisteswissenschaft, gerade heute von neuem nach dem Wesen der Romantik zu fragen."

[20] Further details in Werner Mahrholz, Literargeschichte und Literarwissenschaft, "Kröners Taschenausgabe," vol. 88, Leipzig, 1932². The following books and their dates of publication are significant: Reinhold Steig, Heinrich von Kleists Berliner Kämpfe, Berlin and Stuttgart: Spemann, 1901; Ferdinand Josef Schneider, Die Freimaurerei und ihr Einfluß auf die geistige Kultur in Deutschland am Ende des XVIII. Jahrhunderts, Prolegomena zu einer Geschichte der deutschen Romantik, Prague, 1909; Rudolf Unger, Hamann und die Aufklärung, Studien zur Vorgeschichte des romantischen Geistes im 18. Jahrhundert, Jena, 1911. J. Nadler, Die Berliner Romantik, p. VIII, remarks: "Mit diesen drei Werken . . . setzt die wissenschaftliche, entwicklungsgeschichtliche Erforschung der romantischen Bewegung ein."

[21] Cf. Christoph Bernoulli and Hans Kern, Romantische Naturphilosophie (Jena: Eugen Diederichs, 1926), passim. The terms logocentrism and biocentrism have, un-

that Romanticism cannot be studied successfully through any but a genetic approach, for problems of life are problems of growth. The study of Romanticism is a biological study. The student of romantic literature cannot be interested solely in the dialectic phenomena as such. He must endeavor to penetrate into the life which pulsates in them. This means that problems in Romanticism must be approached not only genetically but rather physiognomically. The individual productions are not to be viewed and judged as isolated pieces of work. They appear as expressions of the romantic spirit or as physiognomic representations of the romantic character. For the present study this observation is of basic methodological importance.

The physiognomist endeavors to recognize a coherent character from a multiplicity of separate traits. These traits, however, belong together and form an organic whole. None of them has any meaning in isolation, and each one is supported in its expressive significance by a multiplicity of other homogeneous traits. The physiognomist endeavors to visualize a whole, but he does not believe that he can attain completeness by an exhaustive survey of all the individual traits which he is able to record. On the contrary, he considers it his task to recognize the whole in each part and to interpret significant parts in terms of the whole. It is interesting to find allusions to the methodological implications of a physiognomic approach to the study of literary history in Friedrich Schlegel's references to Winckelmann. "The first amongst us," Schlegel wrote,[22] "who recognized the prototype (*Urbild*) of perfected mankind in the creations of art and of antiquity, the

---

fortunately, been abused in one-sided exaggeration. Cf., e.g., Werner Deubel, "Umrisse eines neuen Schillerbildes," *Jahrbuch der Goethe-Gesellschaft,* XX (1934), 1ff., and the aggressive but just criticism of it in Walter Gresky, *Schillers Garten in Jena* (Sondershausen, 1935), p. 24: "Von Goethe unterscheidet sich Deubel wohl darin, daß er eine einzelne, zufällig vorgefundene Ausdrucksform seelischen Lebens, nämlich das 'gleichsam instinktmäßige' Verhalten zur allgemein gültigen Norm für die Äußerung seelischen Lebens überhaupt erhebt und demgemäß alles, was an Schiller anders ist denn jene besondere Form, als Verderbnis und Vergiftung seiner Natur zurückweist. Der Verfasser der 'Umrisse eines neuen Schillerbildes' dürfte in diesem Punkte logozentrisch voreingenommen urteilen, statt biozentrisch unbefangener einer möglichen Vielseitigkeit des inneren Menschen mit mehr Billigkeit gegenüberzutreten."
[22] Friedrich Schlegel, "Ideen," 101, *Prosaische Jugendschriften,* edited by Jakob Minor, Vienna, 1906².

first who spoke about them in divine inspiration was Saint Winckelmann." He read the ancients as *one* poem.[23] He understood them as the books of a bible, for what we call the Bible is one book and yet a system of books, each one of which repeats the spirit of the whole. It is in this sense[24] that

all the classical poems of the ancients are inseparably connected, that they form an organic entity and, considered closely, that they are just one poem, the only one in which poetry itself appears in perfection. In a similar fashion all the books in a perfect literature are to be but one book, and in such an eternally growing book the gospel of mankind and culture (*Bildung*) shall be revealed.

With these last remarks Schlegel referred obviously to an ideal fulfillment of the romantic promise.

Romantic literature is not the perfect literature which Schlegel announced, but it strove toward perfection and visualized its future as an uninterrupted growth. To read romantic literature in its own spirit, we should read it as a bible, i.e., as a muliplicity of books which yet are one. It must be our endeavor to recognize a coherent movement from a great number of works which may be assumed to belong together and to form an organic whole. None of them has a satisfactory meaning in isolation, and the expressive significance of each one finds support in a multiplicity of homogeneous others. We try to conceive of Romanticism as a living whole, yet we do not believe that we can attain completeness by an exhaustive survey of all the various works which have come down to us. On the contrary, we consider it our task to recognize the romantic spirit in its representative works and to interpret these works in terms of the totality of the romantic endeavor. As a matter of practical methodology this means that the student of Romanticism must endeavor to visualize a given problem with all its implications on the basis of a general acquaintance with its representative expressions. For purposes of presentation

[23] Friedrich Schlegel, "Athenäums-Fragmente," 149, *Jugendschriften*.

[24] F. Schlegel, "Ideen," 95; also in *Novalis Schriften,* III, 362, with Hardenberg's note: "Bibel ist ein Gattungsbegriff unter dem Büchergeschlecht. Er subsummiert nach Arten und Individuen. Die Bibeln sind die Menschen und Götter unter den Büchern . . . Ihr Ursprung ist schlechthin unerklärlich . . . Eine Bibel schreiben zu wollen—ist ein Hang zur Tollheit, wie ihn jeder tüchtige Mensch haben muß, um vollständig zu sein."

he will then elaborate his views, of which he must know in advance that they are correct at least in principle, by documenting them with material from a variety of available sources. The selection of these sources cannot be regulated by objective criteria, for each one might be replaced or duplicated by a multiplicity of homogeneous others. Completeness is here no ideal which one should strive to attain, for a given characterological trait is always represented by an unlimited number of individual manifestations. Nor is it objectionable that the determination of the amount and provenance of the material to be adduced is often a matter of accident or intuition, for our interest does not concentrate on individual authors or outstanding works but rather on biotic facts which must be pointed out where they happen to be visible. This describes briefly the method used in the present study. It is a dangerous method but the only one available for a physiognomic interpretation of the biological significance of literary events.

A last peculiarity of the physiognomic approach remains to be noted. Through it the historian of literature becomes an historian of civilization. The biotic facts to which his interest is devoted do not manifest themselves in literature alone. They are often more clearly visible in other domains of cultural endeavor and force the literary historian to disregard the traditional limits of his field of investigation. It is not only his right but actually his duty to cross into adjacent spheres and to attempt a clarification of his "literary" problems by a comparative study of contemporary philosophy, economics, religion, politics, art, science, etc.[25] However, contemporaneity in this sense is not simply a matter of external chronology. It is rather concerned with the degree of inner maturity, and this, indeed, is a value which it is often not at all easy to appraise. It is certainly true, as Korff remarks,[26] that a great many of our physical contemporaries, e.g., live mentally in the Middle Ages, or, to refer to a more specific illustration,

---

[25] This does not mean that the historian of literature has a right to view literary phenomena as "determined by social forces," by philosophical, religious, or economic factors. The physiognomic approach is not causalistic. It is phenomenological and adheres to the principle that the proper study of the historian of literature is the history of letters.

[26] Cf. H. A. Korff, *Geist der Goethezeit*, p. 2.

that many traits of nineteenth-century peasant art belong spiritually to the Seventeenth Century.[27] Phenomena of this sort are visualized by direct, intuitive perception. They depend on the supposition of a possible transition of creative energies from one cultural sphere to another.[28] At times these energies accelerate the development in one field to an extraordinary degree, while others are left well-nigh barren. It seems, indeed, possible to speak with reference to cultural phenomena of a physical as well as of a mental age, and the two, just as in the case of human beings, do not necessarily coincide. For the historian of Romanticism, however, the situation is considerably simpler. We may conceive of cultural growths as endless campaigns in which scattered detachments are constantly engaged in minor or major encounters while others retire or rest. The decades around 1800 appear then in European and still more in German cultural life as a total war in which all the arms and all the units are active at the same time. Romanticism has had its effects, which need not mean its success, in all the spheres of human endeavor. If the student of Romanticism, or, to pursue the simile above, the reporter of the romantic war, visits the various fields of battle, he finds that causes and war cries are everywhere about the same.

A certain totalitarianism is a basic characteristic of all romanticism. J. G. Rademacher, a physician of the romantic era, points out that

it is impossible to succeed in knowing a part of a whole without knowing the whole, for the part is not only connected with the whole but depends on it in a constant exchange of cause and effect in such a way that it attains its real significance and essence of character only through this exchange.[29]

For the present discussion this means that romantic literature attains its real significance only if it is considered as a representation of the whole of romantic culture. Furthermore, this totality

[27] Cf. Joseph Maria Ritz, *Bauernmalerei*, Leipzig, 1935.

[28] Cf. E. K. Fischer, *Deutsche Kunst und Art*, Dresden: Sibyllen-Verlag, 1924.

[29] Johann Gottfried Rademacher, *Rechtfertigung der von den Gelehrten mißkannten, verstandesrechten Erfahrungsheillehre der alten scheidekünstigen Geheimärzte und treue Mittheilung des Ergebnisses einer 25jährigen Erprobung dieser Lehre am Krankenbette* (Berlin, 1843), I, 120. Quoted from Franz Peuten, *Johann Gottfried Rademacher* (Greifswald, 1933), p. 51.

which we call the romantic world is not the sum of all of its parts but an organic whole. Its parts are physiognomic repetitions of each other and of the whole. In the study of Romanticism the discrimination between adjacent or related fields becomes an impossibility. There are no adjacent fields; there are merely various manifestations of the romantic spirit. Their classification is always artificial and at best of purely methodological significance.

The following chapters are concerned with science and literature in the romantic era. These, it is obvious now, are to be regarded, not as separate, tangential fields of expression, but as two aspects, identical in physiognomy, of the general movement that marked Germany's cultural life in the transition from the Eighteenth to the Nineteenth Century. They are to be studied, not in terms of the influence which one may have exerted upon the other, but, briefly and boldly, in their physiognomic identity. The exclusion of other forms of expression of the romantic mentality is arbitrary and regrettable but not fatal. Their significance, physiognomically speaking, would have to coincide with that of science and literature; just as the expansion of the field of investigation beyond the limits of what is traditionally called literature cannot aim at producing anything basically new, but merely at setting old knowledge in new relief and at shedding new light on old facts.

The assertion that science and literature are identical depends on a number of conditions which seem to have been fulfilled in romantic thought. Their analysis is the topic of a first introductory chapter. Harmonious co-operation of science and literature should manifest itself in poetry of Lucretian scope. This is the theme of two chapters which precede and follow the remainder of the study. The first of these chapters, "The New Lucretius," illustrates the problems inherent in modern Lucretian poetry by reference to Wieland and other preromantic writers. The final chapter summarizes these problems as an explanation why the cosmic trend in romantic poetry did not produce a universal poem. The discussion of the Lucretian endeavor in the Eighteenth Century points to the question of man's relation to the surrounding world as the basic problem of all modern universalism. The attempts to overcome man's isolation from nature are exemplified by reference to the problem of the gap between man and the animal realm. This is further discussed in terms of the problem of evolution and as an epistemological problem in so far as a conscious integration of man into the order of things presupposes the possibility of universal knowledge. Through all these analyses it will have become apparent that the elaboration of a modern cosmology encounters particular difficulties because of the fact that the modern mind conceives of the cosmos as infinite. Infinity is an emotional experience. However, it represents also a cosmological problem which may be said to have brought about the idea of a universal organism. This idea contrasts with mechanical causalism, for it permits the conception of even an infinite cosmos as an ordered whole. The question of man's function in the universal organism is not merely a problem of evolution. It is to be qualified as the question of man's spiritual function in universal life. One of its aspects is the question of a special vital fluid. Its solution is found in the conception of an organic hierarchy of nature in which man is the highest development, the prototype and model of all existence. The views thus elaborated may be said to represent the romantic view of the world. Romantic thought is biocentric thought. In it the phenomenal world is viewed as a physiognomic representation of universal life. The last chapter, on the romantic world poem, is thus preceded by a discussion of the romantic conception of physiognomics.

II

SCIENCE AND LITERATURE

THE RELATIONSHIP between literature and the exact sciences is a
problem which has often been attacked. If this relationship were
a very peaceful one, it would not be problematic and there would
be no reason to analyze it. Those, however, who undertake its
analysis are generally not at all disinterested. They suffer somehow from the fact that science and literature treat each other so
often with extreme hostility, and they will not rest until they
have proved that the two are not only compatible but basically
in need of each other. When Sir Ronald Ross, e.g., formulated
the problem by stating that he wondered "in what witches'
cauldron of folly the absurdity was brewed that poetry and science are enemies,"[1] it was a foregone conclusion that he would
succeed to his own satisfaction in proving them to be very peace-
fully inclined toward each other.

Such a proof is not very difficult. Logic supports it, and the
facts which refuse to conform may finally be labeled as facts
which should not be. The late Calvin Thomas based a representative discussion of this kind on Goethe's "Wanderers Nachtlied II."
The first six lines," he observed,[2] "are simply statements of fact.[3] They

[1] Sir Ronald Ross, "Address before the Royal Institution on June 4th, 1920,"
Notices of the Proceedings, XXIII (1920-1922), 207.

[2] Calvin Thomas, "Poetry and Science," *The Open Court,* III (1889), 1730.

[3] This observation must not be taken too literally. The first six lines of "Wanderers
Nachtlied II" contain, as a matter of fact, a great deal more than mere factual statements. On their peculiar sound structure, cf. Professor Martin Schütze's edition of
Goethe's Poems (Ginn and Company, 1916), p. 199. Beyond this there are several
individual words with more than factual meaning. "Vögelein" and "Walde" have
modulating suffixes, the one hovering between diminutive and hypocoristic value, the
other, still more vaguely, suggesting the weightiness of an archaism in addition to its
former grammatical function. Finally there are at least two metaphors. The word
"Hauch" is an anthropomorphism, and "In allen Wipfeln spürest du . . ." starts out
with so general a place of action that *spüren* in its primary sense could hardly be per-
formed in it. It would have to be *sehen* if a *Hauch* could be seen; or the locative
would have to be replaced by a starting-point locution: "Aus allen Wipfeln . . ."
implying a coming from there. As it is, the words are chosen so that the "you" must

are the raw material of either science or poetry according to the nature
of the mental synthesis to which they may be related by what follows.
If the author had related them to some statement, say, concerning the
atmospheric conditions of Mt. Kickelhahn at a peculiar time of the day,
they would have been science; as it is he related them to his own personality, giving us a glimpse of a perturbed soul longing for peace and
they are poetry.

The difference between poetry and the exact sciences becomes
thus a very simple one: both find their raw material in the world
of actual phenomena. If a given individual is merely curious to
learn something about these phenomena, he is a scientist; if he
strives to establish a relationship between himself and these
phenomena, he is a poet. Both these urges, the curiosity about
external phenomena and the desire to establish some sort of contact with them, are fundamentally human. They belong closely
together. Now it is inconceivable that a human being should be
curious about anything in the outside world unless it be in preparation for communion with it, nor can the longing to establish a
direct contact with external phenomena be understood except as
the expression of a very deep urge to know about them. The
scientific and the poetic craving are really but variations of the
same impulse, and it becomes necessary to conclude, as Professor
Thomas did, that poetry and science, which "have so far gone
hand in hand and have played parts of equal prominence and
value in the history of humanity," will continue to be linked up
with each other, "for both have their roots deep down in primal
human instincts that are imperishable."[4]

One cannot help feeling, however, that it would be quite easy
to construct an equally peaceful theoretical relationship between
any other two forms of the human search into the unknown. Indeed, even the history of the eternal war between the various
religions and the exact sciences shows an impressive list of armi-
stice proposals of just this sort. "The basis of all scientific work,"

---

actually be understood to do the "sensing" in all those places to which "in all the
tree tops" refers. This is a truly pantheistic expansion of "your" soul. Cf. also Professor Schütze's remark, loc. cit.: "The distinction of the song is limited to the first
six lines."

[4] C. Thomas, "Poetry and Science," p. 1730.

says Einstein, for instance,[5] "is the conviction that the world is an ordered and comprehensive entity, which is a religious sentiment. My religious feeling is a humble amazement at the order revealed in the small patch of reality to which our feeble intelligence is equal." Yet such an ideal conception, in which religion becomes the rock underneath the superstructure of science, remains the achievement of rare individuals or groups[6] and does not affect the rule to which it is an exception. The verdict suggested by history's account would much rather be of the pessimistic tenor of J. W. Draper's statement that the divergence betwen religion and science "has increased so much, that it has become an absolute opposition," and further, that no peaceful settlement is imaginable, so that "one of the antagonists must give way."[7]

Ideally and theoretically, science and religion are not only made for smooth co-operation, they actually belong together, and each may be taken as the essence of the other. Exactly the same could be said about the relationship of science and poetry, or of science and literature in general. The practical situation, in contrast to the ideal, is also very much the same in both cases. The antagonism of science and literature, just as that of science and religion, becomes at times so strong that no other solution seems possible but that one of the two "must give way." This is, briefly, the impression one gets from a first superficial review of representative situations in which science and literature actually meet.

There is, first of all, the problem of didactic poetry. A poem that imparts scientific knowledge can be called poetic only in so far as it imposes on its subject matter a certain nonscientific mode of presentation; it is scientific in so far as its material escapes poetic assimilation. Science and poetry remain separate as content and form. Or rather, since form separate from content

---

[5] Albert Einstein, *Cosmic Religion with Other Opinions and Aphorisms* (New York: Covici-Friede, 1931), p. 98.

[6] For a discussion of this conception of science among the Puritans, cf. Robert K Merton, "Science, Technology, and Society in Seventeenth-Century England," *Osiris,* IV (1938), 2.

[7] John William Draper, *History of the Conflict between Religion and Science* (1875), (New York: Vanguard Press, 1926), p. 76.

cannot possibly be anything poetic, the scientific content ceases
to be scientific whenever it has been successfully moulded into
poetry. Santayana summarized this observation in the simple
statement:

The reasonings and investigations of philosophy [this term embraces
natural philosophy and thus what we should call the natural sciences]
are arduous, and if poetry is to be linked with them, it can be artificially
only, and with a bad grace.[8]

A specific instance which comes to mind when science and
literature are mentioned side by side is that of the so-called
naturalistic school toward the end of the Nineteenth Century.
However, the respect which this literary movement felt for the
"minor facts"[9] of science was inspired by a serious endeavor to
settle down to the basic business of life, to leave behind the playful manipulation of empty verbal beauties, and to establish an
understanding contact with those forces which make us and direct
us as human beings. The faith in what has been called the "minor
facts" of science lasted as long as the belief that they were the
essential determinants of human behavior, for these determinants
were being pursued and not the facts of science as such. They
consequently had to undergo a striking metamorphosis as finer
and more ambitious methods of investigation were developed and
applied.

They had to recede," as Eloesser[10] formulates it, "from proximity in
time and space and finally had to escape altogether from countable time
and measurable space to a sphere where the creative energies of dream
and myth and fairy tale grow independent of them. Naturalism is always
a new start, a reinvigoration through reattainment of the solid earth,
but it will always have to end in romanticism or symbolism, for it must
reach out above or below the terrestrial realm.

Indeed, the earliest traces of such transscientific tendencies are
almost always contemporaneous with the beginnings of naturalism. And the only lesson which is to be derived for our purposes

[8] G. Santayana, *Three Philosophical Poets*, p. 10.
[9] Félix Berteaux, *Panorama de la littérature allemande contemporaine* (Paris:
Kra, 1928), p. 43, coins (or cites?) the expression "petit-faitalisme."
[10] Arthur Eloesser, *Die deutsche Literatur von der Romantik bis zur Gegenwart*
(Berlin, 1931), p. 407.

from the noble experiment called scientific naturalism is the old
wisdom which Strindberg reformulated in the statement: "A poet
must know a great deal, perhaps even everything. But woe unto
him if we can notice how much he knows."[11] That is, indeed, what
August Wilhelm Schlegel had in mind when he cited as one characteristic of the poetic genius that he knows more than he knows
that he knows.[12]

So far then it would seem that scientific material injected into
the poetic body is received there as an alien substance which must
be metabolized or expelled. That is, at any rate, the impression to
be gathered from the following illustration, which is extreme but
highly characteristic, as only caricatures can be. It is taken from
a volume called *Poems of Science* (1931) which was offered as a
"sincere beginning" and as "a prophecy of the coming performance":[13]

> 2,222,222,222,222,222,222,222,222,222 tons of mass!
> With metal core, hot calcium, hot gas . . .[14]

[11] Quoted as an oral statement by Carl Ludwig Schleich, *Besonnte Vergangenheit,*
kleine, etwas gekürzte Ausgabe (Berlin: Rowohlt, 1922), p. 203.
[12] "Athenäums-Fragmente," 172, ascribed to August Wilhelm by J. Minor. Cf.
F. Schlegel, *Jugendschriften.*
[13] William Pallister, *Poems of Science* (New York, 1931), p. XIII.
[14] W. Pallister, *Poems of Science,* p. 60. The entire volume of Pallister's *Poems of
Science* contains but one poetic line: "Life is a rainbow in a cosmic storm." In it
only the expression "cosmic storm" can be related to modern science, while the
image as such has a long history of its own, sometimes dependent on, and always
related to, the well-known cave parable of Plato. For illustrations from Goethe,
cf. Julius Schiff, "Naturwissenschaftliche Gleichnisse in Goethes Dichtungen, Briefen
und literarischen Schriften," *Goethes naturwissenschaftliches Denken und Wirken*
(Berlin: *Die Naturwissenschaften,* 1932), pp. 60, 65f., 75. There is Faust's monologue
in the first scene of the second part with the climax: "Am farbigen Abglanz haben
wir das Leben." In the preface to *Versuch einer Witterungslehre* (1825) Goethe
wrote: "Das Wahre, mit dem Göttlichen identisch, läßt sich niemals von uns direkt
erkennen." This is the essence of the older rainbow metaphor, which did not simply
signify that life is a peculiar whirl of electrons and that we might as well get used
to it. For poetically still more powerful variations of the same motif, cf. Friedrich
Hölderlin, "Empedokles," *Sämtliche Werke,* edited by Friedrich Michael, 1 vol.
(Leipzig: Insel-Verlag, n.d.), p. 382:
> O Iris' Bogen! über stürzenden
> Gewässern, wenn die Wog in Silberwolken
> Auffliegt, wie du bist, so ist meine Freude!
Further, *ibid.,* p. 417, Empedokles on Aetna, speaking to Pausanias:
> Sieh', Liebster! anders ist es mir und leichter schon
> Und freier atm' ich auf, und wie der Schnee
> Des hohen Aetna dort am Sonnenlichte

That we have to do with "poetry" should be obvious from the words "gas" and "mass" which rime. Apparently the deeper reason why the author of this passage thought it poetic is that the enthusiasm which he derived from his work in the laboratory was for him essentially the same as that which poetry can afford. This, however, proves merely that essentially the same emotional experience can be released by science as by poetry and naturally also that the same kind of enthusiasm may spur the poet's and the scientist's ambition. This would simply mean that we have returned to Professor Thomas' statement that science and poetry alike "have their roots deep down in primal human instincts which are imperishable."[15] In their abstract purity they are perfectly compatible and perhaps even a necessary complement of each other, but this observation can only serve to make their actual and practical incompatibility the more striking.[16]

> Erwarmt und schimmert und zerrinnt und los
> Vom Gipfel wogt . . .
> Und über den stürzenden Gewässern
> Sich blühend Iris' stiller Bogen schwingt,
> So rinnt und wogt vom Herzen es sich los,
> Das Schwere fällt und fällt, und helle blüht
> Das Leben, das ätherische darüber.

Also Carl Gustav Carus used the image repeatedly, e.g., in *Zwölf Briefe über das Erdleben* (Stuttgart, 1841), p. 12: "Denke dir einen senkrecht, glatt und breit niederstürzenden Wasserfall. Dies sei das ewig Werdende, das rastlos bewegte Phänomen der chaotischen Naturelemente an sich, und nun denke dir die Schatten der Bildsäulen einer an den Wassersturz herangebauten Galerie, welche von den Strahlen der Sonne auf dieser stürzenden Wasserfläche gezeichnet werden. Jene Bildsäulen seien aber die Gleichnisse der göttlichen Ideen, jener Urbilder, durch welche aus dem Chaos des allgemeinen Werdenden oder dem Naturelemente, hier unter dem Gleichnis des stürzenden Wassers ausgesprochen, bestimmte Gestalten hervortreten."

[15] Cf. p. 15, n. 4.

[16] A meeting of poetry and science in their abstract purity is beautifully described in Walter de la Mare's most perfect sonnet, "The Happy Encounter," in *Poems* (London, 1920), I, 73:

> I saw sweet Poetry turn troubled eyes
>   On shaggy Science nosing in the grass,
>   For by that way poor Poetry must pass
> On her long pilgrimage to Paradise.
>
> He snuffled, grunted, squealed; perplexed by flies,
>   Parched, weather-worn, and near of sight, alas,
>   From peering close where very little was
> In dens secluded from the open skies.

The metaphor which equips science and poetry with roots extending deep down into primal human instincts has its parallel in another which unites them in their final vision. "The vision of philosophy [which again includes science] is sublime," says Santayana in continuation of the passage quoted above.[17] "The order it reveals in the world is something beautiful, tragic, sympathetic to the mind, and just what every poet, on a small or on a large scale, is always trying to catch." Poetry and art in general, the sciences with philosophy as their superstructure, and finally also religion, all participate in this vision. Art strives to recreate what science endeavors to prove, and both draw their energies from the certitude which only faith can give. "Poetry is the end. Science is the means. Religion is the mental posture which desires this end and has faith in this means."[18]

Science and poetry spring from the same psychic depths and are united in one sublime vision of universal scope. This ontogenetic assertion may be developed into a phylogenetic one. Flaubert, for one, had this latter sense in mind when he expressed the idea that art and science will "meet again at the top after having separated at the base."[19] This is a triadic faith in a future reattainment of what the past once possessed. The actual present belongs to a period of transition. It has broken away from a first golden age and strives to establish it again on a higher plane. In terms of such a belief the problem of the relationship of science and poetry has narrowed down to the question as to why their intermediate realities should face each other in hostile antagonism although their origins, like their final visions, are inseparably

---

But Poetry in bravery went down,
  And called his name, soft, clear, and fearlessly;
Stooped low and stroked his muzzle overgrown;
  Refreshed his drought with dew; wiped pure and free
  His eyes; and lo! laughed loud for joy to see
In those grey deeps the azure of her own.

[17] Cf. p. 17, n. 8.

[18] Oliver Ellis, *Poetry and Science and Other Essays in Prose* (Manchester: Sherratt, 1924), p. 30.

[19] Gustave Flaubert, *Œuvres complètes,* édition du centenaire (Paris, 1922), V: *Correspondance,* I, 434: "Plus il ira, plus l'art sera scientifique, de même que la science deviendra artistique; tous deux se rejoindront au sommet, après s'être séparés à la base."

merged. The explanation can hardly be found in a difference of method; it cannot simply be a matter of misunderstanding between two partners who have chosen different paths in the pursuit of consciously identical goals. The Flaubert phrase just quoted has a remarkable parallel in Goethe's complaint that "people had forgotten that science developed out of poetry" and in his further assertion that "they might well unite again on some higher plane."[20] This has a double significance. Goethe implies that the current conceptions of poetry and science do *not* view them together, not even in their origin or final vision. As for a possible reunion of the two, Goethe refers in the context to one of his own works as to a tangible example of what the co-operation of science and poetry can achieve. He is not concerned with an asymptotic ideal.

However exceptional Goethe's conception may be, it does prove that it is possible to understand science and poetry as integral parts of some higher entity which current usage would call neither science nor poetry and which yet embraces both. Why then is not this the general conception? It seems that poets have devoted more thought to this question than scientists. A wealth of quotations could be adduced to show that poets on the whole look down upon science and feel it to be wanting.[21] The essence of all such

[20] Goethe, "Zur Morphologie. Schicksal der Druckschrift," *Werke* (Sophienausgabe), second series, VI, 139: ". . . nirgends wollte man zugeben, daß Wissenschaft sich aus Poesie entwickelt habe; man bedachte nicht, daß nach einem Umschwung von Zeiten beide sich wieder freundlich, zu beidseitigem Vorteil, auf höherer Stelle gar wohl wieder begegnen könnten."

[21] Cf. also Ralph Brinckerhoff Crum, *Scientific Thought in Poetry* (New York, 1931), especially pp. 3f.: "Coleridge . . . regarded science as the antithesis of poetry . . . Poe believed that a poem should be written solely for the poem's sake . . . Keats' well-known toast in execration of Newton for destroying the poetry of the rainbow . . . Emerson could boast that the poet alone knows anatomy, chemistry, vegetation, and animation . . ." As for Emerson, the context from which Crum quotes, "The Poet," in *Essays,* second series (Boston, 1876), p. 24, seems indispensable since it modifies the significance of the verb "to know": "All the facts of the animal economy—sex, nutriment, gestation, birth, growth—are symbols of the passage of world into the soul of man, to suffer there a change, and reappear a new and higher fact. He [the poet] uses forms according to the life, and not according to the form. This is true science. The poet alone knows astronomy [!], chemistry, vegetation, and animation, for he does not stop at these facts, but employs them as signs. He knows why the plain or meadow of space was strewn with these flowers we call suns, and moons, and stars, why the great deep is adorned with animals, with men, and gods; for, in every word he speaks he rides on them

material may be summarized in words applied by a contemporary scholar to Wordsworth and Thoreau. For them "the truth of poetry is superior to the truth of science, for it is based upon the universal and the general rather than upon the idiosyncratic and the particular."[22] Science, from this point of view, does not "deal primarily with truth. It deals with facts as something unrelated to human life, and robs them of their symbolical meaning."[23] This factual science, however, is quite different from the science of which Goethe knew that it had joined poetry in the creation of his works on natural phenomena. Indeed, science, as the term is currently used, means at least two basically different things. Both are embraced in the description which states that science is "ordered knowledge of natural phenomena." But knowledge is wisdom and knowledge is power. As wisdom, science serves man's urge to gain deeper and deeper insight into the nature of his relation to the surrounding universe. It helps him—ever anew—to formulate and solve the problem of his rank and function in the order of things. This is the science which appears in Blake's prophecy:[24]

---

as the horses of thought." Poe summarized his thoughts regarding the present problem in his "Sonnet—To Science." Some of its ideas are like a diluted version of Schiller's "Gods of Greece."

> Science! true daughter of Old Time thou art!
>   Who alterest all things with thy peering eyes.
> Why preyest thou upon the poet's heart,
>   Vulture, whose wings are dull realities?
> How should he love thee? or how deem thee wise,
>   Who wouldst not leave him in his wandering
> To seek for treasure in the jewelled skies,
>   Albeit he soared with an undaunted wing?
> Hast thou not dragged Diana from her car?
>   And driven the Hamadryad from the wood
> To seek a shelter in some happier star?
>   Hast thou not torn the Naiad from her flood,
> The Elfin from the green grass, and from me
> The summer dream beneath the tamarind tree?

[22] Fred W. Lorch, "Thoreau and the Organic Principle in Poetry," *PMLA*, LIII, 1 (March, 1938), p. 295.

[23] Lorch substantiates this statement by references to *Henry David Thoreau's Writings*, Walden Edition (New York, 1906), IX, 155f.; XVI, 164-175; XVIII, 23 and 171.

[24] William Blake, *Vala*, "Night the Ninth Being the Last Judgment."

Urthona rises from the ruinous Walls
In all his ancient strength to form the golden armour of Science
For intellectual War. The war of swords departed now,
The dark Religions are departed & sweet Science reigns.

Such science, indeed, can be at odds with religion only when it must take the place held formerly by dubious faiths. It is itself religion, although of a purer and truer and more resplendent kind. This is the science whose relation to the arts, to literature, to poetry is one of co-operation dependent on identity of basic roots and final vision.

On the other hand, science as an ordered system of that knowledge which means power to man has nothing either in its methods or in its goal to serve as a basis for co-operation or for a mutual understanding with religion or the arts. This is the science which Blake detested because, as he put it in beautifully confused technological metaphors,[25] it harnessed

the Loom of Locke, whose Woof rages dire,
Washed by the Water-wheels of Newton.

It settles the problem of man's place in the order of things by stipulating that it is his mission to enslave nature, to harness and exploit her, quite in contrast with all other creatures, which can survive only by trying to conform to nature's demands.[26]

[25] William Blake, *Jerusalem.*

[26] It is interesting to observe that the present begins to doubt the validity of this conception of the difference between man and animal. A striking symptom of this state of affairs may be seen in the popularity of a book like Alexis Carrel's *Man the Unknown* (New York: Harper, 1935), whose German translation seems to have been as successful as its American original. The main problem of this book is the question whether or not man will be able to adjust himself to the new environment created by technological progress. The author's optimism is, strangely enough, based upon his conviction that a fuller scientific investigation of man's needs and functionings will enable him to transform his supercivilized environment in such a way that it will represent a new "natural" environment which should make no demands upon his biological mechanism with which it cannot readily comply. Cf., in contrast, J. B. S. Haldane's *The Last Judgment,* a scientist's vision of the future of man (New York and London, 1927), which equips our descendants with the power to transform even their own bodies. Julian Huxley has the same idea in his essay "Religion and Science: Old Wine in New Bottles," *Essays of a Biologist,* New York: Knopf, 1923. He speaks there of the possibility that "the evolutionary methods of psychozoic organisms may become conscious" so that "they come to direct their own evolution instead of having their destinies shaped by the blind forces of natural selection." More radical than Carrel's book is Edgar Dacqué's reappraisal of the concept of adaptation in his essay "Außen und Innen der organischen Entwicklung,"

The idea that it is the function of science to establish an *imperium hominis* over nature[27] produced at least part of that arrogant optimism which is so characteristic of the Nineteenth Century. It survives in the popular conception of science even now and seems to be responsible for most of the difficulties which confuse the problem of the relationship between science and art. It demands further elucidation.

In the course of the Nineteenth Century technological advance became the well-nigh exclusive goal of the sciences.[28] Their generally recognized object was "to extend and consolidate man's dominion over nature."[29] A science of this sort cannot, obviously, produce "sublime visions," for it must seek to work out logical systems which have nothing to do with metaphysical implications or aspirations. Their sole function is to serve as the basis for mathematical formulas covering the customary behavior of natural phenomena. These formulas, which are called natural laws, have but one criterion: their predictions must never fail, and that means little more than that they must be technologically useful. Contrasting this situation with the past, Wundt formulates delightfully:[30] "In the Seventeenth Century God gave the laws of nature, in the Eighteenth nature did it herself, and in the Nine-

---

Corona, VI (1936). On p. 135 we read: "Ebenso bedeutet der Verfall der Entwicklungskraft auch eine zu weit getriebene Spezialisation der Gestalten, die sich nicht mehr mit einem naturgemäßen Anpassen an bestimmte Lebenserfordernisse und Lebensräume begnügt, sondern sich in einem austreibenden Formenwillen ergeht, das stark den Zusammenhang mit den Umwelterfordernissen vermissen läßt und damit zur sinnlosen Formenspielerei werden kann." Cf. also Oskar Ewald, "Kultur und Technik," *Logos,* III (Tübingen, 1912/13), 275ff.

[27] Francis Bacon. Cf. also *Advancement of Learning,* II: "I stake all on the victory of art over nature in the race."

[28] England got its "Institution of Civil Engineers" as early as 1818, Prussia its equivalent in 1821. These dates may be taken as marking the beginning of a consciously fixed course which was not to be changed on the whole till well into the most recent past. Cf. Conrad Matschow, "Aus der Geschichte des technischen Vereinswesens," *Forschungen und Fortschritte,* XII (1936), 347f. The Prussian organization was the "Verein zur Beförderung des Gewerbfleißes in Preußen." It was chartered on January 15, 1821, but plans for such an association reach back to March, 1771. The VDI (Verein Deutscher Ingenieure) was founded much later, on May 12, 1856. It had its roots in a technological students' organization, active under the name of "Die Hütte" since 1846.

[29] Eric Nordenskiöld, *The History of Biology* (New York: Knopf, 1928), p. 277.

[30] Wilhelm Wundt, *Philosophische Studien* (Leipzig, 1883ff.), III. Quoted after Johannes Maria Verweyen, *Naturphilosophie,* "Aus Natur und Geisteswelt," vol. 491 (Leipzig: Teubner, 1919²), p. 55.

teenth the individual scientists take care of that task." Surely, an idea like Baader's, that natural laws are inviolable because of the Creator's reliability,[31] must appear childishly mystical to a representative mind of the Nineteenth Century.

It is difficult not to admire the technological achievements of the natural sciences in the Nineteenth Century. These achievements are ends which justify their means. They justify the metaphysically arid notion that it is the task of the natural sciences to elaborate unfailing rules of prediction for the behavior of natural phenomena. They justify, in other words, the transformation of one group of sciences into something we had better call tool sciences of technology. It is, however, quite a different matter when the ideal of predictability and consequent domination affects naturally alien spheres and becomes the recognized ideal of sciences with a basically different structure. How far this actually happened, may be gathered from a few representative quotations.

With respect to medicine, Max Neuburger, whose authority in matters concerning the history of this science can hardly be challenged, stated in 1906 that it was the aim of all medical research to "transform the art of the old masters into teachable technique," and the striving for this aim he considered "the essence of the entire revolution in the art of healing" which the Nineteenth Century has brought about.[32] The science of medicine has always held a position halfway between the mental and the so-called exact sciences. It is, therefore, not very surprising that the achievements of the other natural sciences caused medicine in the Nineteenth Century to think of the human body as of a mechanism functioning according to mathematical laws which permitted the codification and learning of all possible forms of intervention with their predictable results.

However, also the science of language seems to have been under a similar influence. Jespersen[33] explains:

[31] Cf. David Baumgardt, *Franz von Baader und die philosophische Romantik* (Halle, 1927), p. 330. Baader thought of Genesis, 8, 22: "While the earth remaineth, seed-time and harvest, and cold and heat, and summer and winter, and day and night shall not cease."

[32] Max Neuburger, *Der Arzt Ernst Freiherr von Feuchtersleben* (Vienna, 1906), pp. 13f.

[33] Otto Jespersen, *Language, its Nature, Development, and Origin* (New York: Henry Holt, 1922), p. 65.

When in the beginning of the Nineteenth Century philosophers began to divide all sciences into the two sharply separated classes of mental and natural sciences, linguists would often reckon their science among the latter. There was in this a certain amount of pride or boastfulness, for on account of the rapid rise and splendid achievements of the natural sciences at the time, it began to be a matter of common belief that they were superior to, and were possessed of, a more scientific method than, the other class.

This supposed superiority of the "exact" sciences was due to their absolute faith in the principle of causality. There was, of course, nothing to prevent the mental sciences from applying to their subject matter also the axiom of the sufficient cause, but they, on their part, deemed it important to be allowed to submit to a mathematically applicable law of causation.[34] Indeed, in the era of Positivism one went so far as to attempt to extend this ideal to the fields of history and sociology. Thus we have in Scherer's *History of the German Language* the amazing statement that

the aims of the science of history are fundamentally related to those of the natural sciences, in so far as we investigate the powers of the mind in order to dominate them, just as physical powers are forced into human serfdom with the help of the natural sciences.[35]

A still more brutal formulation of the same thought comes from a discussion of the aims and methods specifically of the science of literature. It was Georges Renard who wrote in 1900:

Mankind will learn to govern as far as possible the obscure forces which it now obeys without knowing that it does. It will take a step toward that liberty which is the only one within its range, a liberty which consists of knowing the play of natural laws in order to be able to command the forces of aesthetic pleasures.[36]

The conception of the task of science as implied in the material just presented did not, it is true, gain absolute control in any of the cultural disciplines. For these it is today already a matter of hardly more than historical interest. The situation continues to be different with respect to those sciences which are naturally

---

[34] Cf. Otto Ritschl, *Die Causalbetrachtung in den Geisteswissenschaften*, Bonn, 1901.

[35] Wilhelm Scherer, *Zur Geschichte der deutschen Sprache* (1878²), p. XIII.

[36] Georges Renard, *la Méthode scientifique de l'histoire littéraire* (Paris: Alcan, 1900), p. 500.

called upon to co-operate with technology. However, it must be recorded at least in passing that a significant reorientation seems recently to have occurred also in the natural sciences. Their stubborn muteness when interrogated on matters of more than purely technological import, such as matters metaphysical or epistemological, began to strengthen the suspicion that they were perhaps quite incapable of assisting man in the elaboration of his views concerning his own metaphysical significance because they were not made to view but to reckon.[37]

This dissatisfaction with the metaphysical aphasia of our sciences is one of the clearest manifestations of a very general crisis. Its symptomatic significance exceeds the range of a few vague allusions, but the phenomenon itself can easily be characterized in a brief sketch. The sciences are accused of having ceased to be human sciences. They are told to make it again their main business to clarify man's relation to the world of realities. Their results are called meaningless, at least in so far as they are concerned with the construction of an objective world detached from man as a center of vision. This, it may be asserted, is the deeper significance of the controversy about the concept "objective" which has been particularly vehement in latter-day Germany. Dacqué's statement, e.g., that "even the confirmation of mere facts is impossible without some previous judgment metaphysically conceived"[38] indicates clearly that the struggle against "ob-

[37] Walter Kossel suggests in his article "Zu Philipp Lenards 50jährigem Doktorjubiläum," *Forschungen und Fortschritte*, XII (1936), 247f., that a future historian of science will see the essential contribution of our era in the fact that "it penetrated into the inner structure of matter and solved the problem of its unity." It is highly significant that voices are heard which doubt the validity of even this claim to immortality advanced by the sciences. Conrad Weygand, "Gestalt und molekularer Aufbau der Kohlenstoffverbindungen," *Forschungen und Fortschritte*, XII (1936), 400f., says: "The formation of theories concerning the structure of matter has not proceeded from the visually given crystal, which is the sensually most tangible and geometrically most orderly configuration of matter, but rather from hypothetical complexes of concepts of atoms and molecules. A very general problem, not at all limited to special disciplines within the natural sciences, is thus that of gaining insight into the nature of matter proceeding from actual—not from idealized—configurations. This problem, thus seen, reduces all our concepts concerning the structure of matter, of the atom, the molecule, the crystal, to purely historical significance. It is a question at present how far these concepts will be at all capable of answering actual questions of realistic import."
[38] E. Dacqué, "Außen und Innen der organischen Entwicklung," p. 133. A striking parallel is to be found in F. Schlegel, "Athenäums-Fragmente," 226: "Da man immer

jectivity" is really a struggle for a metaphysical rehabilitation of the sciences.[39] This means, in other words, that scientific knowledge shall again lead to wisdom and not only to power.

Such a redistribution of emphasis in the endeavors of the sciences is not being witnessed for the first time. It seems rather to have been a general characteristic of all "romantic" movements. Thinking more specifically of the age around 1800, Cysarz, indeed, ventures to generalize that "it was probably the greatest act of liberation achieved by Romanticism to have emancipated the sciences from their serfdom in the pursuit of practical goals."[40] It is true, a great variety of observations pertaining to a variety of spheres of human endeavor have been adduced in support of the idea that a striking affinity connects the present with the early decades of the Nineteenth Century; but the notion that scientific knowledge must be made to assist man in the elaboration of a

---

so sehr gegen die Hypothesen redet, so sollte man doch einmal sagen, daß etwas ist, ohne zu sagen, was es ist. Indem man sie denkt, bezieht man Fakta schon auf Begriffe, und es ist doch wohl nicht einerlei, auf welche. Weiß man dies, so bestimmt und wählt man sich selbst unter den möglichen Begriffen die notwendigen, auf die man Fakta jeder Art beziehen soll. Will man es nicht anerkennen, so bleibt die Wahl dem Instinkt, dem Zufall, oder der Willkür überlassen, man schmeichelt sich reine solide Empirie a posteriori zu haben und hat eine höchst einseitige, höchst dogmatizistische und transcendente Ansicht a priori." This is only a minor bit of evidence to characterize Dacqué as an essentially romantic thinker.

[39] Cf. Staatsminister Rust's address on the occasion of the 550th anniversary of the University of Heidelberg (June, 1936), "Nationalsozialismus und Wissenschaft." It is an impressive rejection of what Rust calls "voraussetzungslose Wissenschaft." The reasoning in this address becomes difficult only when Rust stipulates that the "Voraussetzungen" of German science must needs be German. If we agree, for argument's sake, to such an infusion of metaphysical significance into a political concept, we begin to understand what is meant, e.g., by a "Deutsche Physik" distinct from the physics of other nations. Cf. Philipp Lenard, *Deutsche Physik*, IV, Munich, 1936ff. This idea is not a modern invention. It was of Lorenz Oken that A. Huschke said in 1851 that he had established morphology as a German science and as German property. Further details in Karl Friedrich Jakob Sudhoff, *100 Jahre deutscher Naturforscher-Versammlungen* (Leipzig, 1922), p. 33.

[40] Herbert Cysarz, *Erfahrung und Idee* (Vienna and Leipzig, 1921), p. 215. Cf. F. Hölderlin, "Dichterberuf" (second version):
> Zu lang ist alles Göttliche dienstbar schon,
> Und alle Himmelskräfte verscherzt, verbraucht
> Die Gütigen, zur Lust, danklos, ein
> Schlaues Geschlecht, und zu kennen wähnt es
> Wenn ihnen der Erhabne den Acker baut,
> Das Tageslicht und den Donnerer, und es späht
> Das Sehrohr wohl sie all und zählt und
> Nennet mit Namen des Himmels Sterne.

metaphysically valid conception of his own existence is certainly one of the most important claims which the present is making in essentially the same terms as the age of more than a century ago.

It must be admitted that the idea that man is destined to become the ruler over all nature was not at all unknown to the romantic era. Fichte prophesied in 1799 in his *Appellation to the Public*[41] that a time was to come when nature would be "subjected and transformed into an obedient and passive instrument." This, however, is contrasted with a past in which we were slaves of nature because we were still a product of the world of the senses from which only the highest ethical ideals can grant redemption. An *imperium hominis* of this sort has evidently little to do with the endeavor to usurp mastery over nature for purposes of utilitarian exploitation. On the contrary, it is a rule which presupposes wisdom rather than power and is quite compatible with the Goethean attitude which has been characterized as the exact opposite of those trends in the sciences "which strive to subject nature intellectually even though that be possible only by destroying her."[42]

Here as elsewhere Goethe represents clearly what was really characteristic of his entire age. Romantic science, it may be asserted, knows nothing of the motive of power in the materially practical sense of the word. Heinse in his virile individualism could still maintain that "it elevates man that nature must serve him";[43] Schiller spoke of nature as loving the bonds which man imposes upon her and conceived of an everlasting struggle in

---

[41] Johann Gottlieb Fichte, *Die Schriften zu J. G. Fichtes Atheismus-Streit,* edited by Hans Lindau (Munich: Georg Müller, 1912), p. 147.

[42] Ernst Barthels, *Goethes Wissenschaftslehre in ihrer modernen Tragweite* (Bonn, 1922), p. 99. Cf. also Carl Gustav Carus, *Goethe, zu dessen näherem Verständnis* (Leipzig, 1843), p. 88. "Nicht eine ursprüngliche analytische Tendenz seines Geistes . . . noch weniger irgend das Bedürfnis in die Untersuchung der Natur für Zwecke des praktischen Lebens einzugehen, brachten ihn der Naturwissenschaft näher, sondern, wie Plato sagt, daß die Philosophie überhaupt mit der Bewunderung beginnen müsse, so war es bewundernde Liebe und tieferes Vereinleben mit der Natur, welches ihn nöthigte, auch einer wissenschaftlichen Naturbetrachtung sich angelegentlich zu widmen und hinzugeben." For further material, cf. Ricarda Huch, *Die Blütezeit der Romantik* (Leipzig, 1920[11]), especially the chapter "Apollo und Dionysus."

[43] Wilhelm Heinse, "Hildegard von Hohenthal," *Sämmtliche Werke,* edited by Carl Schüddekopf (Leipzig, 1903-1910), V, 48f.

which we are engaged to maintain our rule;[44] but the Romanticists, as Goethe before and with them, did not see the necessity of subduing nature, and neither the romantic poets nor the romantic scientists knew anything but filial love for her.[45]

A loving science of nature! The expression must sound ridiculous if one does not perceive its sublime implications. A science, as Friedrich Schlegel put it,[46] which is disinterested and which is practiced for its own sake must turn out to be poetry as soon as it uses words as its medium of expression. Upon this basis it is no longer possible or even desirable to distinguish between science and poetry. As far as science assists man to establish or maintain his tyranny over nature it has nothing in common with art, either in its "roots" or "final vision." When science is engaged in disinterested exploration of nature, it is linked in co-operation with religion and art; it merges with them not only at "top and base" but again and again in their everyday realities. A science of power is bound to clash with religion and art. A science of wisdom maintains with them a truly romantic friendship of progressive identification. "Natural scientists and poets," says Hardenberg in a bold generalization of his own conception,[47] "have always spoken *one* language and thus presented themselves as *one* family." The younger Friedrich Schlegel does not tire of demanding that "all art must become science and all science art."[48] The physicist Ritter is confident that his science will earn the rank of an art as soon as it has come of age.[49] Even E. Th. A. Hoffmann has one of his characters exclaim enthusiastically: "The golden gates are

[44] Cf. Schiller, "Die Künstler," lines 10f.:
    Herr der Natur, die deine Fesseln liebet,
    Die deine Kraft in tausend Kämpfen übet . . .
[45] Cf. Henrich Steffens' review of Johann Christian Reil's book on the *Pepinieren* (Halle, 1804), in Marcus' and Schelling's *Jahrbücher der Medizin*, I (1806), 2. Here Steffens emphasizes the definiteness of Reil's distinction between *science* and *technology*.
[46] Cf. Friedrich Schlegel, "Gespräch über die Poesie," *Jugendschriften*, II, 354.
[47] In "Die Lehrlinge zu Sais," *Novalis Schriften*, I, 16.
[48] Friedrich Schlegel, "Kritische Fragmente," 115, *Jugendschriften*. It seems that Schlegel did not deem it inconsistent to state also the exact opposite. Cf. "Kritische Fragmente," 61: "Streng genommen ist der Begriff eines wissenschaftlichen Gedichts wohl so lächerlich wie der einer dichterischen Wissenschaft."
[49] Johann Wilhelm Ritter, *Die Physik als Kunst* (Munich, 1806), p. 59.

open, and science and art kindle with *one* ray the sacred yearning which is to unite all men in one church."[50]

Poetry which is science must expand individual contacts with outside phenomena into vast systems of universal scope. Science which is poetry must similarly integrate its fragments of knowledge into a universal plan. Korff expresses this as follows:

Reason cannot get along without imagination, but neither can imagination without reason. The wedlock of the two is, however, of such a peculiar kind that they must wage a struggle of life and death, while they are capable of attaining their greatest achievements only in close co-operation. The result of this combat is called science when reason plays in it the leading part; it is poetry when the leading part has been taken over by imagination; it is, finally, philosophical intuition when reason and imagination co-operate harmoniously.[51]

The essence of romantic poetry is thus perhaps philosophical, but then the essence of romantic science is also philosophical. It is in their philosophical co-operation that romantic science and romantic poetry think themselves capable of elaborating a truer and richer conception of God's Creation.

This view becomes clearer through a discussion of one of its most characteristic expressions: the quest for a new Lucretius. In it the genesis of Romanticism may be traced back into the Eighteenth Century.

[50] Ernst Theodor Amadeus Hoffmann, *Sämmtliche Werke* (Serapionsausgabe), edited by Leopold Hirschberg (Berlin, 1922), I, 95.
[51] H. A. Korff, *Geist der Goethezeit*, I, 28.

III

THE NEW LUCRETIUS

In 1784 Georges Louis Le Sage published in the memoirs of the Berlin Academy an essay entitled "The Newtonian Lucretius."[1] In it he undertook to show

that the first Epicureans could have discovered without much effort the laws of universal gravity and of its mechanical cause if only they had had as sane a system of ideas about cosmography as several of their contemporaries, to whom they neglected to listen, actually had, and about geometry only a part of that knowledge which was quite common at the time. The famous laws of Kepler would have been merely particular and inevitable corollaries of the general insight which these ancient philosophers could have gained through [an understanding of] the mechanism, as such, of nature.

"The same conclusion," Le Sage continued, "applies also to the laws of Galileo on terrestrial heavy bodies"[2] and, in fact, to all the pivotal principles of the exact sciences as they have developed since the "restoration of the arts and sciences."[3]

Rejecting the possibility that this world was created for us by the gods,[4] Lucretius had attempted to build the universe out of eternally falling atoms. As they collide in their fall, they arrive by trial and error, as it were, at those configurations which are necessary for the establishment of our world.[5] The central diffi-

[1] On Le Sage, cf. also Johann Carl Fischer, *Geschichte der Physik seit der Wiederherstellung der Künste und Wissenschaften bis auf die neuesten Zeiten* (Göttingen, 1801-1808), VI, 18ff., with further references to Kant and Schelling.

[2] Georges Louis Le Sage, "Lucrèce Newtonien," *nouveaux Mémoires de l'académie de Berlin* (Berlin, 1784), p. 404.

[3] This picturesque phrase is taken from the title of J. C. Fischer's *Geschichte der Physik*. Here it is used in complete awareness of the importance of Professor Lynn Thorndike's warning in *Science and Thought in the Fifteenth Century* (New York, 1929), p. 134: "There was no turning point and marked improvement from medieval to modern times, but only the usual historical continuity."

[4] Lucretius Carus, *De rerum natura*, edited by Hermann Diels (Berlin: Weidmannsche Buchhandlung, 1923), II, 180f.; and literally once more, V, 198f.:
Nequaquam nobis diuinitus esse creatam
naturam mundi, quae quam stat praedita culpa.

[5] Lucretius, *De rerum natura*, I, 1026ff.:
Omne genus motus et coetus experiundo
tandem deueniunt in talis disposituras,
qualibus haec rerum consistit summa creata.

culty, as Lucretius saw it, derives from the fact that there is no answer to the obvious question why falling atoms should concur at all. It would seem so much more natural for them to pursue their downward rush for eternities on end without the occurrence of the slightest collision to start the all-important initial diversity of configurations. To force them to collide Lucretius had to open a sort of back door through which a creative will penetrated into the system in the disguise of an original inclination[6] of the falling atoms.

For Le Sage this vulnerable spot in the Lucretian system was of outstanding interest. It seemed to him that he could substitute a purely mechanical principle for the mysticism of an original inclination, succeeding thus where Lucretius had failed. "If the disciples of Epicurus," Le Sage reasons,[7] "had been as much persuaded of the sphericity of our globe as they were disposed to suppose it to be flat, instead of making their atoms move almost parallel, they would not have hesitated to ascribe to them movements perpendicular to the surface of a ball." The atoms could then have collided without the intervention of an original inclination. A variety of accidental atomistic configurations would have resulted, and the process we call creation would have begun all by itself. There would have been no need to trouble a Creator or His like about it. Upon this basis Le Sage proceeds to derive the laws of Galileo, Kepler, and Newton and implies that the Epicureans could have done the same if they had been patient enough to collect all the available data.

Nevertheless, what Le Sage obtains by this procedure cannot simply be described as a Newtonian system. The Epicureans had failed to attain Newton's truths because they overlooked the one means which could have helped them to replace the mysticism of their original inclination by a more rational principle. Newton, on the other hand, had failed to attain a system of Lucretian self-sufficiency for reasons which Le Sage does not state explicitly but which he seems to have perceived at the basis of the asser-

[6] Lucretius, *De rerum natura*, II, 292 :
　　　　　Id facit exiguum clinemen principiorum.
[7] G. L. Le Sage, "Lucrèce Newtonien," p. 406.

tion "hypotheses non fingo"[8] in which Newton expressed his refusal to investigate the ultimate cause of gravity. The reasons for this attitude on the part of Newton are obvious. The term "gravity" cannot, it seems, have signified for him an ultimate cause. It was rather a mere scientific symbol which "explained" the phenomena of motion only in the sense that it reduced their complexity by demonstrating the possibility to conceive of them as dependent on one common factor. Everything else had to remain hidden in "God's unfathomable will, which we have to accept without question."[9] From Le Sage's point of view the situation was naturally much simpler. Newton had failed to find an ultimate cause of material motion because he was not sufficiently conversant with the Lucretian system. The "Newtonian Lucretius" of Le Sage is thus at the same time a "Lucretian Newton." It not only tries to show what the Epicureans could have achieved if they had accepted certain premises which were to become the basis of Newton's deductions; it also criticizes modern science for not having elaborated a universal system of Lucretian self-sufficiency. It is in terms of these two observations that an evaluation of the historical significance of Le Sage's contribution will have to be undertaken. Before we proceed in this direction it is necessary to show that the Frenchman's criticism of Newton is characteristic of a significant trend of his entire age.

When Newton refused to theorize about the causes of gravity, he did so because he knew that it is not the business of science to attempt an explanation of God's basic decisions. This was essentially the same attitude as that of Robert Hooke, who had stated in 1667 that matter and motion "are what they are, powers created by the Almighty to be what they are and to act as they

[8] For a lucid exposition of this problem as far as it concerns Newton, cf. J. M. Verweyen, *Naturphilosophie*, pp. 29f.

[9] This wording is taken from Friedrich Gundolf, *Paracelsus* (Berlin: Bondi, 1928), p. 55. Having spoken of Paracelsus' Christian trust, Gundolf continues: "In einem weit helleren und reiferen Stadium der Naturwissenschaft wiederholt sich das nämliche Verhältnis eines unerschrockenen Naturforschers zum positiven Christenglauben: Newton sah die Schwerkraft nicht als letzte Ursache an, sondern als menschliche Erklärung für Erscheinungen deren Ursache Gottes unergründlicher, hinzunehmender Wille sei. Auch Newton widmete sich mit grüblerischem Eifer der Bibelauslegung . . ." Cf. also Friedrich Wilhelm Joseph von Schelling, *Von der Weltseele* (Hamburg: Perthes, 1798), p. 28.

do, which are changeless and which in their totality neither increase nor diminish."[10] Almost a century later the situation had not changed, as may be gathered from d'Alembert's summary statement: "The nature of motion is a riddle for philosophy."[11] Soon, however, this riddle had ceased to be enigmatic. It might be said that it came to be posited as an *Urphänomen*, that is to say, as one of those phenomena "which are fully explained as soon as they have been mentioned."[12] Motion was no longer a riddle but simply a fact. It remained inexplicable but merely because it was basic and universal, not because it was covered by a veil of mystery which human eyes could not pierce. Motion was understood as one of the essential qualities of matter so that it became impossible to conceive of matter at rest. The "Ogni cosa si muta" of Giordano Bruno[13] or the "Panta rhei" of Heraclitus seemed to have come to the fore again.

From this point of view it is but natural that Le Sage should have been shocked by Newton's refusal to consider gravity as "explained" by the idea that motion is a universal quality of matter. Kant went one step farther and proved that the idea is actually, if not explicitly stated, at least implicitly contained in Newton's views. In 1786 he wrote:[14]

It is generally assumed that Newton did not deem it necessary for his system to suppose an immediate attraction of matter but that he allowed the physicists full freedom to explain it at their pleasure, without confusing his principles with their play of hypotheses, for he practiced the most severe abstinence of the pure mathematician. But how could he think he had a basis for his statement that the general attraction of bodies, actuated by them at equal distances [from them], stands in

---

[10] Quoted from Hooke's *Micrography* (1667) in Ludwig Darmstaedter, *Handbuch zur Geschichte der Naturwissenschaften und der Technik,* Berlin, 1908².

[11] Jean le Rond d'Alembert, *Traité de dynamique,* new edition (Paris, 1758), in the preface: "La nature du mouvement est une énigme pour les philosophes."

[12] Cf. Goethe, *Sämmtliche Werke,* III, 280: ". . . ein Urphänomen, das man nur aussprechen darf, um es erklärt zu haben." A striking, though indirect, expression of Goethe's attitude is contained in a letter of his to Schiller, dated October 19, 1796: "Überhaupt sind alle . . . die sich aufs Negieren legen . . . wie jene Bewegungsleugner zu behandeln: man muß nur unablässig vor ihren Augen gelassen auf und ab gehen."

[13] Giordano Bruno, *le Opere italiane,* edited by Paul Lagarde (Göttingen, 1888), I, 5, in the dedication of "Candelajo" to Signora Morgana.

[14] Immanuel Kant, *Metaphysische Anfangsgründe der Naturwissenschaften* (Riga: Johann Friedrich Hartknoch, 1786), pp. 65f.

direct proportion to the quantity of their matter, if he did not assume that all matter, that is to say *as* matter and thus through its essential quality, actuated this force of motion?

After this time the idea that motion is a universal quality of matter seems to have become a commonplace. It appears, e.g., explicitly and implicitly in Schelling,[15] in Oken,[16] and in romantic poetry it is too generally represented to need special documentation.[17]

One cannot help feeling that this trend must have been conditioned by what might be called loosely a pantheistic leaning. Motion becomes a quality of matter because the thinkers of the time find it unbearable to conceive of the behavior of things as secondarily determined by an added factor. Precisely this must be seen at the basis of Le Sage's impatience with Newton's cautious self-limitation. Newton, after all, had given "the reputation of scientific clarity and order to the universe,"[18] and it was really but a completion of his work if one attempted to trace this order without reference to factors hidden in "God's unfathomable will."[19] The conviction that "Order is Heaven's first law," as Pope[20] had put it, was insufficient as long as it had to be coupled with a constant "Presume not"[21] which represented the warning that a further description of the nature of that order transcended the powers

---

[15] E.g., in J. W. Schelling's basic thought, *Weltseele*, p. VIII, that the organic principle has priority over the principle of mechanism.

[16] Cf., e.g., Lorenz Oken, "Lehrbuch der Naturphilosophie" (1809), in Chr. Bernoulli and H. Kern, *Romantische Naturphilosophie*, p. 2: "Alle Ruhe in der Welt ist nur relativ, ist nur eine kombinierte Bewegung. Eine Ruhe gibt es nur im Ewigen, im Nichts der Natur."

[17] One illustration in lieu of many: F. Hölderlin, *Werke*, p. 381, has Pausanias complain: "Und alles soll vergehn!" Thereupon Empedokles replies:
> Vergehn? ist doch
> Das Bleiben gleich dem Strome, den der Frost
> Gefesselt. Töricht Wesen! schläft und hält
> Der heilige Lebensgeist denn irgendwo,
> Daß du ihn binden möchtest, du, den Reinen?

[18] Thus stated by George W. Gray in his article "Our Greater Galaxy," *Yale Review*, XXV (Autumn, 1935), 60-75.

[19] Cf. p. 34, n. 9.

[20] Alexander Pope, "An Essay on Man. Address'd to a Friend," IV, 47, *Epistles to a Friend* (London, 1733f.), IV, 47.

[21] *Ibid.*

of the human mind. In Le Sage's work Newtonian[22] science did finally "presume." Here it became at length the basis for a speculative construction of Lucretian dimensions. This is Le Sage's historical importance. He had the courage to elaborate a system which embraces the totality of all natural phenomena and to interpret them as products of material motion: a totalitarian system with one central speculative although not transcendental principle! This is the aspect of Le Sage's work which fifteen years later aroused the admiration of even his most vigorous opponent. It was Schelling who hailed the "Newtonian Lucretius" as having marked the reawakening in physics of the speculative spirit which had been dormant for so long.[23]

This exhausts the historical importance of Le Sage's work. It marked a beginning and signified that eighteenth-century science understood that the time had come for an attempt to adjust all the scattered bits of its knowledge into one general system of truth.[24] This, however, does not mean that the particular system which Le Sage presented was in any sense an adequate outline of views characteristic of his entire age. The last decades of the Eighteenth Century are surprisingly rich in poetry of Lucretian ambitions. Yet none of the works which could be grouped under this heading seems to show a direct dependence on Le Sage's essay. This is highly significant, for it indicates that the poets (who are the embodiment of their age) could not be satisfied with a conception which tried to retrace the universe in terms of Newtonian or Lucretian mechanics.[25] An attempt to show what a representative new Lucretius in the poetic sense

[22] The previously discussed differences between Newton and Le Sage do not affect the bases of the latter's work. These remain Newtonian.

[23] Cf. Friedrich Wilhelm Joseph von Schelling, "Einleitung zu dem Entwurf eines Systems der Naturphilosophie," §3, in Paul Kluckhohn, *Weltanschauung der Frühromantik*, "Deutsche Literatur, Reihe Romantik," IX, 63.

[24] Cf. L. Thorndike, *Science and Thought in the Fifteenth Century*, with a motto from P. Liron, *Singularités historiques et littéraires*, I (1738), preface, p. XII: "Il viendra un temps pour l'histoire comme pour la connoissance de la nature, où la lumière succédant tout à fait aux ténèbres tous ces morceaux épars prendront d'eux-mêmes leur place et s'ajusteront au système général de la vérité."

[25] For a specific discussion of Lucretian attempts, cf. chapter XIII, "Cosmic Poetry."

would have had to convey will confront us with a variety of intricate problems.

It has been said by a contemporary German literary historian[26] that it was the mission of the age of classic-romantic idealism "to recast the basic religious and ethical contents of historical Christianity in the monistic and individually determined moulds of thought as these were indicated by modern forms of inner and outer experience." A universal poem which might claim to be a representative portrayal of the classic-romantic cosmos would have to achieve such a recasting in monistic moulds of the totality of man's experiences about the universe and its structure. With such a demand we have left Le Sage far behind, for in his universal mechanism there was no man to claim special attention and, obviously, no historical Christianity to be recast in monistic moulds of thought. However, at this point the question arises whether historical Christianity, as a fairly monotheistic religion, was really incapable of supplying such moulds from the funds of its traditional dogma. To be sure, a religion whose God entertains only secondary and, as it were, politely social relations with His universe cannot possibly assist man in his endeavor to comprehend the world as an ordered and organized whole. The idea of an absentee God who wound the clock and left is not, however, generally Christian. It is the property of an extreme Deism, and of this it can naturally be asserted that it could not supply those monistic moulds of thought.

Eighteenth-century Deism has rarely, if ever, attained to such an extreme position, but the difficulty just alluded to had to concern as well, although to a lesser degree, all the other possible forms of the idea of an extramundane God. A case in point is Brockes' work, *Earthly Delights in God*. It is doubtless the most important of those poems[27] which Fritz Strich describes as having "wished to view nature from the standpoint of modern religion as the an-

[26] Rudolf Unger, *Herder, Novalis und Kleist,* "Deutsche Forschungen," IX (Frankfort-on-Main, 1922), 13.
[27] Cf. Fritz Strich, *Die Mythologie in der deutschen Literatur von Klopstock bis Wagner,* 2 vols., Halle: Niemeyer, 1910. Uz' "Theodicy" and Dusch's "The Sciences" belong here. The tradition extends to Tiedge's "Urania."

cients had viewed it from the standpoint of their mythology."[28]
Yet it is quite remarkable that this definite standpoint does not
produce anything like structure, system, or totality. The absence
of these could not, to be sure, impress the poet as a shortcoming
of his work. His plan provided for nothing but an encyclopaedic
compilation of poetic discussions of a multitude of objects. They
were held together by the common denominator referred to in
the title *Earthly Delights in God*. The question, however, which
one cannot help asking is precisely why it is that such a common
reference to God did not transform this universal cyclopaedia into
a structured cosmology. The answer is to be sought in the
strange rôle which this sort of poetry must needs assign to its God.
On the one hand He may be considered as the real and general
theme, for it is He who represents the basic principle of the poem
as of the world of objects which it treats. Yet He somehow keeps
aloof from all the ephemeral concerns of His poet. The net of
words succeeds in catching many objects of great beauty, but
their God, who made them, who should be in them, seems always
to escape a moment prior to the draft. It is taken for granted
that God is the creator and ruler of the world, that it is He who
operates the great chain of being. The only possible function of
poems like those of Brockes is thus to illustrate over and over
again the previously known grandeur of God and never to convey
either an understanding of how the chain of being must be what
it is or a new experience of its creator and active principle. A
Christian Lucretius, on the other hand, could indeed be characterized only in contrast to everything said about the *Earthly Delights*. Instead of being a versified encyclopaedia it would have
to be a work of concentrated vision. Its strict organization would
mirror an equally rigid cosmic order, and in its views of the
Creation we should obtain a view of the Creator. *Deus sive natura*
would have to be its theme.

Wieland's poem on *The Nature of Things* (*Die Natur der
Dinge*, 1750) is, from this point of view, a remarkable hybrid.
It has, as it were, two Gods. The one, who actually bears the name

[28] F. Strich, *Mythologie*, I, 138.

of God, looks at His creation from without as a judge and correc-
tor, interfering occasionally with its course and even with His
poet's work. Then there is another, without a name and without
commands, who reveals himself in the living order of His world
with its eternal growth and evolution. Through his allusions to
this second God Wieland becomes a "precursor" of Goethe and
Hardenberg. His poem becomes a significant expression of that
quest for a new poetic mythology of nature which is generally
associated with the age of classic-romantic idealism. To document
this, it is necessary to give a detailed analysis of the most
striking passages of the poem.[29]

His purpose, Wieland states (p. 14) is to present a plan of the
cosmos, "that most perfect work of God," which resulted from the
co-operation of all the qualities of its maker. A list of certain
specific characteristics of it follows.

[The universe] is without limits in time and space and will last as
long as God's power can act. It contains an infinity of spiritualities,[30]
all of which bear the likeness of God, and all of them grow more and
more similar to their prototype (*Urbild*). The most complete union with
God is the goal toward which all of them strive and which all will attain
(*erhalten*). The laws of motion are perfect, harmonious and simple.
Spirits move according to the rule that their vitality and force increase
in proportion to the number of ideas which they absorb. Their force
grows thus incessantly, for nothing can hamper them. Bodies move
according to the rule imposed upon them by perfect harmony with the
spiritualities. The universe as a whole contains all possible forms of
beauty and passes through all possible changes. Every distinction, however, will finally be assimilated to one basic purpose, which is the greatest
and best that could be imagined.

This brief program demonstrates with sufficient clarity how
greatly Wieland was indebted to Leibnitz and Plato. With respect
to the latter he refers particularly to the *Timaeus*. As for Leibnitz, he does not feel sure that it suffices to call him "the German

---

[29] Christoph Martin Wieland, *Werke* (first series of *Gesammelte Schriften*), edited
by the Prussian Academy of Sciences (Berlin, 1900ff.), I¹, 5-128. References to the
poem are given in the text. Pages refer to prose passages, Roman numerals to books
I to IV, Arabic numerals to the lines counted separately for each book. In important
cases the footnotes repeat quotations in their German original.

[30] *Geistigkeiten.* Wieland uses this word sometimes as a synonym for *Monaden*,
more often, however, to cover his own substitute for Leibnitz' monads.

Plato."[31] A more adequate way of honoring him seems desirable (p. 5). The idealistic dualism which Wieland's system represents cannot, nevertheless, be classed and filed as a youthful attempt to concoct a versified Leibnitz. He states expressly (p. 5) that it seems to him "that Leibnitz did not carry the idea of harmony as far as would have been possible. It was by making use not only of Leibnitz' doctrine but also of the opinions of other thinkers that he [Wieland] reached finally the system of which the following poem presents an outline."[32]

The arrogance with which it is then announced, not only that certain Leibnitzian views will be attacked, but that the whole of Leibnitz will be surpassed, may, of course, be overlooked as an excusable aberration of youth. If a young man of seventeen is carried away by enthusiastic polemics until he finally calls a Leibnitz a man of "cloudy views" behind an "impertinent brow" (frecher Stirne), one may pass on without comment, especially since the phrase about the "German Plato" was uttered in virtually the same breath. Underneath this arrogance there is, however, a sturdy pride. This certainly needs no apology, for it is fully justified. When Wieland declares (p. 5) that "majesty, simplicity, beauty and harmony, all of them in the highest possible degree, are the soul of the universe" and when he adds (p. 6) that "the entire universe consists of spirits and bodies whose movements correspond to each other in their minutest details," he obviously has not reached the point where he thinks he surpasses Leibnitz. Nor do we hear anything revolutionary about the nature of God. His existence is evidenced by the existence of nature (pp. 15ff.) and made plausible by the fact that all peoples and races are familiar with the idea of a Creator. The remainder of the first book is devoted to a disproof of the Epicurean

[31] On Wieland's indebtedness to Leibnitz, cf. Emil Ermatinger, Die Weltanschauung des jungen Wieland (Frauenfeld, 1907), especially pp. 12-24; on Wieland and Plato's Timaeus, ibid., pp. 27-30. The phrase "The German Plato" is traditional. Cf. Charles Bonnet, la Palingénésie philosophique (Geneva, 1769), p. 262: ". . . le Platon de la Germanie."

[32] "Ich habe geglaubt, daß der Herr von Leibnitz diese Harmonie noch nicht so weit getrieben, als es möglich ist, und indem ich mir seine Lehrsätze und die Meynungen andrer Weisen zu Nutze gemacht, bin ich auf den Lehrbegriff gerathen, von dem dieses Lehrgedicht einen Entwurf giebt . . ."

cosmogony, the illusions of pantheists and "naturalists," who confuse God with nature or consider a rigid mechanism which they call God the first cause of all things.

The second book deals with the origin of the world, a problem, we are told, which cannot possibly be solved by any system of emanation (p. 36). The Creator was concerned only with souls and spirits, and all matter is merely a necessary means of clothing the immaterial. These thoughts refer back to the introductory prose passage mentioned above. In it Wieland tried to clarify his position with regard to Plato. For this philosopher, he says, the world was one single animated and reasonable being which contained within it all the others, which are less perfect. This view may be poetically beautiful, but it is wrong. It is certainly true, Wieland continues, that the world contains all animals, but it is not true that the world itself is an animal. For, in contrast to Plato's universal sphere of finite dimensions, we can prove that the world is infinite. Plato animated the individual spheres of his universe, and it is but logical that he should have proceeded to do the same with the universal sphere. However, since we do not conceive of a universal sphere which is finite, we cannot consider anything but God as the soul of that infinity which we call the universe. The meaning of the term "soul of the universe" must, of course, be purified (*gereinigt*) to such a degree that it stands only for that being which moves the world and supports it in its reality. Then there will be nothing sacrilegious in its identification with God.[33]

A further clarification of the notion "God" is not attempted. The analogy of God's relation to the world with that of individual souls to matter is deemed sufficiently removed from human rationality through repeated insistence on the world's limitlessness. The conclusion which one would expect, "Presume not God to scan,"[34] is most remarkably avoided. Later on, it is true, there follows a passage (IV, 350) which warns that "no human mind can unveil the nucleus of things."[35] This sounds like a variation

[33] It is interesting to observe that Pope had not taken any such precaution. Cf. "Essay on Man," I, 256f.:
        All are but parts of one stupendous Whole:
        Whose body Nature is, and God the Soul.
[34] Cf. p. 36, n. 21.
[35] "O still! Der Dinge Kern enthüllt kein irdscher Geist."

of Haller's famous passage: "Into the innermost of nature no created mind will pierce; blessed is he to whom she shows the outer shell."[36] Yet Wieland has only the premise, not the conclusion. To be sure, he does not reach Goethe's categorical rejoinder: "Nature has neither nucleus nor shell";[37] but although he admits the impossibility of further penetration, he proceeds in his third book to clarify the problem of the interdependence of kernel and shell.

First of all, Wieland rejects the views of those who hold the world to be composed of atoms. The same treatment is administered to Leibnitz and his monadology. This thinker, Wieland declares, found harmony; he even found ideas where Newton and Gassendi found nothing but inanimate dust (III, 19f.). Despite this advance, a new theory of the relation of mind and body must be developed (III, 255ff.). Reason shows how matter and mind are separated. The latter thinks and feels. It works but it cannot suffer. The body acts and suffers; and matter remains extended however much it may be divided. It will never be entirely dissolved, just as the spirit will never be transformed into a body to lose its sensitivity and to behave like a machine. The spirit which can think yet cannot move will never receive an impression directly from another spirit. Matter, however, does have the virtue, given it by God, to move and to transmit motion to other bodies.

One feels tempted to interrupt here to ask why it should at all be necessary to suppose the existence of something nonmaterial if matter itself has the capacity to move. The answer is found in the peculiar idea, expressed in a previous passage, that God was concerned with souls and spirits and that matter is only a sort of secondary drapery. Many forget, Wieland emphasizes (III, 301), that the spirit cannot be impressed by matter and are misled into

---

[36] This quatrain is known because Goethe used it in his ritornello "Allerdings. Dem Physiker." It runs:

> Ins Innre der Natur
> Dringt kein erschaffner Geist;
> Glückselig wem sie nur
> Die äußre Schale weist.

[37] "Allerdings" and "Ultimatum":

> Natur hat weder Kern
> Noch Schale . . .

accepting a misinterpreted statement of Aristotle to the effect that a nervous fluid is poured into the soul, flowing from there into the body, where images are produced which are broken into spirit and radiate then at an inconceivable speed.[38]

Wieland, in contrast to young Schiller,[39] rejects the idea of a special fluid mediating between body and soul. Various theories which depend on it are presented in outline only to be ridiculed as a sort of warning example.[40] His own view appears in repeated but consistently vague references. As noted above, he conceives of matter as a substance of which there is only enough to clothe the spirit. It seems thus that matter is held to be somehow dependent on the spirit. However, a clearer analysis of the nature of this dependence fails to appear. Despite such a lack of precision, Wieland pursues his thought to sublime heights. This is strikingly illustrated by the climactic conclusion of the third book (III, 751ff.):

The suns which move above in luminous whirls, the planets, the air and the ocean, and everything we see, are not mere matter aging without a soul. No, they are spiritualities which we perceive because their bodies supply them with form.[41]

This is an extraordinary passage which claims in itself a basic reappraisal of the entire poem in which it occurs. The fact that the

---

[38] The original seems to permit several interpretations:
> Vergessend, daß ein Geist vom Stoff nicht leiden kann,
> Nimmt man vom Stagyrit miskennte Sätze an,
> Und läßt den Nervensaft sich in die Seel' ergießen,
> Und diese in den Leib hinwieder, herrschend, fließen.
> Die Bilder drücken sich in unsern Körper ein,
> Hier formt ein flüchtig Naß der Dinge Wiederschein,
> Der unbegreiflich schnell zu Geist gebrochen stralet,
> Und ein empfindbar Bild ins Ungedehnte malet."

[39] Cf. Schiller, *Über den Zusammenhang der thierischen Natur des Menschen mit seiner geistigen,* 1780.

[40] In 1750, however, Wieland had to take this idea more seriously than Schelling in 1798. Cf. *Weltseele,* p. 296: "Diejenigen, welche eine Wechselwirkung zwischen Geist und Körper dadurch begreiflich zu machen glauben, daß sie zwischen beyde feine, ätherische Materien als Medium treten lassen, sind wahrhaftig nicht scharfsinniger, als jener, der glaubte, wenn man nur einen recht weiten Umweg machte, müßte man endlich zu Land—nach England kommen."

[41]
> Die Sonnen, die sich dort in lichten Wirbeln drehn,
> Planeten, Luft und Meer, und alles was wir sehn,
> Ist nicht ein bloßer Stoff, der unbeseelt veraltet,
> Nein, Geistigkeiten sinds, die uns ihr Leib gestaltet.

thought as such belongs unmistakably to the tradition of Platonism must not be considered as very important.[42] What counts is the peculiar and personal tenor in which this Platonism is presented. Thus considered, Wieland's thought that physical phenomena are merely the sensually perceptible manifestations of life appears as an amazingly premature "forerunner" of Goethe's wisdom: "Am goldnen Abglanz haben wir das Leben."[43]

The fourth book, which summarizes Wieland's cosmogony, explains at the same time how the peculiar panpsychism just discussed came into being. The most vexing problem in the way of any such reasoning is that of the gaps between the different realms of nature. A brief digression on the history of these gaps seems necessary for a juster appreciation of Wieland's nonchalance in crossing them.

The concise division of all natural phenomena into three distinct realms, mineral, vegetable, and animal, had begun as a convenient help for systematic descriptions. Soon it was construed as of basic significance. In 1675 Leméry distinguished between three kinds of chemistry pertaining respectively to the three realms of nature. In 1682 these three chemical disciplines were set up by Emanuel König as corresponding to three different kinds of matter. Having been accepted as a matter of course, this notion

[42] Plato's "idea" can be understood in so many different ways that the interpretation becomes always the creative property of the interpreter. Cf. A. O. Lovejoy, *The Great Chain of Being*, p. 36 and notes. Two fundamentally contradictory conceptions are quoted there in Constantin Ritter's formulation "that the Platonic idea is the expression of the simple thought that every rightly formed conception has its solid basis in objective reality" but "that the doctrine of an other-worldly realm of ideas was not held by Plato as a rigid dogma," and in Shorey's words that "the hypostatized ideas are Plato's Ding-an-sich, deliberately accepted with full perception of the apparent absurdity of the doctrine from the point of view of common sense."

[43] This is at the same time the quintessence of Carus' philosophy, and Carus is doubtless the most significant representative of an achieved synthesis of what is normally called classicism and romanticism. This may serve to emphasize further the importance of Wieland's thought. In Carus the idea appears again and again, generally expressed by his favorite word "darleben." Cf. Carl Gustav Carus, *Organon der Erkenntnis der Natur und des Geistes* (Leipzig, 1856), pp. 148f.: "Im Begriff des Organismus sind wir gewohnt, Alles zusammenzufassen, was wir erkennen als eine durch die Einheit einer Idee bedingte und überall bestimmte gegliederte Mannigfaltigkeit, so zwar, daß eben diese Mannigfaltigkeit, woran jene Idee sich offenbart, uns nun gleichsam als das Werkzeug (Organon) dieser Idee erscheint und als solches das Wesen derselben bethätigt und in bestimmten Wirkungen darlebt."

was turned by general consciousness into a commonplace. It is well known that the exact sciences at a more advanced level had to struggle to rid their subject matter again of this artificial division. The early Nineteenth Century (cf. Wöhler) succeeded only step by step in proving that there could be but one kind of matter. After it had been demonstrated that inorganic matter was inanimate and basically different from organic matter, it became necessary to prove that organic matter was really also inorganic and thus as inanimate as inorganic matter. Previous to this twofold reorientation, continuity in nature was sought, on the whole, in some form of panpsychism; during and after it we watch the slow advance of a materialistic monism. The common endeavor of both lines of thought was to uphold the principle of continuity in nature: not to admit of any gaps between the realms.

Wieland passes from the realm of inanimate matter into that of the organisms with a slightly too optimistic reliance on the powers of the microscope. Some day, he declares, the microscope will show that all matter is organic. Already Leeuwenhoek, Needham, Hooke, and Swammerdam have shown how apparently dead particles of substance are fairly swarming with life. They saw (IV, 85) with strongly armed vision what the human eye is normally not fitted to behold. With the help of their glasses they found all matter animated and even the solid rock interwoven with worms.[44]

The transition from the vegetable into the animal realm and farther into man's private domain, Wieland achieves with even greater unconcern. Does not, he asks (IV, 153), the structure of plants in form and shape show a striking similarity to that of "other" animals? As for man: "Admit," Wieland exclaims (IV, 304), "sublime man, admit at least in secret that you are of the same class as these abject beasts!"[45] He refuses to consider any

[44] Du, Leeuwenhök, zeigst uns mit scharf bewehrten Augen,
Was Menschenblicke sonst nicht zu bestralen taugen.
Du zeigst den ganzen Stoff durch Gläser nur belebt,
Und wie der harte Fels selbst von Gewürmen webt.

[45] Gesteh, erhabner Mensch, zum mindsten im Vertrauen,
Du bist von gleichem Stamm mit dem verworfnen Vieh . . .

of the traditionally enumerated differences between man and beast. Not even art or science are peculiar to us. The only thing we might possibly say in favor of man's excellence is that he has progressed the farthest along a path on which all the other creatures follow. This, if taken literally, must needs lead to a sort of theory of evolution. It is, indeed, meant to be taken literally, for the passages of Wieland's poem which follow do present a most amazing exposition of such a theory, not at all, of course, in the sense in which the term evolution is now generally understood, but in a sense peculiar to Wieland and to the age immediately following his own.

Here we may feel confident that we have reached the point where Wieland is sure that his thought has soared beyond the heights of Leibnitz. How far this belief was justified is naturally another matter which need not be taken up in this connection. It suffices to record that the problem whether or not there are already in the works of Leibnitz traces of a transformistic conception of the hierarchy of nature is still an open one.[46] However that may be, Wieland's poem does present, so far as this investigation goes, the earliest poetic expression of a nonstatic view of nature. As such it differs fundamentally from all those descriptions of the hierarchy of the universe which Western thought had produced in uninterrupted continuity since the days of Plato.[47] Professor Lovejoy has stated that "one of the principal happenings in eighteenth-century thought was the temporalizing of the Chain of Being." This means that "the *plenum formarum* came to be conceived by some, not as the inventory but as the program of nature which is being carried out gradually and exceedingly slowly in the cosmic history."[48] The importance of this step from "inven-

---

[46] Cf. A. O. Lovejoy, *The Great Chain of Being*, p. 366. With regard to the problem of Leibnitz' attitude concerning static or temporal plenitude in nature, Lovejoy states that the adoption by Leibnitz of transformism in a rudimentary form is recognized by E. Ràdl in his *Geschichte der biologischen Theorien seit dem Ende des 17. Jahrhunderts*, I, 72; by Buchenau and Cassirer in *Leibniz: Hauptschriften zur Grundlegung der Philosophie*, II (1906), 26; and by Thienemann in *Zoologische Annalen*, III, 187.

[47] Cf. A. O. Lovejoy, *The Great Chain of Being*.

[48] A. O. Lovejoy, *The Great Chain of Being*, p. 244.

tory" to "program" can hardly be exaggerated.[49] Wieland was certainly one of the first[50] to take it.

Let us return to the poem and take up those sections which develop Wieland's views on a temporal succession of all the grades in the hierarchy of beings. The animals, he agrees (IV, 399), are at present not what we are; but if in distant times their future good luck advances them to our present level, then a similar process will have advanced us beyond them to a superior community. This is the new significance of the old "Panta rhei," that worlds and stars and man and animals and plants and microbes and units of matter, that everything is not only in incessant flux but in incessant ascension. Indeed, the poet asserts (V, 293), in the marrow of matter you can read the cause: Is not the entire world a universe of spiritual beings hidden from us through their bodies and shaped into a thousand different forms because the hand of order placed them next to those like them? Is not in the ethereal spaces above each star also an animal which some day must suffer death? This is the basis: the spiritualities which are ascending in

[49] It was customary until recently to pursue modern theories of evolution back to their roots in romantic thought and to consider men like Oken and Goethe as forerunners of Darwin. This is correct only if one admits that one basic idea can present itself under two diametrically opposed forms. To defend Goethe against the reproach of descendentalism one need not rely on Nietzsche's jingle:

> Dieser braven Engelländer
> Mittelmäßige Verständer
> Nehmt ihr für Philosophie!
> Darwin neben Goethe setzen,
> Heißt die Majestät verletzen:
> Majestatem genii.

It is often stated that the essential difference between Goethe's and Darwin's evolutionary ideas consists in the fact that Goethe did not think in terms of deployment in time. This does not go very far. Goethe's evolution, as that of all the other Romanticists, was born out of their more or less mystic understanding of growth, and growth, obviously, implies expansion in temporal progression. The presence of temporal transformism in Wieland may support this contention. Cf. chapter V, "Time and Eternity." On Darwin and Goethe, cf. Hans Wohlbold, "Die Naturerkenntnis im Weltbild Goethes," *Jahrbuch der Goethe-Gesellschaft,* XIII (1927), especially pp. 44f., where Darwin is called a forerunner of Goethe and descendentalism a first step toward a fuller understanding of the principle of metamorphosis.

[50] Cf. chapter IV, "The Unity of Organic Nature," especially the discussion of Georg Friedrich Meier; also chapter VIII, "Type and Organism," especially the discussion of Robinet.

constant transformation.[51] They amaze our senses, for their bodies as the vehicle of their souls must carry them in harmony with their inner state. Connecting this with the earlier notion (p. 14) that the spiritualities by absorbing ideas are bound to grow incessantly and unhampered, Wieland proceeds to trace their phylogenetic advance (V, 363). Slowly and in due order the lowliest species (*Geschlecht*) awakens from its slumber to join the host of plants, and moved by the breezes of spring it animates the valley and blossoms in the dales. The humble folk of flowers claim a similar right. They die and wither away, only to rise to the realm of animals. Then the mild air is filled with the rustling of wings which strive in old faith to reach the flower-covered hills, where they bloomed once themselves.[52]

The sixth book must needs be an anticlimax after this grand flight of fancy. All creatures are destined to reach perfection and bliss. Their life together and more especially the life of human creatures in society is regulated by virtue. This is, on the whole, the conclusion which also Pope had reached in his *Essay on Man:*

> That true Self-Love and Social are the same;
> That Virtue only makes our Bliss below.[53]

In Wieland's words (p. 117): "Virtue alone connects our private happiness with general happiness."

The attempt to assign to Wieland's poem its due place in the history of thought does encounter certain complications. The

---

[51]   Ist in ätherschen Reichen
Ein Stern nicht selbst ein Tier, das einst der Tod wird bleichen?
Hier liegt der stille Grund, den, ganz im Stoff versteckt,
Der forschende Verstand, durch manchen Schluß entdeckt,
Die Geistigkeiten sinds, die ändernd sich erhöhen . . .

[52] So wachet allgemach und nach der Ordnung Lauf
Das unterste Geschlecht vom alten Schlummer auf,
Und mehrt der Pflanzen Schaar; bewegt von Frühlingswinden
Beleben sie das Thal, und blühen in den Gründen.
Der Floren düftig Volk hebt sich durch gleiches Recht,
Wenn es verblühend stirbt, zum thierischen Geschlecht.
Denn rauscht die laue Luft von flatterhaften Flügeln,
Die alte Liebe treibt sie den gewohnten Hügeln
Und jungen Bluhmen zu, wo sie einst selbst geblüht.

[53] A. Pope, "Essay on Man," IV, 390f.

work belongs to a series of endeavors to find a viewpoint from which all life can be conceived as essentially homogeneous. Its peculiar conception of a mobile hierarchy within the realm of animation marks the moment, at least in German letters, from which the problem of palingenesis assumes a tangible contour.[54] Its panpsychism, finally, stems from the desire to combine the strictest biocentrism with a conception of life which holds it to be an integral part of the phenomenal world. The date of the poem (1750) makes it an even more astonishing performance. It looks in many respects as though intended to be used as the agenda for several decades of nature study and thought. That it was very slow in losing the good will of its author is easily understood. In 1770 Wieland wrote a supplement to an earlier note of reintroduction; and by this time he had apparently nothing left for the product of his seventeenth year but harsh criticism and biting ridicule (p. 128). The note itself, which accompanied a second edition, is dated 1762. In it Wieland states, by the way, that he wrote his poem without any knowledge of Pope's *Essay on Man,* a fact which may be emphasized since it adds to the interest of a number of unmistakable parallels between the two works. The motive for writing the note of 1762, however, was Wieland's feeling that his poem could not face the public for a second time unless accompanied by explanations and apologies. It seemed necessary to explain why the author in his more mature years had not undertaken to revise his poem and bring it up to date. The reason for this, as Wieland saw it, was simply that the work was misconceived beyond revision. Thus he could do nothing but apologize and promise that he would not do it again (p. 129).

The essence of Wieland's criticism is that he finds it absurd that a Lucretian form was used for a basically anti-Lucretian

---

[54] Cf. Rudolf Unger, "Zur Geschichte des Palingenesiegedankens im 18ten Jahrhundert," *Deutsche Vierteljahresschrift für Literaturwissenschaft,* II, 2 (1924), 273: "So ergibt sich auch in Hinsicht des Palingenesieproblems eine kontinuierliche, wenn auch wirklich sozusagen unterirdisch verlaufende Gedanken- (und mehr vielleicht noch Gefühls- und Phantasie-) Strömung die von Leibniz her neben oder unter der offiziellen Aufklärung zum Sturm und Drang führt, sich hier mit neuer Lebenskraft erfüllt und zuletzt in die Romantik einmündet. Leibniz, der junge Kant, Bonnet und Novalis sind sozusagen ihre Meilenweiser . . ." It is in this continuity that Wieland must be assigned a definite function.

purpose. This is more far-reaching than may be immediately apparent. The anti-Lucretian purpose is evidenced by the modernism of the poem, by its Christian or at least generally religious inspiration. The Lucretian form, on the other hand, is considerably more than the organization of the entire subject matter into six books, the versified presentation and similar externals. Herder may be called upon to explain. In the year of Wieland's death there were to be published in the *Adrastea* samples of Knebel's translation of the original *De rerum natura*. Herder contributed a brief introduction. He used this opportunity to characterize Lucretius as a typical representative of all those "who take Promethean rather than divine delight in knowing about the solid order of nature and in living safely within it."[55] It is this delight, Herder continues, which explains the "note of triumph with which Parmenides and Empedocles, and Lucretius after them, announce the victory of their wisdom." All of this leads finally to the rhetorical question whether this triumphant note differed in any way from "the language used in later times by the Bruno's, the Campanella's, and whoever else believed to understand and to have grasped the true order of nature."

To his list from Parmenides to Campanella, it seems for the moment, Herder might have added the name of Wieland. After all, the only thing Wieland could possibly have in mind when he criticized the Lucretian form of his poem must have been precisely that proud and triumphant tenor which Herder considered as the essential Lucretian characteristic. However, the explicit reason why Herder emphasized this point beyond any other was his longing and perhaps envious veneration for thinkers who "understood and had grasped . . . the solid order of nature and lived safely within it." This was so much more than modern times could ever hope to achieve. Instead of attaining such a state, we must be contented with striving for it. Instead of knowing about the solid order of nature, we must have faith in it. Finally, instead of celebrating the "victory of our wisdom" in a poetic presentation of universal truths, we must let the path be the goal and constant preparation a more honest substitute for an illusory

[55] Johann Gottfried Herder, *Adrastea*, IX (1803), 103ff.

achievement. The deeper significance of Wieland's self-criticism is doubtless that he had come to look upon his youthful performance as an illusory achievement. He had presented a great variety of problems, and these he had understood and grasped. However, he had added to them a corresponding variety of solutions, and these were the product of reading and thinking; they were, as Herder would have put it, "merely made."[56] Reason had been called upon to elaborate a plan of the cosmos although it was acknowledged that this cosmos transcended the sphere of what reason can cover.

Wieland's Lucretian poem is then, after all, not the modern Lucretius, and Wieland's name should not be added to Herder's list. However, the problems which young Wieland undertook to solve are the problems with which a modern Lucretius would have to cope. Thus, before pursuing the discussion of modern Lucretian attempts[57] we shall have to present a number of these problems, observe their relentless development throughout the age of classic-romantic idealism, and emphasize their "modern" (romantic) insolubility. This will explain why the task of a modern Lucretius is significant only as long as it remains a task and not through illusory solutions which, naturally, can never be converted into a final settlement. The problems themselves will claim greater attention than should be their due as mere preparations for a final Lucretian discussion. They will assume the importance of ends in themselves, and the path will have become the goal.

[56] Herder used this expression in his criticism of the first *Götz*.
[57] Cf. chapter XIII, "Cosmic Poetry."

IV

THE UNITY OF ORGANIC NATURE: MAN AND ANIMAL

Poetry," says Ricarda Huch,[1] "has always presupposed a uniform and universally living world. It has had animals speak and act with reason, has even quite often assigned to them superior and mysterious powers and has placed them amidst gods and men as their equals. Yet a specifically romantic view can be clearly distinguished. It does not, in childlike naïveté, identify man and beast. It rather remains always aware of their inequality ("The animals shun him, for he, man, is different," sings Hölderlin[2]); but reaching beyond the actual separation there is always in the romantic view a hopeful longing for the possibility of reunion.

To be sure, a detailed investigation would have to amend this statement in various ways[3] but its general validity can hardly be challenged. It seems obvious that nothing but the romantic endeavor to achieve a complete integration of man into the natural order of things[4] can be held responsible for this romantic longing to conquer the hostility of nature's other creatures, to open up paths of communication with the realm of animals so that these would no longer have to shun man but could live in harmony with him, their elder brother and more mature friend. The background of this state of affairs needs an historical clarification.

The problem of man's place in the order of things dates back to the beginnings of modern science. When Hardenberg conceived the plan to "continue Hemsterhuis' idea about the significance of the Copernican hypothesis for the picture of the world in

[1] Ricarda Huch, *Ausbreitung und Verfall der Romantik* (Leipzig, 1920⁹), pp. 123f.
[2] F. Hölderlin, "Der Mensch," V, 1ff.:
  . . . ihn scheun
  Die Tiere, denn ein anderer ist, wie sie,
  Der Mensch; nicht dir [Mutter Erde] und nicht dem Vater [Helios],
  Gleicht er . . .
[3] Ernst Elster, *Heines Werke* (Leipzig: Bibliographisches Institut, 1924), III, introduction to "Atta Troll," seems to be preparing such an investigation by presenting a list of animal stories from Gellert to Reuter.
[4] Cf. chapter XI, "Man the Measure of all Things."

53

our imagination,"[5] he was undoubtedly interested in the fact that man had ceased to be the Lord of Creation and the measure of all things[6] when he and his globe had ceased to be the center of the universe. If this plan had been carried out in the form of an historical essay, Hardenberg might have begun by presenting a threnodic analysis of Bacon's statement that "it is a false assertion that the sense of man is the measure of things" and that "the human understanding is like a false mirror, which . . . distorts and discolours the nature of things by mingling its own nature with it."[7] After this first attack upon the very basis of man's privileged position in the order of things, the struggles of the Seventeenth Century might have been interpreted as man's resistance against the necessity to "recognize the dynamic nature of all life, which, quite in the spirit of the Ptolemaic system, had been evaluated for thousands of years from the viewpoint of static existence."[8] With the complete breakdown of the static hierarchy of nature, the position of Lord of Creation held for so long by man would then have been abolished. The Eighteenth Century, finally, would have become the period of man's definite resignation and—as though history would illustrate that beautiful maxim of Christian faith according to which only he can be victorious who has submitted—at the same time the period of a first hope for man's re-enthronment. By giving up all claims to a privileged position in nature, man, as it were, would have acquired the right to claim equality with the *other* members of the animal kingdom.[9]

[5] *Novalis Schriften,* III, 264.

[6] Cf. chapter XI, "Man the Measure of all Things."

[7] "Novum Organum," I, 41, *The Philosophical Works of Francis Bacon,* edited by John M. Robertson (London, 1905), p. 264.

[8] P. Meißner, "Die geistesgeschichtlichen Grundlagen des englischen Literaturbarocks," *Forschungen und Fortschritte,* XI (1935), 435f.

[9] It seems that the phrase "man and the *other* animals" would yield a very interesting motif study. The mutation of attitude which it would reveal is probably suggested in outline by the changing terminology in C. G. Carus' chronological bibliography of works on animal psychology. Cf. p. 58, n. 22. The literary material would probably grow more positive from the Storm-and-Stress on. There is, e.g., W. Heinse, "Hildegard von Hohenthal," *Werke,* V, 55: "Wahrscheinlich übertrift das Ohr des Menschen an feiner und mannigfaltiger Aufnemung und Unterscheidung der Töne auch das Ohr aller andern Thiere." Another passage is quoted from MS by Walther Brecht, *Heinse und der ästhetische Immoralismus* (Berlin, 1911), p. 73: "Plato will, daß die Weiber die nehmliche Erziehung haben, wie die Männer . . . Die Amazonen

As their equal he might then try to justify a new claim for a position of *primus inter pares*. The last stages of such a survey might merge with what Brecht had in mind when he suggested that all the preoccupations of modern thought are somehow co-operating in the attempt

to represent man, who was chained to this globe, who was no longer the center of the universe, at first in his smallness, but then more and more clearly in his greatness, as transferring everything that had been external authority into himself as its creator.[10]

The problem of the relationship between man and beast has, then, for our purposes two clearly distinguishable major aspects. First there is the endeavor to find a place for man in the animal kingdom, to break his isolation, to bridge the gap between him and the *other* animals, to deny all human privileges in the conviction—as Pope put it[11]—that "Nature's Children all divide her Care." Second, there is the endeavor to assure man, as an animal and despite his "identity" with his fellow creatures, a privileged position at the top of a newly conceived hierarchy of nature. That these two aspects of the problem should be construed as psychologically interdependent is evidenced by the striking observation that an allusion to one of them is very often followed by a reference to the other. Herder stated in 1774 with characteristic aggressiveness: "It really seems as though all the great men of the century"—he had mentioned Helvetius, Rousseau, Voltaire, Buffon, Maupertuis—"wanted to contribute to a vilification of the human race in metaphysical as well as in moral and physical

---

hätten gezeigt und zeigten noch, daß sie dazu fähig wären. Man könnte noch hinzufügen, daß dieß auch in der Natur bey andern Thieren sey." For a summary of attitudes up to 1747, cf. Leonora Cohen Rosenfield, "Pardies and the Cartesian Beast-Machine," *PMLA*, LII, 3 (September, 1937), p. 763, n. 3: "Finally, by 1747, man was included among the automata, with the appearance of La Mettrie's *l'Homme-machine*"; also George Boas, *The Happy Beast in French Thought of the Seventeenth Century*, Johns Hopkins Press, 1933.

[10] W. Brecht, *Heinse*, p. 54: ". . . daß die gesamte moderne Geistesbewegung darin bestanden hat, alles Transzendentale in Funktionen von uns selbst zu verwandeln; den auf die Erde, die nicht mehr Mittelpunkt der Welt war, unrettbar festgebannten Menschen erst sehr klein, dann aber doch wieder sehr groß, größer denn je zu machen, dadurch, daß man nun alles, was sonst äußere Autorität war, in ihn als Erzeuger verlegte."

[11] A. Pope, "Essay on Man," III, 43. For Wieland's stronger expression, cf. p. 46, n. 45.

concerns."[12] After this hint at the eighteenth-century trend to identify man and beast,[13] Herder continues in the immediate sequence to express his conviction that it is this trend itself which will finally lead to a nobler rehabilitation.[14]

It was obviously first of all the science of anatomy to which a clearer understanding of man's animal structure was due. The Sixteenth Century already had advanced sufficiently in the comparative study of animal organisms to make it possible for Pierre Belon to publish in 1555 a monograph on birds in which he insisted on the parallelism of their bone structure with that of land animals. He went so far as to include sketches of the skeletons of bird and man with parallel nomenclature. The "bloody Seventeenth Century" deserves this name not only because of its great war! It has justly been called a "brilliant epoch"[15] in the history of anatomical research. It was, however, the early Eighteenth Century which consolidated the results of this research into comprehensive anatomical systems.[16] In 1744 Alexander Monro published the first handbook of comparative anatomy. Four years later came La Mettrie's *Man a Machine* with its familiar insistence on identity of structure in all vertebrates.[17] In 1754 Diderot summarized the entire situation in this classical statement:[18]

[12] Johann Gottfried Herder, "Älteste Urkunde" (1774), p. 64, *Sämmtliche Werke,* edited by Bernhard Suphan (Berlin, 1877-1913), VI.

[13] Cf. also "Ursprung der Sprache" (1772), *Sämmtliche Werke,* V, 21f.: "Condillac und Rousseau mußten über den Sprachursprung irren, weil sie sich über diesen Unterschied zwischen Mensch und Tier so bekannt und verschieden irrten: da jener (*Traité sur les animaux*) die Thiere zu Menschen und dieser (*sur l'Origine de l'inégalité*) die Menschen zu Thieren machte." Herder, whose thought gravitates around the organic principle, rejects nevertheless all intimations of a possible bridging of the gap between man and beast! We observe here a clash of the theologian with the naturalist in Herder and see the rupture which goes through the very center of Herder's existence.

[14] The same brusque juxtaposition in Wieland's *Die Natur der Dinge.* Cf. chapter III, "The New Lucretius."

[15] E. Nordenskiöld, *History of Biology,* p. 173.

[16] It is perhaps symptomatic that S. van den Spickel had known the intermaxillary bone in man as early as 1626 without, however, assigning to it any importance beyond that of any other anatomical detail. Goethe's rediscovery, it is true, came only in 1784, but it was the result of a systematic search inspired by faith in a basic principle.

[17] The term "vertebrate" is not La Mettrie's. It was introduced by Lamarck in 1801.

[18] Denis Diderot, *Pensées sur l'interprétation de la nature* (1754), §XII. The English translation makes use of A. O. Lovejoy, *The Great Chain of Being,* p. 278.

It seems that Nature has taken pleasure in varying the same mechanism in an infinity of different ways . . . When one considers the animal kingdom, and observes that among the quadrupeds, there is not one of which the functions and the parts, above all the internal parts, are not entirely similar to those of another quadruped, should one not readily believe that Nature has done no more than lengthen, shorten, transform, multiply, or obliterate certain organs? . . . Who would not feel persuaded to believe that there has never been but one primary being, prototype of all beings? But whether this philosophic conjecture be admitted with Doctor Baumann (Maupertuis) or rejected with M. de Buffon, it will not be denied that it is necessary to adopt it as an hypothesis essential to the progress of experimental physical science, to the discovery and the explanation of those phenomena which depend upon organization.

This last suggestion of Diderot's serves again to elucidate the philosophical background of the progressive animalization of man. To be sure, it was the progress of a nonmetaphysical science which seemed to force man to admit (not only "in secret"[19]) his animal kinship. Yet the motives behind this scientific development cannot be interpreted otherwise than as the metaphysical craving for a complete integration of man into the natural order of things. The most serious obstacle in the path of such an integration was the fact that man possessed an organ which had not been found in animals. This was his soul. Here one reverts to Descartes, in whose doctrine animals are simple machines, obeying their reflex mechanisms, while man, through the privilege of his free soul, is the independent arbiter of his own behavior. It is obvious that such a doctrine could not hide its metaphysical sterility for any length of time. The newly discovered anatomical identity of all animals, according so beautifully with the conception of continuity in nature, could not possibly correspond to an unbridgeable heterogeneity in the psychic realm. Goethe felt that the intermaxillary bone had to be found in man because it was present in all the other vertebrates. In like manner many of his contemporaries felt that animals had to have a soul if man had one. This explains the impatient undertone in Hagedorn's otherwise casual question whether it is really true "that one knows of no deeper source of the activities of animals than the expectance of situations similar to others previously encountered" and

[19] Cf. p. 46, n. 45.

whether science has not finally observed "in their tricks the power to think out possibilities, that is, the power of reason which is the guiding star of man."[20] It explains also the enthusiasm with which Wieland greeted the publication in 1750 of Georg Friedrich Meier's *Essay of a New Doctrine about the Souls of Animals.*[21] It will be recalled that Wieland stated in the introduction to his poem *On the Nature of Things* (p. 5) that he felt prepared to surpass Leibnitz. Later it became apparent that he had referred particularly to his presentation (IV, 399ff.) of a nonstatic hierarchy of nature, in which man can only excel through a comparative superiority over his fellow animals. A hierarchy of this kind depends on the idea of an unqualified identity of man and beast in all structural principles, also with regard to the soul. The courage to accept this last implication Wieland seems to have owed to Meier's essay on the souls of animals.[22] He acknowledged his obligation with extraordinary pathos (V, 447):

[20] Friedrich von Hagedorn, "Der Biber," last strophe.

[21] Georg Friedrich Meier, *Versuch eines neuen Lehrgebäudes von den Seelen der Thiere*, 1750. Cf. D. Spitzer, *Darstellung und Kritik der Tierpsychologie Georg Friedrich Meiers*, Bern, 1903. The following paragraphs are also indebted to E. Ermatinger, *Die Weltanschauung des jungen Wieland*, especially pp. 25ff.

[22] This does not mean that Wieland was simply dependent upon Meier. The thought of an animated *and* mobile hierarchy of nature was apparently no longer uncommon at the time. Cf. also p. 64, n. 34. A bibliography of works concerned with the problem of an animal soul is offered by Carl Gustav Carus, *Vergleichende Psychologie* (Vienna, 1866), chapter III, "Verschiedene Auffassung der vergleichenden Seelenlehre zu verschiedenen Zeiten," pp. 19-24. Meier's work is not mentioned. A summary of this reasoned bibliography is, nevertheless, valuable. The mere terminology used in its titles is suggestive of the changing conception of the problem of the animal soul up to the time of Carus' writing. For Descartes' *Discours de la méthode pour bien conduire sa raison* (Paris, 1724), Carus has only a reference to vol. I, p. 306, where it was stated that we have as little right to suppose a purpose in the activities of animals as in the movement of a stone falling earthward through the effects of gravity. With Leibnitz' *Nouveaux essais sur l'entendement humain* (1704), published by Raspe in 1765, Carus groups Bullier's *Essai philosophique sur l'âme des bêtes* (Amsterdam, 1727), and the writings of Condillac (cf. p. 56, n. 13), Leroy, and others, and excuses their failure as being due to an undeveloped physiology. Cf. p. 59, n. 23. The next is J. A. Reimarus, *Allgemeine Betrachtungen über die Triebe der Thiere, hauptsächlich über ihre Kunsttriebe*, Hamburg, 1760. Carus acknowledges the seriousness of these investigations but finds too strong a prejudice due to the influence of an entirely materialistic psychology. W. Bingley's *Animal Biography or Anecdotes of the lives, manners and economy of the animal creation*, which appeared in a German translation by J. A. Bergk (Leipzig, 1804), offers, according to Carus, little more than the anecdotes promised in the title. The same holds true for Just. G. Henning, *Von den Ahndungen der Thiere*, Jena, 1783. Fried-

O Meier," he exclaims, "whom the wise in all Germany read with delight, from whose mouth the honey of Plato is flowing, how clearly did you prove to us the possibility that also in beasts the value of the soul may grow! Nature solved for you that intricate knot, which even Leibnitz avoided only by means of machines.[23]

Meier had presented his views in explicit opposition to the Cartesian conception that animals are mere reflex mechanisms. His conclusions were based less on empirical data than on ethical and logical considerations. These forced him to assert that animals have memory, imagination, ability of anticipation, a certain creative power, and also a means of communicating with their kind. This last point would mean that they have a language not altogether different from the language of man. These contentions, taken together, stipulate the existence of an animal soul. They are, however, Meier seems to reason, quite self-evident, if one ad-

rich Cuvier's *de la Sociabilité des animaux* (1825) is deeply indebted to the work of the author's brother Georges. His later material was used by P. Flourens, *de l'Instinct et de l'intelligence des animaux, résumé des observations de Frédéric Cuvier*, Paris, 1841. A fourth edition of this work appeared in 1860 and differed from its predecessors in no longer mentioning the name of Cuvier. Oken's influence is discernible in D. Scheitlin's *Versuch einer vollständigen Thierseelenkunde*, II, Stuttgart and Tübingen, 1840. Finally there is Benno Matthes, *Betrachtungen über Wirbelthiere, deren Seelenleben und die Stellung derselben zum Menschen*, Dresden, 1861.

For the future Carus demands a genetic treatment of problems in animal psychology. For the first attempts in this direction, he states, we are indebted to Oken and Scheitlin. It may be supposed that the following decades endeavored to get along without the term "Tierseele." This is no longer the case. In April 1935 the *Forschungsstelle für Tierseelenkunde* was founded in Münster. Cf. Werner Fischel, "Aufgaben und Ergebnisse der vergleichenden Seelenkunde," *Forschungen und Fortschritte*, XI (1935), 364.

[23] Having asked what reason there is that could possibly justify our refusal to grant a soul to animals, Wieland continues:

    O Meyer, den mit Lust das kluge Deutschland liest,
    Von dessen weisem Mund platonscher Honig fließt,
    Wie deutlich hast du uns die Möglichkeit gelehret,
    Daß sich auch in dem Vieh der Seele Werth vermehret.
    Dir löset die Natur des Knotens schwierig Band,
    Aus welchem Leibnitz sich kaum durch Maschinen wand.

Cf. C. G. Carus, *Vergleichende Psychologie*, p. 20: "Selbst große Geister, wie Leibnitz, der sein System der prästabilierten Harmonie auch auf das Verhältniß der Thierseele zum Thierkörper anwendete, konnten hier kein wirkliches Licht aufstecken, da ihnen selbst die Leuchte der wahren Physiologie abging, die Lehre vom Entwickeltwerden der Seele aus dem Unbewußten aber noch überhaupt nicht existierte." This was written in 1866, but it sounds as though Carus had wanted to annotate Wieland's passage quoted above.

mits, as one can hardly fail to do, that animals have organs of
sense perception and that they manifest affects, virtues, and vices.
What they lack is intelligence in the narrower sense, i.e., the
capability of forming general ideas, abstract judgments, and general conclusions. The relation of the soul of the animal to its body
may be explained in terms of the concept of pre-established harmony. These souls are monads and thus immortal. "When an animal dies, its soul survives and lives throughout eternity unless
it be that God destroys it, which is not, however, a likely assumption on any grounds." Leibnitz' doctrine of gradation of monads
assumes then in conjunction with Meier's animal souls a clearly
temporalized form.[24] The souls of animals pass through many
metamorphoses and may finally reach the maturity of human
souls. "It is possible," Meier concludes, "that animals representing the lowest class should be promoted through death into a second, from there into a third and finally, again through a transformation, they may become reasonable beings and spirits."

Meier's contribution may then be appraised as consisting of
two major items. He accepts the identity of man and animal as
a consequence of undeniable facts established by the science of
comparative anatomy. He supplies this identity with a metaphysical basis by assigning a soul to all the members of the animal
realm. Secondly, Meier deprives the opponents of man's animalization of their one and only tenable basis of resistance. He avoids
what Herder calls the "vilification"[25] of man by heeding the obvious fact that the human animal is after all considerably more
than a mere animal. Meier achieves a synthesis of the material
thesis that man is an animal with its spiritual antithesis that man
is the Lord of Creation. He does so in the conception of a mobile
hierarchy in nature, or, in other words, in a theory of evolution.[26]
However, the identification of these two concepts must be justified
by a new approach.

In the most general sense evolution signifies the development
of one natural phenomenon from another. Its problems concern

[24] Cf. p. 47, n. 46.
[25] Cf. p. 56, n. 12.
[26] Meier supplies thus the basis for Wieland's evolutionism. Cf. chapter III, "The
New Lucretius" and Wieland, *Die Natur der Dinge,* IV, 399ff.

thus individual aspects of the axioms of continuity and unity of nature. The solutions of these problems are to demonstrate the interdependence of all single items in the realm of things. When applied to the narrower sphere of organisms this may be understood in two different ways. There is, on the one hand, the obvious, but none the less mysterious, interconnection between the generator and the generated, the creation of individuals in the image of their parents. This is, in more modern terms, the ontogenetic problem. It may be called upon to establish an actual consanguinity between all the various members of one species. On the other hand we have the parallel question of a similar interconnection between entire species. This is the problem of phylogenesis. The parallelism between the two is, it seems, merely a matter of analogy. We conceive of species as entities and observe similarities between them which are as striking as those which led in the case of individuals of one species to the assumption of a direct blood relationship. This specific assumption is repeated in generic terms and leads to a conception which may be called upon to establish some sort of kinship between a variety of species.

At this point an important note must be inserted. In modern usage "evolution" refers always to the second of these two types of organic interdependence. That is a semantic practice which must be heeded. However, this does not mean that the concept of evolution may be narrowed further so that it refers exclusively to the idea that the kinship between different species must be explained by physical descent. This is only one special form of the protothought of evolution. It is exclusively characteristic of the Nineteenth Century and should always be qualified as the evolution of Lamarck, or Darwin, or as evolution by descent, selection, etc. It is also to be noted that the term evolution as used in the Eighteenth Century[27] designated generally a peculiar con-

---

[27] Occasionally also in modern works which refer to the Eighteenth Century. This practice can hardly be avoided, but it is very dangerous. Cf. *The New International Encyclopaedia*, s.v. "Epigenesis": "More critics than one have mired themselves by failing to realize that 'evolution' in the Eighteenth Century meant the preformation theory, not evolution in the modern sense of the word." Quoted by George Reuben Potter, "Mark Akenside, Prophet of Evolution," *Modern Philology*, XXIV (1926), 55-64.

ception of ontogenesis. A brief discussion of this ontogenetic "evolution" must precede the attempt to discover in it elements which, "by analogy" or otherwise, may have led to the phylogenetic conception which Meier (and Wieland) seemed to have in mind.

In 1660 Jan Swammerdam had formulated for the first time, as it appears, the idea that the evolution of an individual is merely the deployment of what is prearranged in the germ. Haller, Spallanzani, and Bonnet accepted the theory that the earliest created *ovum* contained, always one within the other, the germs of all the individuals of its entire posterity. These thinkers were called the "ovists." Others ascribed a similar rôle to the *spermatozoön*. They were thus the beneficiaries of Leeuwenhoek's discovery of spermatozoa in 1677 and were called the "spermists." "Ovists" and "spermists" together formed the school of the so-called evolutionists. It seems, by the way, that only the materially absurd element in these views was overcome by Wolff's *Epigenesis* of 1768. It may be regarded as a resurrection of William Harvey's epigenesis in *De generatione animalium* of 1651 and must be interpreted as a theory of at least potential preformation.[28] All these investigations and theories are concerned with the connection of individuals to their producers. It is, however, a striking observation that a great portion of this work was done by men who devoted a special interest to insects. This cannot have been accidental, and it certainly was not without important effects. In the case of insects the evolution of the individual presents itself as an actual palingenetic ascent from grade to grade along a scale of living things. The vital germ which comes from the egg does not simply assume the shape of one individual of one species. It rather experiences several deaths and births under our very eyes. It lives the lives of several quite different creatures. A rational effort is actually needed if we want to recognize such an obviously "phylogenetic" series as after all nothing but a sequence of stages in an ontogenetic growth. We need not assume that Meier or any of his

[28] For an almost contemporary, although less complete systematic survey of the foregoing, cf. Christoph Girtanner, *Über das Kantische Prinzip für die Naturgeschichte* (Göttingen, 1769), pp. 2off.

contemporaries who held similar views reasoned in this slightly childish fashion, but we can arrive at their conclusions by suggesting that all animals undergo a metamorphosis[29] similar to that of insects. They live, as we know them, the lives of caterpillars. When they die they reach the chrysalis stage, and their next life corresponds to that of butterflies.

The most comprehensive exposition of the idea of a possible palingenetic ascension from grade to grade within the scale of living things is that presented by Charles Bonnet. The essentials of his doctrine were conceived as early as 1745. Their philosophical and metaphysical implications, however, were allowed to mature for almost another quarter of a century until they finally found expression in the famous *Philosophical Palingenesis* of 1769. This publication met with a lively reception[30] which proves that it did not have to arouse a new interest in its subject matter. This was abroad as is also evidenced by the fact that Meier and Wieland published their thoughts on "evolution" during the gestation period of Bonnet's work.[31] It is not easy for us today to extract the essential

[29] The very word "metamorphosis" may have been given its new vogue by these entomologists. It seems to play a more important rôle in the writings of Bonnet than in those of his predecessors. It has, indeed, been suggested that Goethe took it from him. Cf. René Berthelot, *Science et philosophie chez Goethe* (Paris, 1922), p. 21: "C'est à lui [Bonnet] que Goethe paraît avoir emprunté le mot même de 'métamorphose'."

[30] Not always favorable, however. Schiller, "Philosophie der Physiologie" (1779), *Sämmtliche Schriften,* edited by Karl Goedeke (Stuttgart: Cotta, 1867-1876), I, 87, wrote about Bonnet: "Mit unverzeihlichem Leichtsinn hüpft der französische Gaukler über die schwersten Punkte dahin, legt Dinge zum Grund, die er niemals beweisen kann, zieht Folgen daraus, die kein Mensch, ausgenommen ein Franzose wagen kann. Seine Theorie mag seinem Vaterland gefallen, der schwerfällige Teutsche entrüstet sich, wenn er den Goldstaub weggeblasen, und unten nichts als Luft sieht." The passage, it is true, aims mainly at Bonnet's theory concerning the formation of concepts through perception.

[31] There is consequently no occasion to investigate a possible direct influence of Bonnet on Meier or Wieland. On Bonnet and other German thinkers, cf. Robert Hering, "Der Prosahymnus 'Die Natur' und sein Verfasser," *Jahrbuch der Goethe-Gesellschaft,* XIII (1927), 141: "Those chapters which Bonnet, as a faithful adherent to biblical truth, had written about miracles and revelation and about their compatibility with the results of the natural sciences, were translated by Lavater in 1769. F. H. Jacobi's mental development was decidedly influenced by him [Bonnet] during Jacobi's sojourn in Geneva. His conversation with Goethe in Bensberg and Cologne must have centered in questions of this nature, and Spinoza as its problem was assigned to it only at a later time . . . Bonnet's influence on Tetens, who in turn affected Kant, as also his correspondence with Haller made him furthermore a significant factor in the development of physiological psychology." In one of Heinse's

principles from the *Philosophical Palingenesis*. Unger has described it correctly as consisting of a mass of "fatiguingly roundabout discussions"[32] of technical detail which may interest the historian of biology but which conceals the underlying ideology. For the present purpose it suffices to assert that Bonnet conceived of an uninterrupted succession of grades from the lowest vegetable organism to the most perfect animal. This succession was mobilized by imperishable germs of the soul which death could not affect but whose life could be continued only in connection with a new and possibly more highly organized body.

The clearest formulation of his views Bonnet himself gave in the following passage.

I have often interrupted my contemplations to think of this marvelous gradation which prevails amongst all living beings from the lichen and polyp to the cedar and to man. The same sort of progression which we discover today between the different orders of organized beings will no doubt continue to be observed in a future state of our globe. But it will follow different proportions, and these will be determined by the degree of possible perfectibility of each species. Man will leave to monkeys or elephants this first rank which he now occupies amongst the animals of our planet. In this universal rearrangement of the animal kingdom, it might very well happen that there would appear a Newton or a Leibnitz amongst the apes or elephants and a Perrault or a Vauban amongst the castors.[33]

In this conception, which is certainly not devoid of sublime beauty, man has found his place in the order of things. As an animal he belongs to the animal kingdom. That he is nevertheless superior to all other animals means simply that he has advanced farthest along the path of unlimited perfectibility. Thoughts of this general tenor had to be common property[34] be-

---

book lists, published by W. Brecht, *Heinse,* p. 105, Bonnet is indirectly represented by the item: "Due Opinioni del S. Carlo Bonnet, confutato dal Conte Abbate Alfonso." This seems to be concerned with the problem of resurrection.

[32] R. Unger, "Zur Geschichte des Palingenesiegedankens," p. 266.

[33] Ch. Bonnet, *Palingénésie,* pp. 202ff.

[34] The Eighteenth Century already seems to have experienced their spontaneous generation in a number of independent cases. Bonnet, and Meier and Wieland before him, cannot be considered as altogether isolated representatives of a nonstatic conception of the order of things. In a great many cases, however, it is not at all easy to determine whether a given author does actually conceive of the "plenum formarum," as Professor Lovejoy (cf. p. 47, n. 48) puts it, "not as the inventory but as the pro-

fore it could be felt that man's position in nature gave him duties
and rights with regard to his less advanced brothers in the ani-

---

gram of nature." The reason for this difficulty seems to be that skillful writers in-
stinctively make use of terms of motion to describe what they really intend to present as a static hierarchy of things. There are, evidently, no general criteria which
permit of distinguishing this sort of "motion," i.e., the poetic device which Lessing
observed in Homer's description of the shield of Achilles, from an actually progress-
ing ascension. There can be no doubt with respect to the prose of Meier and Bonnet.
If Wieland's poetic expressions were not sufficiently clear in themselves, their dependence on Meier could be used to ascertain their "mobilized" intention.

The following two examples are somewhat more ambiguous. A careful examina-
tion, however, seems to succeed in interpreting them correctly as nonstatic. The first
is taken from Mark Akenside. On this author, cf. also G. R. Potter, "Mark Akenside,
Prophet of Evolution." Potter justifies the title of his essay by emphasizing Akenside's reference to the influence of the environment on the transformation of animals.
This aspect of the matter is of no importance for the present purpose. In contrast to
Potter, who finds the second edition of Akenside's poem on *The Pleasures of the
Imagination* more clearly "evolutionistic," we use the text of the first edition of
1745. Cf. *The Poems of the Pleasures* (Philadelphia, 1870), pp. 82f. In the second
book there is a conversation between the old sage Harmodius and an apparition on
whose transparent robe "in mystic signs engraved" was to be read "his office high
and sacred name, genius of human kind." Harmodius is scolded for having lamented
the cruelty and futility of life. Opening to him a vision of the beauties of nature, the
apparition then explains the purpose of the Creator who

> So fix'd the dates of being, so disposed
> To every living soul of every kind
> The field of motion and the hour of rest,
> That all conspired to his supreme design,
> To universal good: with full accord
> Answering the mighty model he had chosen,
> The best and fairest of unnumber'd worlds,
> That lay from everlasting in the store
> Of his divine conceptions. Nor content,
> By one exertion of creative power
> His goodness to reveal; through every age,
> Through every moment up the tract of time
> His parent hand, with ever new increase
> Of happiness and virtue, has adorn'd
> The vast harmonious frame: his parent hand
> From the mute shell-fish gasping on the shore
> To men, to angels, to celestial minds,
> For ever leads the generations on
> To higher scenes of being; while, supplied
> From day to day with his enlivening breath,
> Inferior orders in succession rise
> To fill the void below. As flame ascends,
> As bodies to their proper center move,
> As the poised ocean to th' attracting moon
> Obedient swells, and every headlong stream
> Develops its winding water to the main;
> So all things which have life aspire to God,
> The sun of being, boundless, unimpair'd,
> Centre of souls.

mal realm. Then only could it become a painful experience that "the animals shun him"[35] although he, man, longs for their friendship to forget for a moment his sublime and miserable lot of being branded, in spite of everything, as an irretrievable apostate from nature.[36]

When it became possible to ascribe a soul to all the members of the animal kingdom, man, we found, could be integrated at least philosophically into the order of things. His distinctness was no

---

The idea that God's parent hand leads the generations on from the mute shellfish to celestial minds seems to be conceived as referring to an actual ascension because otherwise there would be no need to have inferior orders rise to fill the void below.

The second example is one of the few fragments which Écouchard-Lebrun (1729-1807) wrote in addition to the only completed third book of his poem on nature. Casimir Alexandre Fusil, *la Poésie scientifique de 1750 à nos jours* (Paris, 1918), p. 63, gives its date as 1760, but adds: "Nous reconnaissons ici l'influence des travaux de Trembley et de Bonnet." The first alexandrine sounds like a French translation of Goethe's "Und so lang du das nicht hast, dieses stirb und werde . . ."

> Rien ne périt, tout change, et mourir c'est renaître.
> Tous les corps sont liés dans la chaîne de l'Être.
> La nature partout se précède et se suit . . .
> De l'homme aux animaux rapprochant la distance,
> Voyez l'homme des bois lier leur existence.
> Du corail incertain, né plante et minéral,
> Revenez au polype, insecte végétal.
> Sur l'insecte étonnant l'être se ramifie,
> Et présente partout les germes de la vie.
> De son corps divisé soudain réparateur,
> Il renaît plus nombreux sous le fer destructeur.

"L'homme des bois" is the ape. Line 4 finds its explanation in Ch. Bonnet, *Palingénésie*, p. 202: "Le Naturaliste . . . observe qu'entre deux Classes ou deux Genres voisins, il est des Espèces mitoyennes . . . qui dérangent plus ou moins ses distributions méthodiques." A wealth of material concerning the eighteenth-century idea that the ape could be considered as the "espèce mitoyenne" between animal and man is presented by A. O. Lovejoy, *The Great Chain of Being*, p. 234. It is, by the way, an ironical coincidence that the same ape helped later on to draw a new dividing line between man and beast. Cf. Friedrich Tiedemann, whose comparative studies of man and ape were begun in 1826. The brain of the orang was found to have greater similarities with that of the lower apes than with that of man. In 1837 Tiedemann compared the brain of the orang with that of negroes. The result remained the same. The "insecte" in line 8 is still the "polype." It is, finally, the expression "l'être . . . présente partout les germes de la vie" which seems to prove that Lebrun was thinking in terms of a nonstatic hierarchy.

[35] Cf. p. 53, n. 2.

[36] F. Hölderlin, "Hymne an die Freiheit," VIII, 5ff.:

> Einer, Einer nur ist abgefallen,
> Ist gezeichnet mit der Hölle Schmach;
> Stark genug, die schönste Bahn zu wallen,
> Kriecht der Mensch am trägen Joche nach.

longer basic but merely relative. The same result, it might be suggested, could have been obtained by denying also to man the privilege of a soul instead of extending it to all his lower brethren. This would have led to an extreme materialistic monism. A conception of peculiar interest is that which accepts the compromise not to deny the existence of a soul but to conceive of it as substantial, i.e., composed of elements not basically different from those of other natural phenomena. A soul of this sort, even though taken as the exclusive property of man, could not separate him irreparably from the realm of nature. The endeavor to find a place for the soul in the order of physical phenomena deserves a brief discussion at this point, for it may be construed as depending on the same quest for a unified conception of nature as the problem of the connection of man and beast. It can, furthermore, be pursued beyond the time when a structural identity of man and animal had become a truism.

The presence of spiritualistic beliefs in the Eighteenth Century is not very surprising. A system like that of Swedenborg is beautifully rational. The realm of the spirits seems to be organized on the basis of exactly those principles which human reason devised for the organization of our earthly existence. As to the behavior of the spirits themselves, it is soothingly plausible and quite adapted to the needs of a mind whose wisdom cannot reach beyond the sphere of its five senses. A time which produces a Swedenborg will not find it hard to listen to a Cagliostro.[37] Having observed that a serious thinker converses with spirits and associates with them on a footing of equality, one cannot hesitate to consider as a serious thinker a man who calls such spirits as other people call their dogs and has them appear in their concrete, if somewhat threadbare, materiality. Such a materialization of the spirit is obviously related to the typical tendency of the Eighteenth Century to represent all forces in nature, mysterious and otherwise, by a special kind of substance: one for light, another

[37] Even Wieland lumped men like Swedenborg, St. Martin, and Mesmer with Cagliostro and others as deceitful mystagogues who took advantage of the public's stupidity and love for the phantastic. Cf. Christoph Martin Wieland, "Euthanasia," *Sämmtliche Werke* (Leipzig: Göschen, 1853-1858), XXX, 105ff.; also F. Strich, *Mythologie*, I, 200.

for electricity, one for gravity, one for heat, one for animation, one for magnetism, etc. *ad infinitum* and *ad absurdum*. As the philosophical representative of early German Romanticism, Franz von Baader ridiculed this trend as early as 1792:[38]

If we are to suppose for each and every manifestation of force one special kind of matter, I can see no end of these chemical personifications. What we need most will finally be a matter which makes matter, since we decided that matter as such should not be capable of any manifestation of force of its own.

Yet the basic motive behind all these crude materializations was doubtless nothing but the desire to ascertain an unqualified homogeneity of all natural phenomena, whether physical or mental, concrete as well as abstract; and this motive was known to Baader and his fellow romanticists as it had been known to the Eighteenth Century. This is strikingly illustrated by an observation of Unger's.[39] In a discussion of Bonnet's palingenetic ideas he calls attention to a passage in Herder's essay on the ancients and their representation of death which refers to the bodily resurrection of Christ. "How this heavenly doctrine," Herder exclaims,[40] "changes at the same time the most delicate supernatural hope into a noble sensuality!" The context confirms Unger's impression that Herder voices here a yearning for a synthesis of two tendencies, one toward spiritualization and the other toward sensualization. It is perhaps not quite clear what such a synthesis would represent. Its monism, however, would doubtless conceive of body and soul as *one* phenomenon viewed merely in two different categories. This is, indeed, a generally romantic ideal, but unless we wish to think here of Goethe, it would not be easy to point to an actual instance of its realization. It seems that the synthesis of the spiritual and the sensual tends to crystallize *in statu nascendi* as a one-sided monism either purely materialistic or purely idealistic in character.[41]

[38] Franz Xaver von Baader, "Ideen über Festigkeit und Flüssigkeit," *Gren's Journal*, II, 222-47, or *Sämmtliche Werke*, edited by Franz Hoffmann, 15 vols. (Leipzig, 1850-1860), III, 181-202. Cf. also Hoffmann's editorial note to p. 186.

[39] R. Unger, *Herder, Novalis und Kleist*, p. 12.

[40] J. G. Herder, *Sämmtliche Werke*, V, 674.

[41] This helps to explain the fact that such extreme materialists as Karl Vogt or Haeckel surprise us at times with thoughts anticipated by typical Romanticists like

It is not only the subject matter of Herder's essay which brings to mind Hardenberg's fifth "Hymn to Night." We find there the same synthetic quest, and it is fascinating to observe how the younger thinker dissolves it in a sort of highly sensual spirituality. After an introductory invocation of the mythical past, Hardenberg reaches his first reference to death as the one dread which spoiled the general bliss of that golden age. Nevertheless, man succeeded in depicting death as "a quiet youth who comes and extinguishes the light and rests." This Hardenberg interprets as an escape from the horrors which death must have been when it meant the dissolution of life into brute matter. It was then a lifeless night, and "night remained a mystery not solved." Death depicted as a handsome youth is interpreted as only a poetic creation of the longing of a pre-Christian imagination. Quite in keeping with Hardenberg's magic idealism, such a dream of wish fulfillment must, nevertheless, correspond to something real. When the long period of preparation had passed, when Christ was born, a singer came from Greece to Palestine and greeted the Messiah: "Thou art the youth . . . Thou art Death . . ." This then might be called the Copernican achievement of Christ: Till then life was light and death was fearful darkness. Henceforth life is but a dream and light but a splinter of eternity. When that dream is over, the real life begins as "*one* continuous night of bliss." Death

---

Hardenberg or F. Schlegel. A psychological explanation of the monistic tendency toward extremes of pure idealism or pure materialism seems to be hinted at in Hölderlin's distich "Guter Rat":

> Hast du Verstand und ein Herz, so zeige nur eines von beiden!
> Beides verdammen sie dir, zeigest du beides zugleich.

An interesting light is thrown on the question by Ignatius Paul Vitalis Troxler, "Metaphysik" (1828), in Chr. Bernoulli and H. Kern, *Romantische Naturphilosophie,* p. 243: "Die Seele hat man . . . ungeachtet Alles beseelt ist, säkularisiert und mit einer kleinen Pension ins obere Dachstübchen verwiesen; dafür muß sie Magds-dienste tun; sie hat das Haus auszukehren, Fremden aufzumachen und zu leuchten, Wasser und Holz zu tragen, das Böse zu flicken, das Schmutzige zu waschen, zu kochen usw., denn sie ist nur um des Hauses willen da, ja nichts anderes als das haushaltende Haus selbst. Zuweilen ist ihr erlaubt, noch in ihrer alten Tracht zu erscheinen, und dann nennt man sie verächtlich Verstand und Begehrensvermögen und wirft ihr alle andere Titel vor, als ob sie damit vergeblichen Lärm gemacht und die guten Scholastiker, besonders aber den Reflexionsmenschen Aristoteles geäfft hätte. Tritt sie als Vernunft auf, so sieht man in ihr zu viel Ökonomie und tadelt ihre Nüchternheit; allenfalls als Einbildungskraft, das heißt jetzt so viel als *folle de la maison,* darf sie sich zuerst noch anmelden, und wer sie als solche aufführt, hat sich am wenigsten zu schämen, ihr noch das Gnadenbrot gereicht zu haben."

is no longer the end but the beginning of life. At the same time we have here Hardenberg's own Copernican achievement: What we call death is no longer the dissolution of life into brute matter but rather the dissolution of a brute body into the infinite ocean of life, for what we call life and everything our senses perceive is but a spark of the Spirit imprisoned in a narrow dream of an unreal reality. There is no soul which could free itself from the body. There is rather a body which longs for redemption and reintegration into the Soul which is called God and which appears in the thoughts of the poet as *one* continuous night of bliss.[42]

The cruder forms of "sensualization of the soul" are characteristically lacking during the *Blütezeit* of Romanticism. They appear again at the time of its decay and deteriorate quickly into a more or less pronounced materialistic spiritualism. A rather moderate version of this is presented by Schubert[43] in a striking metaphoric formulation:

As the digesting body retains from food, whose dead and decaying remains it rejects, a nutritive juice, which is transformed into new flesh, so, it seems, the soul retains from the dying visible body a something which may be called an invisible body; a germ of immortality, in which there is a regenerative power, able to reproduce in due time what has been lost and to rebuild from transformed dust a new, visible body.

A particularly interesting work in this tradition is Jung-Stilling's *Theory of Spiritualism*. The essence of its discouragingly involved teachings is skillfully hidden in paragraphs 9 and 10 of a summary in section five. There[44] we read:

Animal magnetism proves beyond a doubt that we have an inner man, i.e., a soul which consists of the divine spark, of the eternal spirit which

---

[42] Cf. the hymn in its entirety, *Novalis Schriften*, I, 60-64. The passages quoted *verbatim* read in the original: "Ein sanfter Jüngling löscht das Licht und ruht . . . Unenträtselt blieb die ewge Nacht . . . Der Jüngling bist du. Du bist der Tod . . . Nur *eine* Nacht der Wonne."

[43] Gotthilf Heinrich Schubert, "Geschichte der Seele" (1830), in Chr. Bernoulli and H. Kern, *Romantische Naturphilosophie*, p. 131.

[44] Heinrich Jung-Stilling, *Sämmtliche Schriften* (Stuttgart, 1837), VI: *Theorie der Geisterkunde*, p. 610: "§9. Der thierische Magnetismus beweist unwidersprechlich, daß wir einen innern Menschen, eine Seele haben, die aus dem göttlichen Funken, dem Vernunft und Willen habenden ewigen Geist und einer von ihm unzertrennlichen Lichthülle besteht.—§10. Die Lichtmaterie, die elektrische, die magnetische, die galvanische Materie und der Aether scheinen alle ein und das nämliche Wesen unter verschiedenen Modificationen zu sein."

has reason and will, and a covering of light which is inseparable from it. The matter of light, the matter of electricity, that of magnetism, and that of galvanism as also ether seem to be one and the same thing in different modifications.

We have here a perfect case of the decline of a romantic idea. Hardenberg thinks of reality as a "bewitched" spark of the universal soul. Schubert tries to assure a connection of the soul with matter by ascribing to it a physical constituent which can develop into a new physical body, a thought conceived by analogy with the regeneration of plants from a potential preformation in their seeds. Jung-Stilling, finally, "materializes" the soul and gives it a "body" which is not basically different from the "substance" of light and a number of other materials quite common in physical nature. This last conception of a "material" realm of the spirits is strangely reminiscent of Swedenborg. It is a spiritualism of the "five senses."[45] Its purpose is not[46] to rationalize a biocentric faith in palingenetic immortality but merely to conceive of a realm from which the spirits can descend upon us in our less eternal but only slightly more terrestrial existence.

Of Jung-Stilling's *Theory of Spiritualism* Achim von Arnim wrote to Brentano that he felt it to be a wonderful book, "so deep and yet so very human, just like a Greek mythology."[47] It is indeed a strange sort of mythology, but we must remember that we have ventured ahead in time and have reached the period in which "magnetism and somnambulism were the surrogate for a lacking

---

[45] The phrase "philosophy of the five senses" was used derogatorily by Blake. Cf. Georg Fuchs, *Deutsche Form* (München, 1906), p. 28. H. Jung-Stilling says explicitly, *Theorie der Geisterkunde,* p. 609: "In unserm gegenwärtigen natürlichen Zustand können wir auf keinem andern Wege zu irgend einer Erkenntniß erschaffener Dinge gelangen, als durch unsere fünf sinnlichen Werkzeuge."

[46] Cf. H. Jung-Stilling, *Theorie der Geisterkunde,* p. 619: "§40. Die Seelenwanderung ist in den Gesetzen und in der Natur des Geisterreichs *nicht* gegründet . . ."

[47] Cf. Reinhold Steig, *Achim von Arnim und die ihm nahe standen,* 3 vols. (Stuttgart, 1894-1913), I, 261. Arnim reviewed Jung-Stilling's book in Gubitz' *Gesellschafter,* I, 1817. The review was reprinted in *Unbekannte Aufsätze und Gedichte,* "Berliner Neudrucke," third series, I, 17ff. Cf. also F. Strich, *Mythologie,* II, 153. Arnim's line of reasoning sheds remarkable light on the present problem. Poets, he feels, will not dispense with apparitions. Animal magnetism, however, has removed apparitions from the sphere of fancy. The prophetic powers which Jung described as manifestations of psychic disturbances are sacred and healthy in poetry. The conclusion is that Jung-Stilling's theory might become a real mythology if only the nation could produce a Dante who could succeed in linking up that system with the understanding of the universe which the present (Arnim's) age has attained.

mythology," not only for Hoffmann, about whom this remark was originally made.[48] When young Goethe wrote:[49] "The world of the spirits is *not* closed!" he thought of the bliss which elevation into it through mere communion with nature had meant to him. Hardenberg copied and emphasized the thought:[50] "Indeed, the world of the spirits is opened for us. Its revelation is always at hand!" This "world of the spirits," however, was our world. To see it, to enjoy life in it, nothing had to be done but to bathe the oppressed soul in the rosy light of dawn. The world of the spirits which Jung-Stilling had in mind was a world of ectoplasmic spectres. A path leads to it, but, as Börne expressed the thought in a related context,[51] "it crosses a shaky and rotten bridge. Below there is a threatening abyss, and the frightened wanderer dares neither to advance nor to retreat and waits undecided till the pillars collapse." It is E. Th. A. Hoffmann's art which Börne wishes to describe in this passage. He proceeds, however, as though he wanted to characterize the mythology which Arnim hoped to see derived from Jung-Stilling's spectral system:

It opens up realms which are haunted by ghosts, it betrays the life of lifeless things and brings to light the hidden threads by which man is guided, it lets every flower appear as the lurking eye of a spectre and

[48] F. Strich, *Mythologie,* II, 306.
[49] Goethe, *Urfaust,* lines 93ff.:
> Die Geister Welt ist nicht verschlossen,
> Dein Sinn ist zu, dein Herz ist todt.
> Auf! bade, Schüler, unverdrossen
> Die irdsche Brust im Morgenroth.
[50] *Novalis Schriften,* III, 111: "Die Geisterwelt ist uns in der Tat schon aufgeschlossen—Sie ist immer *offenbar.*"
[51] Ludwig Börne, *Gesammelte Schriften,* 3 vols. (Leipzig: Reclam, n.d.), II, 242, "Humoral-Pathologie," review of E. Th. A. Hoffmann's *Kater Murr:* "Kater Murr und die ihnen vorhergegangenen Werke seines Verfassers sind Nachtstücke, nie von sanftem Mondscheine, nur von Irrwischen, fallenden Sternen und Feuersbrünsten beleuchtet. Alle seine Menschen stehen auf der faulen wankenden Brücke, die von dem Glauben zum Wissen führt; unter ihnen droht der Abgrund, und die erschrockenen Wanderer wagen weder vorwärts zu schreiten noch zurück, und harren unentschlossen, bis die Pfeiler einstürzen. Das ist seine Stärke, seine Wissenschaft und seine Kunst,—die Geisterwelt aufzuschließen, zu verrathen das Leben der leblosen Dinge, an den Tag zu bringen die verborgenen Fäden, womit der Mensch, und der glückliche, ahnungslos gegängelt wird; jede Blume als ein lauerndes Gespensterauge, jeden freundlich sich herüber neigenden Zweig als den ausgestreckten Arm einer zerstörenden dunkeln Macht erscheinen zu lassen. Es ist der *dramatisirte Magnetismus* . . . Es muß auch solche Käuze geben."

every branch that bends and greets as the extended arm of a destructive and dark power.

The realm of light-bodied souls is a realm of ghosts. To commune with it is infernal punishment. The closing words of Jung-Stilling's work read appropriately:[52] "The Lord who is Love Eternal protect in His mercy the readers of this book from such a frightful fate. Amen!"

[52] H. Jung-Stilling, *Theorie der Geisterkunde*, p. 620: "Der Herr, der Erbarmer, der die ewige Liebe ist, bewahre alle Leser dieses Buches vor diesem schrecklichen Schicksal. Amen!"

V

TIME AND ETERNITY: THE PROBLEM OF EVOLUTION

THE EIGHTEENTH CENTURY, we saw, integrated man into the order of things. It conceived of him as an animal which had so far been more successful than any of its competitors in the advance toward final perfection. All the protagonists of these ideas have at one time or another been labeled "prophets" or "forerunners" of evolution in the nineteenth-century sense of the word.[1] If limited by certain qualifications, such statements are not entirely wrong.

It is Croce who said[2] that

no speculative concept which is really what it claims to be can be entirely lacking in one age and appear suddenly in another. There can only be this difference, that science seems to derive its problems in a given period from one aspect of an idea rather than from another. The idea itself, however, is always there in its totality.

What Croce describes here has been called the "historical mutation of concepts,"[3] a thought which could be further clarified by re-terming it "the metamorphosis of ideas." From this point of view it is equally unsatisfactory to trace modern evolutionary thinking to its "beginnings" in the romantic era and not farther, and to interpret eighteenth-century manifestations of evolutionism as timid prophecies of a coming performance.[4] The younger stage in the metamorphosis of an idea is not necessarily superior to the older, and so far as terms like "prophet" and "forerunner" are

---

[1] Cf. p. 64, n. 34. Of Écouchard-Lebrun, C. A. Fusil, *Poésie scientifique*, pp. 63f., says that his was an attempt "to sing the epic of life as modern science conceives it."

[2] Benedetto Croce, *Teoria e storia della storiografia* (Bari, 1917), p. 246.

[3] John C. Hemmeter, "Mutationen in geschichtlichen Begriffen und der Zusammenhang medizinischer Ideen und Lehren," *Festschrift Max Neuburger gewidmet* (Vienna, 1928), especially pp. 164ff.

[4] Cf., e.g., B. Croce, *Storiografia*, p. 247: "Nobody should suppose that the scientific importance of the concept of evolution had not been felt or anticipated prior to the romantic period. One could investigate its traces in the pantheism of the great philosophers of the Renaissance, especially in Bruno, as also in mysticism, in as much as it involves pantheism; more distinctly still in the . . . conception of history as a gradual education of mankind, in which the successive revelations would have been communicated in less and less elementary textbooks."

meant to imply inferiority as compared with a later fulfillment they should be avoided.

It is the task of the historian of evolution to discern the peculiarities of the process of mutation which differentiate nineteenth-century evolution from all its older forms. It is quite obvious, even for the nonspecialist, that a major characteristic of all modern theories of evolution is their aim to trace physical ancestries from higher into lower forms of life. To put it crudely: the genealogical tree of the director of a zoölogical garden and the genealogical trees of all his individual animals are, from this point of view, not really trees but branch systems, all of which together make up the tree. Allusions to this idea have been found in the writings of Goethe, Hardenberg, Schelling, and other romantic thinkers.[5] In tracing them one should be wary of concluding that the process which Lovejoy called the temporalization of the chain of being leads necessarily to the idea of physical descent. A temporal factor in the conception of nature's hierarchy appears at the end of the Eighteenth and at the beginning of the Nineteenth Century as a matter of course. This, however, it will be shown, does not at all signify that the current ideas on evolution were timidly groping their way toward Darwinian descendentalism. Olshausen's conclusion[6] that Hardenberg "made [the temporal factor] the basis of all his ideas and allowed it to assume a more and more definite shape until it finally became the basic thought of his *Ofterdingen*," is thus really not so revolutionary as it sounds.

The contention that a temporalized conception of the chain of being does not represent an advance toward descendentalism is far from self-evident. It finds support, however, by an analysis of the significance of the temporal factor in question. It has been observed[7] that writers in the Eighteenth Century seem often to

[5] Passages of descendentalistic interest from Goethe are, according to various authorities, *Werke* (Sophienausgabe), 2nd series, VI, 185; VIII, 234; IX, 117; VI, 13; VIII, 223; 3rd series, II, 130; etc. Cf. also Hermann von Helmholtz' address of 1892, "Goethes Vorahnungen kommender naturwissenschaftlicher Ideen," *Goethes naturwissenschaftliches Denken und Wirken*, Berlin: *Die Naturwissenschaften*, 1932.

[6] Waldemar Olshausen, *Friedrich von Hardenbergs Beziehungen zur Naturwissenschaft seiner Zeit* (Leipzig, 1905), p. 72.

[7] Cf. p. 64, n. 34.

describe a natural hierarchy with a possible ascension in time, when they are really concerned with nothing but a stylistic device which mobilizes a static object for purposes of a more effective presentation. Professor Lovejoy states[8] that "it is often impossible to be sure whether . . . [a given author] is speaking of a temporal sequence of stages of evolution or merely of the consecutive steps, i.e., grades in the Scale of Beings." It is considerably less plausible that exactly the same should also be true for a thinker like Schelling. Walzel, however, bases this observation on a brief summary of Schelling's evolutionary system. This takes its start in the basic polarity of repulsion and attraction which manifests itself in gravity, cohesion, elasticity, and certain aspects of chemism. A new polarity of ponderable matter and ether results in light and heat. The next step reaches the phenomena of electricity, magnetism, and galvanism. These represent the transition into the realm of organisms, where a slow spiritualization marks the evolution of the most highly conscious from the most deeply unconscious. Then Walzel continues: "In this sequence of stages Schelling wished expressly to trace a development (*Entwicklung*)." Yet the final conclusion is that "he [Schelling] did not explain whether this transition from the imperfect to the more perfect was also to be an historical fact and a temporal phenomenon."[9] A development which is not necessarily a temporal phenomenon is either an absurdity or presupposes a very peculiar conception of time.

A discussion of the concept of time as held and developed during the decades around 1800 must be set in relief by reference to a larger context. "The philosophers of the Middle Ages," to quote from a convenient historical summary by Carrel,[10]

considered time as an agent concretizing abstractions. To them time, in nature, appeared as completely inseparable from space. In reducing objects to their primary qualities—that is to what can be measured and is susceptible of mathematical treatment—Galileo deprived them of their secondary qualities and duration.

[8] A. O. Lovejoy, *The Great Chain of Being*, p. 364.
[9] Oskar Walzel, *Deutsche Romantik*, "Aus Natur und Geisteswelt," vol. 232, pp. 50ff.
[10] A. Carrel, *Man the Unknown*, p. 162.

"This arbitrary simplification," Carrel concludes, "made possible the development of physics," i.e., we add, of physics as a technological science, which exhausts itself in what might be called spatial thinking. In such a science the notion *time* is basically always only space in disguise. The measurement of time becomes possible only through the "trick" of converting it into space. The spatial thinking of modern science may be contrasted with temporal thinking. This refers, then, to the pre-Galilean tradition, which depends ultimately on the foundations of Western thought as elaborated by Greek philosopher-scientists from Pythagoras to Aristotle.[11]

Greek and medieval temporal thinking as such has, naturally, no direct interest for the present discussion. It is, however, a striking observation that the scientific tendencies of the age around 1800 have often been characterized as akin to those of ancient Greece and medieval Europe. Of Goethe it has been said by Adolf Meyer[12] that "his scientific research was like that of the ancients; Plato and Aristotle would have proceeded in their investigations of natural objects exactly as Goethe did if they had been placed in his position in the history of thought." Similar statements might be made about a great many of Goethe's contemporaries. Joël arrives at the conclusion[13] that the pre-Socratic philosophers of nature "had much the same intellectual preoccupations as the Romanticists, but," Joël qualifies interestingly, "they had them 'naïvely,' to use Schiller's terminology, while the Romanticists have them 'sentimentally,' in a conscious endeavor and with an effort of volition."

Observations of this sort are also valuable since they help to discredit the cumbersome notion that Goethe, in his scientific demeanor, was an isolated phenomenon in his time and age. The romantic respect for the scientific views of the past does not, of course, express itself in explicit use of the more modern construct

[11] Cf. also Karl Buchheim, *Wahrheit und Geschichte,* Leipzig: Hegner, 1935. The introductory chapters are a lucid exposition of the problem of spatial as against temporal thinking.

[12] Adolf Meyer, "Goethes Naturerkenntnis. Ihre Voraussetzung in der Antike. Ihre Krönung durch Carus," *Jahrbuch des Freien Deutschen Hochstifts* (1929), p. 209.

[13] Karl Joël, *Der Ursprung der Naturphilosophie aus dem Geiste der Mystik* (Jena, 1906), in the appendix on "Archaische Romantik."

"temporal thinking." The Greek sciences, like those of the Middle Ages,[14] were held to be characterized by a certain totalitarianism, an identification of what we should distinguish as poetry and science or as science and ethics. It is, however, precisely such an identification which the construct of temporal thinking tries to cover. Temporal thinking alone is capable of biocentric interest, for, as Karl Ernst von Baer put it as late as 1866, "the process of life can be apprehended only in a visualization of time."[15] Temporal thinking alone is capable of an interest in those aspects of a given phenomenon which pertain to life, such as poetics, aesthetics, ethics, etc., as distinguished from the spatially material which alone is susceptible of mathematical treatment.[16]

[14] The name of Paracelsus comes to mind here. His significance for the romantic era would deserve a special monograph. Goethe, Baader, Hardenberg, Rademacher, are the more important mediators.

[15] Karl Ernst von Baer, *Über Zweckmäßigkeit und Zielstrebigkeit* (1866), quoted after Alfred Rosenberg, *Der Mythus des XX. Jahrhunderts* (Munich: Hoheneichen-Verlag, 1936), pp. 394f. The context of Baer's statement will be of further importance: "Wir werden erkennen, daß das Wesen des Lebens nur der Lebens-Prozeß selbst oder der Verlauf des Lebens sein kann. Wir werden dann nicht nach dem räumlichen Sitze des Lebens suchen, da der Lebensprozeß nur in der Anschauung der Zeit verlaufen kann."

[16] Mathematics is here to be taken in the generally accepted sense of the word, not in Hardenberg's sense, and not in the sense which the word *Mathesis* had for some of the later Romanticists. Only thus will it be possible to appreciate fully the significance of Goethe's attitude toward mathematics. Ernst Cassirer, "Goethe und die mathematische Physik," *Idee und Gestalt* (Berlin, 1921), p. 71, gives the following generally important analysis. There is, Cassirer says, a "decisive difference between the principles of mathematical physics and the Goethean vision of nature. Both endeavor to overcome the isolation of individual views and to gain a serial interconnection of phenomena. However, the two make use of entirely different ways and means for the establishment of such an interconnection. The procedure of the exact sciences is on the whole to relate the sensually and empirically given variety of phenomena to another 'rational' variety and to reproduce (*abbilden*) it therein completely. To achieve this transformation into a logical form, mathematical physics must begin by transforming the elements which are to enter into it. The contents of empirical perception must first be translated into purely quantitative and numerical values; then only will there arise the possibility of stating relations based on law; [this is so] because the general significance and the basic pattern of a natural law presuppose the form of an equation of causation. Goethe, on the other hand, demands between the phenomenologically perceptible a new kind of interrelation which leaves the contents of the perception as such inviolate. He demands that the elements be viewed together synthetically. In the exact sciences the synthesis does not so much concern the elements themselves but rather their conceptual and numerical representatives which we insert in their stead." Cf. also Cassirer's condensed summary on p. 74: "The mathematical formula strives to make the phenomena calculable, that of Goethe to make them visible."

The biocentrism of the romantic era signifies thus a revival of temporal thinking. This manifests itself quite often through a certain undertone of yearning and envy in the observation that "the ancients knew of no separation of science and life," so that, as Börne puts it,[17] "they could think their lives and live their thoughts, which were strong and lasting because the entire fullness of life of their creators was impressed upon them."[18] The same envious veneration of classical antiquity may be discerned in the hope of seeing the present achieve a "sentimental" resurrection of the "naïve" first golden age of the Greeks. A striking expression of this optimism was given by Adam Müller in 1808 in a passage which serves at the same time to connect the present problem with the more general one of the quest for a unified vision of nature and spirit.

The conception commonly held by our contemporaries divides all phenomena generally and specifically in two great classes. As though there were one law ruling in the realm of realities and an entirely different law in the realm of ideas and of the products of man's inner nature. That was quite different in the conception of things which the ancients held! Ethics and physics have both the same object!—The realm of law or of ideas is one with the realm of nature or things real!

Thus Müller goes on in his characterization of Greek thought, persisting all the while in an expressive use of the present tense. As though this device were not sufficient to apply his description also to the contemporary situation, he then proceeds with an explicit statement of his conviction that Germany's mission in the

---

[17] L. Börne, "Altes Wissen, neues Leben" (1823), *Schriften*, I, 96.

[18] A very strange passage, which is not quite clear but which seems to mirror a basically different view of the ancients, occurs in A. W. Schlegel's *Vorlesungen über schöne Literatur und Kunst* (1801-1804), edited by Jakob Minor, "Deutsche Literatur-Denkmale des 18. und 19. Jahrhunderts," vols. 17-19 (Heilbronn, 1884), III, 199. Here August Wilhelm speaks of a complete separation of poetry and philosophy in Greek antiquity. This remark is made by way of contrast to a statement about Dante. It is thus perhaps nothing but an ill-considered stylistic device and need not be taken too seriously. The passage reads: "The direct representation of infinity has probably never been achieved as poetically as in the *Divina Commedia*. The ancients could not assign such a task to themselves because of the complete separation of poetry and philosophy. The epic works of their physicists, e.g., those of Empedocles, belonged really to philosophy and took from poetry only diction and rhythm, and if we may judge on the basis of Lucretius, those poems were not constructed symbolically so that their form might have held the infinite object in its reflection."

science of nature as elsewhere is to mediate between modern times and antiquity.[19] The resulting synthesis, to paraphrase Friedrich Schlegel,[20] "would have appeared as a science of life in contrast to the dead science of death of the modern past."

It is this same science of death which Franz von Baader meant to attack when he restated, in the fourth decade of the Nineteenth Century, the romantic creed that it is the task of the present to take up again the tradition of Greek and medieval thought. "It is not at all in physics as a science," Baader wrote,[21] "but only as an observational and experimental technique that we have surpassed the ancients, just as we have surpassed them with regard to moral codes and not at all in morality." He further states that there is to be observed "a progressive shallowing of the natural sciences which has kept pace, especially since the Reformation, with that in theology." As an accusation this means that the science of nature has developed into a mathematically abstract technique through absolute disregard of "time as an agent concretizing abstractions."[22] As an exhortation it means that the science of nature can become again a science of life if it is reborn in the spirit of Greek antiquity or of the pre-Galilean Middle Ages. Spatial-mathematical thinking must be replaced by biocentric thinking, in which the temporal factor animates spatial phenomena with which it is inseparably connected. This, however, is not only an idea of Baader's: it is generally romantic. The endeavor to conceive of time and space as interrelated is representatively illustrated by Adam Müller's statement in the *Doctrine of Opposites:*[23] "Space is that which opposes (*entgegensteht*) time and vice versa. Space is anti-time, time is anti-space. One is not possible without the other." The contention that temporal and biocentric thinking are functionally interdependent may be based on an equally representative quotation from the romantic late-

[19] Adam Müller, *Vorlesungen über deutsche Wissenschaft und Literatur* (1808), edited by Artur Salz (Munich, 1920), p. 119.

[20] In a letter to Boisserée, written in 1810 or later, Friedrich Schlegel referred to his plan of a new philosophy, "die als Philosophie des Lebens (im Gegensatz gegen die bisherige tote Philosophie des Todes) . . . erscheinen soll." Cf. Johannes Nohl, "Franz von Baader, der Philosoph der Romantik," *Euphorion,* XIX (1912), 614.

[21] F. v. Baader, "Religionswissenschaft und Naturwissenschaft," *Werke,* III, 333.

[22] Cf. p. 76, n. 10.

[23] Adam Müller, *Die Lehre vom Gegensatz* (Berlin: Realschulbuchhandlung, 1804), p. 251.

comer Carus. It dissolves our problem in the more general one of *being* and *becoming*,[24] and must be set in relief by the observation that Carus' panpsychism permits the identification of the concept of becoming or growth with that of life. With this in mind, we are to understand that existence necessitates space, that life necessitates time, that purely spatial phenomena are dead, and that living phenomena are always and necessarily time-spatial. Carus' exact words are:[25]

A general, momentary, simultaneous manifestation of the becoming of something which exists eternally, necessitates what we call space. From the ever recurring successive manifestation of being in the phenomenon of becoming is derived the category which we call time.

The discussion may be brought to a head by the tabulation of all the major pertinent utterances of one representative author. We select Hardenberg. In a letter to Friedrich Schlegel he announced in 1799 that he had found a deeper understanding of space and time, that both had been sadly misunderstood in the past but that he was now aware of their personality and creative power.[26] Repeating these words almost literally, Hardenberg proceeds in his private notes with the explanation that the activity of time and space is creative and that the universe hinges upon their relation.[27] Elsewhere he says:

Time and space originate simultaneously, they are probably one and

[24] *Werden* and *Sein*. Cf. also C. G. Carus, *Organon der Erkenntnis*, p. 130. Here it is stated that there does not seem to be another language as fully equipped as German to express this polarity. *Sein* is at times translatable, but it is impossible to find the equivalent of *Werden*. Repeatedly Carus suggests that the expression *das Werdende* should be used instead of the pale loan word *Natur*. Cf., *Organon der Erkenntnis*, p. 135. Considering the importance which Carus attaches to this idea, it is interesting to note that he was fully aware of his dependence on Goethe. Having complained about the lack of understanding for nature which characterizes most of his contemporaries, Carus concludes the discussion in one of his cosmo-biological letters, *Briefe über das Erdleben*, p. 10, by stating: "Dem würde gewiß nicht so sein, wenn das was wir *natura* nach seiner Ableitung von *nascor,* ich entstehe, nennen, und also das im Göttlichen und durch Göttliches rastlos Entstehende, Vergehende und wieder Entstehende anerkennen, in jeder Sprache durch ein eigentümlich gebildetes Wort sich bezeichnet fände!—Die deutsche Sprache, deren innerer philosophischer Sinn und schöne Bildsamkeit sich um so deutlicher hervorhebt, je mehr man in ihre Ramificationen eindringt, würde hier am wenigsten einer schicklichen Wortbildung entbehren, ja sie besitzt eine solche in den Worten von Goethe: 'Das Werdende, das ewig wirkt und lebt.'"

[25] C. G. Carus, *Organon der Erkenntnis*, p. 136.

[26] *Novalis Schriften*, IV, January 20, 1799.

[27] *Novalis Schriften*, III, 265.

the same thing, as subject and object. Space is static time—time is space made variable and flowing. Space is the schema and time is the concept.[28]

"Freedom and immortality belong together as time and space."[29] "Space is a precipitate of time—a necessary consequence of time."[30] "Force is a function of time and space."[31] "Space and time are identical—only reversed—as nature and person."[32] "Is not time perhaps the square of space?"[33] A summary of all these thoughts is finally offered in the statement: "The ordinary present connects past and future by limitation. The spiritual present does it by dissolution."[34]

Most of these formulations were, to be sure, jotted down in the form of private notes. They are not, for that reason, to be taken less seriously. We are not at all dealing with the ephemeral thoughts of a singularly fertile mind but rather with personal expressions of a general attitude. This is confirmed by Oken's categorical utterance: "Time is simply the active thinking of God . . . Created time and creation are one."[35] Is not this merely a bolder restatement of Hardenberg's reference to the personality and creative power of time? Indeed, the two may be combined as but different versions of one basic thought, as the premises of a tautologous syllogism: "God's thinking is time, time is creative, *ergo* the created world consists of God's thoughts." This idea, which is quite common with romantic thinkers,[36] implies that space and time are dimensions of God's thoughts. For God, the visualization of past, present, and future cannot, as it were, necessitate "prolonged" observation. Past, present, and future constitute for Him an added dimension of the object of His creative thought. In His perception a living phenomenon is simultaneously young and old. All the various stages of its development coincide,[37] for God, although his thought produces time, cannot be

[28] *Novalis Schriften*, III, 156.
[29] *Novalis Schriften*, III, 213.
[30] *Novalis Schriften*, III, 291.
[31] *Novalis Schriften*, III, 305.
[32] *Novalis Schriften*, II, 269.
[33] *Novalis Schriften*, III, 31.
[34] *Novalis Schriften*, II, "Blütenstaub," 109.
[35] L. Oken, *Naturphilosophie* (1809), I, 22.
[36] Cf. p. 115, n. 88.
[37] This is what K. E. v. Baer called "Anschauung der Zeit." Cf. p. 78, n. 15. It can

involved in its current.[38] From the human point of view God appears to be standing outside of time in what we call eternity. If a transition into divine spheres were possible for a human soul, it would cease to be carried along by time's relentless drift; it would be emancipated into eternity, and in its vision time would become a mere dimension of external created things. This transformation of time into eternity is a thought of Jacob Böhme. It is quoted by Carus as a basis for his attempt to disentangle the question of time and eternity within the limits of human means and human understanding. The result is a surprisingly simple metaphor. If eternity is compared to a straight line, time may be thought of as a point which moves along it.[39]

There remains one troublesome objection. All these thoughts were conceived by a human mind. Yet they themselves seem to imply that their understanding is open to God alone. There is but one answer to this, however presumptuous it may sound. That which belongs to God is not beyond the reach of man. The symbol of the human mind is a winged Psyche and its name is *anima humano-divina*.[40] "We *are* God,"[41] said Hardenberg, supplying thus the last link in our reasoning. "We *are* God; as far as we are

---

probably be connected, or even identified, with the idea of "intellektuelle Anschauung." On its importance for a rational conception of teleology, cf. p. 88. The logical link is approximately this: God perceives end and beginning as one. His extratemporal position permits such "Anschauung der Zeit." The beginnings of organic growths tend toward their ends as though these ends, which God sees in them, were actually contained in them. There must be something in organisms which might be described as their participation in God's vision. What the subject, God, visualizes in the object, organism, must be experienced in one way or another by that which is beheld as partner in the action of Him who beholds.

[38] Here we sense at the same time the ethos of Goethe's "Grenzen der Menschheit," especially lines 29f. and 37ff.:

> Was unterscheidet
> Götter von Menschen? . . .
> Ein kleiner Ring
> Begrenzt unser Leben,
> Und viele Geschlechter
> Reihen sich dauernd
> An ihres Daseins
> Unendliche Kette.

[39] C. G. Carus, *Organon der Erkenntnis*, p. 138, quotes Böhme: "Wem Zeit ist wie Ewigkeit und Ewigkeit wie Zeit, der ist befreit von allem Streit."

[40] Cf. p. 211, n. 37.

[41] *Novalis Schriften*, II, 142.

individuals, we can only think." This added remark contrasts our thinking, which we do as individuals, with our being, which constitutes us as the totality of the human race. It must be emphasized: Hardenberg does not pretend that we are gods; he identifies the multitude of human beings with the oneness of God. This, then, is the first conclusion: humanity as a whole is like unto God. It occupies a position outside of time in the realm of eternity. Its thought is creative, and time is in its vision but an added dimension of the things it beholds. This is a beautiful thought, but where and how does mankind think and see? The romantic answer is in Friedrich Schlegel's version:[42]

Through its artists mankind becomes one individual. They connect posterity and anteriority in the present. They are the superior soul organ in which the spirits of life of the entire external human race converge.

In art the transformation of time into eternity, of which Jacob Böhme spoke,[43] can be achieved. This is the deep significance of the grandiose picture which Hardenberg draws in the third "Hymn to Night" of a time which moves rapidly away like a thunderstorm beyond the horizon.[44] Hölderlin's ode "Patmos" makes use of the same material in its introductory metaphors, which, it seems, the present discussion can save from being misinterpreted as a mere poetic trick.

> Im Finstern wohnen
> Die Adler, und furchtlos gehn
> Die Söhne der Alpen über den Abgrund weg
> Auf leichtgebaueten Brücken.
> Drum, da gehäuft sind rings
> Die Gipfel der Zeit, und die Liebsten
> Nah wohnen, ermattend auf
> Getrenntesten Bergen,
> So gib unschuldig Wasser,
> O Fittiche gib uns, treuesten Sinns
> Hinüberzugehn und wiederzukehren.[45]

[42] F. Schlegel, "Ideen," 64.
[43] Cf. n. 39 above.
[44] *Novalis Schriften*, I, 57: ". . . Jahrtausende zogen abwärts in die Ferne wie Ungewitter . . ."
[45] F. Hölderlin, "Patmos," 5ff. The force of these declarations becomes still more striking if we contrast the passage with another in which the same basic idea is used

The transformation of time into eternity is, finally, the subject of Hardenberg's poem on "The Wedding of the Seasons."[46] It occupies a central position in *Heinrich von Ofterdingen* and consequently in the philosophy of its author. It is permissible to see in it the solution of Klingsor's tale and consequently of the entire novel. In addition to its individual significance for Hardenberg, this poem plays an important part in Romanticism generally. Its thought, to be sure, was the common and spontaneous property of a variety of contemporary thinkers; but its very form seems to have become the inspiration of the most important work of romantic painting. "The Wedding of the Seasons" can be read as the text for the magnificent fragments of Philipp Otto Runge's *Times of the Day.*[47]

The foregoing analysis of the concept of time as understood by romantic poets and thinkers throws light on their conception of a nonstatic hierarchy of beings. This hierarchy is a temporal phenomenon. It is alive and evolving, but its evolution cannot be perceived by a mind which is itself carried away by the stream of time. There seem to be only stages whose obvious interrelation remains an insoluble riddle. However, let this mind achieve emancipation from time and attain the viewpoint of eternity. The stages of the hierarchy will then represent its temporal dimension. Time is the animating factor which combines the phenomena of nature into one living whole. This is what is meant when stages in the order of things are said to evolve from each other. They be-

---

for purely literary purposes. This is the case in Joseph von Eichendorff, "Julian," V, 30ff., "DNL," vol. 146², edited by Max Koch (Berlin and Stuttgart, 1893) :

> Was der Genius schafft
> In schauderndem Entzücken,
> Wölbt unsichtbar durch die Luft
> Über der Jahrhunderte Kluft
> Demantene Brücken,
> Wo die verwegnen,
> Unsterblichen Fechter
> Getrennter Geschlechter
> Sich freudig begegnen.

[46] *Novalis Schriften*, I, 249.

[47] Cf. also Fritz Strich, *Deutsche Klassik und Romantik* oder *Vollendung und Unendlichkeit* (Munich, 1928³), p. 111. P. Kluckhohn, *Novalis Schriften*, I, 56*, discusses the importance for Runge of Eros' treasure in Klingsor's tale.

long together as the tree and the seed; they are present in each other as "tomorrow is present in today."[48]

In addition, it seems, we have found the principle according to which the relative positions in the hierarchic order of things must be determined. The power of emancipation from time cannot be attributed to God alone. He, to be sure, is not involved in the current of time; He watches its waves from a position in eternity.[49] However, man whom those waves lift and carry and swallow, is at least capable of longing for a similar vision. Indeed, he attains it

[48] Arthur Drews, *Die Lehre von Raum und Zeit in der Nachkantischen Philosophie* (Halle, 1889), p. 25, quotes from Albert Lange, *Geschichte des Materialismus*, 1st edition (1866), p. 254: "Wenn es wahr sein sollte, daß alle Dinge im Universum in Wechselwirkung stehen, und alles nach Gesetzen unwandelbar zusammenhängt, so wäre auch Schillers Dichterwort 'Und in dem Heute wandelt schon das Morgen' im strengsten Sinne des Wortes eine metaphysische Wahrheit, und es müßten auch Intelligenzen denkbar sein, welche dasjenige simultan auffassen, was uns in Zeitfolge entsteht." Drews continues: "Schopenhauer hat diesen Schluß bei seiner Annahme der kantischen Erkenntnistheorie mit Recht gezogen und darauf eine Erklärung der Prophetie und Magie gegründet." It seems, however, that Kant had drawn this conclusion himself long before the time of his *Critiques*. Cf. Immanuel Kant, "Träume eines Geistersehers" (1766), *Gesammelte Schriften*, published by the Prussian Academy of Sciences (Berlin, 1900-1936), II, 379f.: "Every human soul [has] already in this life its place in the world of spirits and belongs to a certain society which corresponds at any given moment to its inner condition with respect to the true and the good, that is, to reason and will. However, these positions of the spirits with regard to each other have nothing whatever in common with the space of our physical world; so that the soul of a person in India may be, as far as its spiritual position is concerned, the closest neighbor of another in Europe; while such as may live, as far as their bodies are concerned, in one and the same house, may be far enough removed from each other with respect to those other conditions. When a man dies, his soul does not change its position but perceives itself to be where, with respect to other spirits, it was already in this life." This basis of telepathy hinges on something which is true "at any given moment." It is not affected by the current of time and becomes thus a basis for magic and prophecy.

[49] This is again Goethe's poem "Grenzen der Menschheit," lines 29ff.:

> Was unterscheidet
> Götter von Menschen?
> Daß viele Wellen
> Vor jenen wandeln,
> Ein ewiger Strom:
> Uns hebt die Welle,
> Verschlingt die Welle,
> Und wir versinken.

A historical study of the motif of "Grenzen der Menschheit" would have to pay particular attention to Goethe's poem. It represents, as it were, the fruitful moment which summarizes an old development and, at the same time, presents this summary as the beginning of something entirely new. Before Goethe the present motif was used as a formula for the matter-of-fact observation that our power of understand-in occasional blissful victories over his lower animal nature. This happens when he is creative as an artist, i.e., as a summary of mankind past and future, or simply as God. The power of eman-

---

ing is inferior to that of God. Illustrations of this attitude abound in eighteenth-century letters. In English there is Pope's "Presume not God to scan." In German we have Haller's warning:

> In's Innre der Natur
> Dringt kein erschaffner Geist.

French is represented by Voltaire's lines:

> Je vous vois dessiner, par un art infaillible,
> Les dehors d'un Palais à l'homme inaccessible;
> Les angles, les côtés, sont marqués par vos traits;
> Le dedans à vos yeux est fermé pour jamais.

For Pope, cf. p. 36, n. 21; for Haller, p. 43, n. 36; for Voltaire, C. A. Fusil, *Poésie scientifique,* p. 40. Cf. also Frédéric II, "Epître sur la faiblesse de l'esprit humain," *Poésies du philosophe de Sans-Souci,* II. The ethos which finds a voice in the passages just quoted may be said to appear in a climactic summary as well in Kant's criticism as in Goethe's "Grenzen der Menschheit." At the same time, however, this poem exhibits an entirely new trait in as much as it is not content with confronting and differentiating human and divine powers. Here a human soul tries to admit its inferiority and succeeds in doing so only on a note of complaint and fatigue. There is something here which cannot refrain from asking "Why?", a something which seems to long to re-establish a new order, if not of equality, at least of equivalence of men and gods. The "Parzenlied" in *Iphigenie* has exactly the same comparison of men and gods, but instead of the note of fatigue there is in it a beginning of envy, almost of accusation, especially in this hammering repetition of a threefold "they":

> Sie aber, sie bleiben
> In ewigen Festen
> An goldenen Tischen.
> Sie schreiten vom Berge
> Zu Bergen hinüber.

From here it is but one step to the nostalgic "Schicksalslied" in Hölderlin's *Hyperion:*

> Ihr wandelt droben im Licht . . .
> Doch uns ist gegeben,
> Auf keiner Stätte zu ruhn,
> Es schwinden, es fallen
> Die leidenden Menschen
> Blindlings von einer
> Stunde zur andern,
> Wie Wasser von Klippe
> Zu Klippe geworfen,
> Jahrlang ins Ungewisse hinab.

If we translate Pope, Haller, Voltaire into the modern vernacular, we get this reasonable advice: "Don't be silly, don't make a fool of yourself by trying to be like God." Goethe and Hölderlin, on the other hand, inspire the remark: "A soul so deeply aware of the narrowness of human life in comparison with the eternal gods, is no longer ephemerally human but divine. Its capability of longing makes it attain an occasional blissful victory over its lower human nature." Thus we have attained, at least potentially, the romantic identification of God and Man.

cipation from time becomes thus the criterion of a given individual's rank in the scale of beings. Troxler says quite categorically[50] that the difference between man and animal is merely this: the higher species of animals which are able to distinguish between the external and the inner world and between past and future are not capable of conceiving of an existence outside of and beyond the spheres of time and space, so that the cognition of time and space, with the corollaries of eternity and infinity, is the prerogative of man alone. Carus' entire system of natural philosophy may be constructed around the basic problem of time and eternity. This contention assumes particular importance in view of the fact that Carus presents us so very often with belated and therefore matured summaries of romantic preoccupations. In the *Organon of Cognition*[51] he states that "it is through being conscious of its own self that the mind becomes able to conceive of a time which is not, for past and future are equally nonexistent in reality." This thought might be taken as merely the psychic substructure of Troxler's differentiation between man and beast. Carus, however, makes it the basis of his entire system of evolution and develops from it those teleological principles through which his views become diametrically opposed to all forms of Darwinian descendentalism. The passage which contains all this *in nuce* reads:

My doctrine of knowledge demonstrates that there is a sort of vision of the past and the future also in the unconsciously creative growth of the individual which is based on something eternal. This fact alone can explain the preformation of all organs in agreement with their future purpose. Actual knowledge of future and past, however, is possible only in the mind which has matured into cognition of its own eternity.[52]

This, it seems, is the basis on which the earlier "mobilization" of the chain of being must be understood. Let us consider the case of Hardenberg. It is doubtless a personal trait that he is fond of connecting the idea with questions of disease and generation:[53]

[50] Ignatius Paul Vitalis Troxler, "Metaphysik *oder* Naturlehre des menschlichen Erkennens" (1828), in Chr. Bernoulli and H. Kern, *Romantische Naturphilosophie,* p. 271.

[51] C. G. Carus, *Organon der Erkenntnis,* p. 140.

[52] Cf. also p. 82, n. 37.

[53] Aside from being conditioned by personal accidents, this factor in Hardenberg's views is also the representation of something generally romantic. The Romanticists

Diseases of plants are animalizations, diseases of animals rationalizations, diseases of stones are vegetabilizations. Should not a stone and an animal correspond to each plant? Plants are deceased stones and animals deceased plants.[54]

These phrases are, to be sure, merely what Hardenberg liked to call *fermenta cognitionis*. An almost systematic presentation of the problem is found, however, in one of his few really good poems in a lighter vein. It is to be identified by its important and charming refrain:

> Ich wußte nicht, wie mir geschah
> Und wie das wurde, was ich sah.[55]

This seems to express nothing but the impatience of a person who has tried, naturally in vain, to see something grow. This something keeps on growing throughout four stanzas, and finally one begins to feel that it is all the work of some sprite bent upon teasing the unfortunate observer. In stanza 5 a tree looks like an animal and beasts seem to try to become human. In stanza 7, the last, men are striving to assume the rank of gods, and one wonders how Hardenberg dared to present the idea of a palingenetic ascension along the scale of beings in such a playful and superficial form. However, the solution of this riddle has been given in stanza 6. There a girl comes along and makes the poet understand that we are not to *become,* but that we *are* gods. Now the refrain has changed:

> Nun wußt' ich wohl, wie mir geschah,
> Und wie das wurde, was ich sah.

Clothed in a charmingly witty form we find in this poem the very essence of romantic evolutionism: The ascension along the scale of beings need not move, since it has attained its goal at any particular moment during its growth. There is a plant in every seed and a god in every man. One of the most important thoughts

---

impress us often as forerunners of Freud or Thomas Mann. Friedrich Hufeland, "Über Sympathie" (1811), in Chr. Bernoulli and H. Kern, *Romantische Natur-philosophie,* p. 48, declares that there is an unmistakable kinship between contagion and biological generation, and similar expressions could be gathered from the works of all the significant romantic thinkers.

[54] *Novalis Schriften,* III, 369.
[55] *Novalis Schriften,* I, 357.

of Herder is, paradoxically formulated, that "only that can become which is."[56] This does not mean that transformation cannot be advance. It simply means that advance, when and where it occurs, is prearranged from the beginning of the process of transformation. This question comes up in Herder's dialogue *God*. It is formulated by Theano as her reaction to Theophron's discussion of palingenesis. "Would this transformation," she asks,[57] "be also an advance?" The answer is characteristically elusive. "Suppose," says Theophron, "it were not; but can you imagine a continued life, an eternally and progressively active force without progressive effects, i.e., progression without progression?" Herder, it is true, rejected most definitely the possibility of a given individual's rebirth as a member of a different realm of nature.[58] Yet

[56] Cf. "Über den Ursprung der Sprache" (1772), p. 42, *Sämmtliche Werke*, V. The same thought, in explicit and implicit formulation, occurs time and again throughout all of Herder's works.

[57] J. G. Herder, "Gott," *Sämmtliche Werke*, XVI, 567.

[58] Cf. "Über den Ursprung der Sprache," p. 42, *Sämmtliche Werke*, V, where Herder rejects the idea of "Stufenverschiedenheit" between man and beast and insists on an unbridgeable "Artverschiedenheit." A systematic defense of this attitude may be found in a letter which Herder wrote, probably in 1769, to Moses Mendelssohn. Cf. R. Unger, *Herder, Novalis und Kleist*, pp. 150ff., where the complete text of this important document is offered for the first time. It contains sentences like these: "If my present dispositions are to serve as the basis for my guessing what the future will be, I shall again become such a mixed creature as I am now . . . Everything in nature remains what it is . . . Here, too, it must be said: quidquid est illud est—I shall be what I am . . . All the circles and spheres in the world are upset if one moves into the other, if man is transformed into an angel, the angel into a god, the animal into man, the stone into an animal . . ." This emphatic insistence on the static character of the hierarchy of beings clashes strangely with Theophron-Herder's statement that "an eternally and progressively active force" produces "progressive effects" which are manifest in the relentless transformation of all created things. As Theophron, Herder seemed to feel that it did not matter whether or not immortality meant an advance for individual souls. Their unceasing transformation sufficed to insure the living coherence of all of creation and a living continuity from one extreme of the hierarchy of beings to the other. In his letter to Mendelssohn, on the other hand, Herder seemed to be horrified by the same idea. But here this idea presented itself in the shape of a doctrine of metempsychosis; it spoke of the possibility of the rebirth of an individual soul as the member of a higher realm of nature. In this form the idea had to clash with Herder's theological convictions. What he rejected was not so much a nonstatic conception of the hierarchy of beings, but rather an unchristian interpretation of it.

Herder's violent dismissal of all intimations of a possible transmigration of souls is no isolated phenomenon. Cf. p. 71, n. 46, for a similar attitude on the part of Jung-Stilling. This is remarkable, for it would seem that a temporalized chain of being, as Professor Lovejoy calls it, must lead to a revival of the doctrine of

this could not prevent him from conceiving of a progressively ascending hierarchy of nature, which he described[59] as moving "from the stone to the crystal, from the crystal to the metals, from these to the realm of plants, from the plants to the animal and from there to man." It goes even farther. Having summarized in the declaration "that man completes thus the chain of final organization as its supreme and last link," Herder proceeds with the assertion "that he [man] marks consequently also the beginning of the chain of a higher species of creatures as its lowest link."[60]

The idea that the past and future history of the hierarchy of things is present in it at any moment throughout its growth is the basis of Herder's exegesis of Genesis. Analyzing *The Oldest Record of Humanity*,[61] Herder accepted it as an authentic account of the history of Creation. This, however, meant for him a description of the present interpreted as the summary of a past evolution. There never was, according to Herder, an historical beginning of the universe beyond that which we can experience at any particular moment of our own temporal existence. His reading of the Judaic history of Creation as the description of the beginning of any normal day is, consequently, no deviation from literalistic principles. It is not an allegorical interpretation in the ordinary sense of the word. It must not be explained as "poetic license" but as a logical consequence of Herder's discussions of "historical" phenomena.

---

metempsychosis. K. Joël, *Der Ursprung der Naturphilosophie*, p. 57, adds this related argument: "Das übermenschliche Lebens- und Selbstgefühl zwingt zum Dogma der Wiedergeburt; das können wir heute an dem Beispiel Nietzsches verstehen—wenn wir es verstehen! Gerade der Individualismus neigt, wie Lessing und Lichtenberg zeigen, zu diesen Dogmen, die sogar der gottlose Hume zu verteidigen weiß.' However, as A. Rosenberg puts it, *Der Mythus des XX. Jahrhunderts*, p. 392, this question is a metaphysical one, and its answer can be made physical only in the shape of a metaphor or a new question. Thus we find it in Lessing, *Die Erziehung des Menschengeschlechts*, §98: "Why should I not return as I grow capable of attaining new knowledge and new skills?" For other aspects of the question of transmigration of souls, cf. Karl Friedrich Burdach, "Die Zeitrechnung des menschlichen Lebens" (1829), in Chr. Bernoulli and H. Kern, *Romantische Naturphilosophie*, p. 196, and L. Oken, "Naturphilosophie," §85. For our purposes we conclude that metempsychosis is a possible but not a necessary consequence of the mobilization of the hierarchy of nature.

[59] J. G. Herder, "Ideen," *Sämmtliche Werke*, XIII, 167.
[60] J. G. Herder, "Ideen," *Sämmtliche Werke*, XIII, 194.
[61] J. G. Herder, "Älteste Urkunde des Menschengeschlechts" (1774), *Sämmtliche Werke*, VI.

A particularly clear case might be made out with reference to his conception of the origin of language. It seems, however, that his views on this subject did not differ fundamentally from those of the following generation. At least as far as the present analysis is concerned, it is quite possible to proceed with a reference to A. W. Schlegel's views, which permit a briefer presentation than those of Herder.[62] For August Wilhelm it would have been perfectly correct to speak of the origin of language in terms of an actual growth, motivated by a physical urge to vent the emotions and to submit such eruptions to the measure and rule of rhythm.[63] He arranges the multitude of present-day languages in a scale of excellence, placing the flexional languages highest because they alone can be qualified as "organic." Their two varieties, the synthetic and the analytic,[64] are to be distinguished with regard to their historical provenance. The beginnings of the former are lost in the darkness of past ages, while all the latter have been created in modern times.[65] Nevertheless, the origin of language as such need not be construed as an historical occurrence which might be traced to a definite temporal date. Language originated always as it originates now, as it will always originate in each and every particular moment, in exactly the sense in which the creation of the world is renewed in every new moment.[66] We create our language as we use it, but it is nevertheless a direct derivation in continued growth from the language of our fathers.

[62] Cf. also Eva Fiesel, *Die Sprachphilosophie der deutschen Romantik 1801-1816*, Tübingen, 1927.

[63] August Wilhelm Schlegel, "Briefe über Poesie, Silbenmaß und Sprache," *Horen*, II (1796). Cf. also Rudolf Haym, *Die romantische Schule* (1870), edited by Oskar Walzel (Berlin, 1920⁴), p. 160, and especially F. Schlegel's review in *Deutschland* (1796) or *Jugendschriften*, II, 7ff.

[64] August Wilhelm Schlegel, *Observations sur la langue et la littérature provençale*, Paris, 1818.

[65] Cf. also O. Jespersen, *Language*, p. 36.

[66] A. W. Schlegel, *Vorlesungen über schöne Literatur und Kunst*, I ("Kunstlehre"), 272. Cf. also R. Haym, *Romantische Schule*, p. 842.

VI

ROMANTIC ANTHROPOMORPHISM: THE BIOLOGICAL PROBLEM

THE HIERARCHY of nature is no conglomerate of heterogeneous constituents. It is characterized by coherence and uniformity. There is an unbroken continuity advancing, as Herder said, "from the stone to the crystal, from the crystal to the metals, from these to the realm of plants, from the plants to the animal, from animal to man; and man marks the beginning of the chain of a higher species of creatures."[1] He is its lowest link and God its highest. That which advances from grade to grade along the scale of beings need not be the substance of individual souls. Herder for one rejected any such idea with extreme violence.[2] Again, with other thinkers, ascension along the scale of beings may actually mean that every individual has lived a complete set of inferior lives on all the levels of nature below its present rank. However that may be, the essence of a mobilized conception of the hierarchy of beings lies in the idea that every individual is, as it were, a preparation for a superior existence. To be a plant means to be ready for the life of an animal. To put it more romantically, there is a longing in every vegetable soul to be admitted into the realm of beasts.

This is the idea which places man at the beginning of a last climb, the end of which is God. "Every good human being," said Friedrich Schlegel, "is becoming more and more like unto God. To become God, to be man, to develop, these are expressions which mean one and the same thing."[3] In Hardenberg we read: "Every human being now living through God and of God (*durch, von*) is to be God himself."[4] Oken, less given to cautious formulations, did not feel that the identification of man and God should be

[1] Cf. p. 91, n. 60.
[2] Cf. p. 90, n. 58.
[3] F. Schlegel, "Athenäums-Fragmente," 262.
[4] *Novalis Schriften,* III, 107.

placed in a distant future. "Man is God fully manifested," he wrote.[5] Franz von Baader, finally, gave his version of the same thought in the more delicate form of a question which has none of Oken's brutal sacrilege. "Should not," Baader asked in 1786,[6] "this eternal longing be a certain proof of our immortality? Of the eternal ascension of the creature toward the creator? Similification! Asymptote!"[7] All these quotations, which are but samples from a rich file of related passages, represent the final development of the eighteenth-century faith in human perfectibility.[8]

[5] L. Oken, *Naturphilosophie* (1809), I, 28.

[6] Fritz Lieb, *Franz Baaders Jugendgeschichte* (Munich, 1926), p. 13.

[7] On the idea of asymptotic perfection, cf. Ferdinand Bulle, *Franziskus Hemsterhuis und der deutsche Irrationalismus des 18. Jahrhunderts* (Jena, 1911), p. 34, with references to Fichte, Hölderlin, Schlegel, Herder.

[8] The peculiar romantic mutation of the idea of unlimited human perfectibility might be elucidated by a detailed study of the motif of the superman in romantic literature. Cf. Ricarda Huch, *Ausbreitung und Verfall der Romantik,* pp. 54f. A similar investigation of the motif of the golden age has been undertaken by Julius Petersen, "Das goldene Zeitalter bei den deutschen Romantikern," *Die Ernte,* edited by Fritz Strich and Hans Heinrich Borchardt, Halle, 1926. Finally, the motif of *veniet tempus* (cf. F. W. Schelling, quotation from Seneca, used as motto of *Weltseele,* part I) would have the advantage of an uninterrupted continuity from the beginnings of the age of Enlightenment. Regarding its romantic mutation, cf. Johann Gottlieb Fichte, *Über die Bestimmung des Gelehrten* (1794), at the end of the second lecture; Friedrich Schleiermacher, *Reden über die Religion* (1799): "A time will come when no Messiah will be needed"; Friedrich von Hardenberg, "Die Christenheit *oder* Europa" (1799), *Novalis Schriften,* II, 84: "Be patient, for the sacred age of eternal peace will and must come." This motif assumes particular importance in F. Schlegel. Cf. *Jugendschriften,* II, 50-56, a review, originally published in *Niethammers Journal* (1795), of *Esquisse d'un tableau historique des progrès de l'esprit humain. Ouvrage posthume de Condorcet,* 1795. Friedrich's enthusiasm concentrates on the phrase, Condorcet, p. 320: "The moment will come when the sun will shine on free men only, who know of no other master than their reason." The central idea of this review appears again in "Athenäums-Fragmente," 227. Last but not least, reference must be made to F. Schlegel's enthusiasm for Lessing. It seems to have been inspired entirely by one sentence of Lessing's, *Die Erziehung des Menschengeschlechts,* §86: "Sie wird gewiß kommen, die Zeit eines neuen ewigen Evangeliums, die uns selbst in den Elementarbüchern des Neuen Bundes versprochen wird." Cf. F. Schlegel's essay on "Lessing," *Lyceum* (1797), especially the conclusion added in 1801, *Jugendschriften,* II, 416; the last lines of the sonnet to Lessing, which is found there, read:

> Es wird das neue Evangelium kommen!
> So sagte Lessing, doch die blöde Rotte
> Gewahrte nicht der aufgeschloßnen Pforte.
> Und dennoch, was der Teure vorgenommen,
> Im Denken, Forschen, Streiten, Ernst und Spotte,
> Ist nicht so teuer wie die wen'gen Worte.

Then Friedrich reiterates in prose that he would have to "honor and love Lessing,

They represent, however, also the final victory of Romanticism's endeavor to re-enthrone man as the Lord of Creation. He who can dare to visualize a shortening of the distance which separates him from God, must be convinced of his absolute superiority over all other creatures. He must consider their realm as his domain. He must feel qualified and destined to become in it the plenipotentiary of the demiurge.

This attitude must be recognized as an extraordinary epistemological optimism. It contrasts sharply with the characteristic epistemological resignation of the Eighteenth Century, which had reached its philosophical fulfillment in Kant's criticism, with its concise definition of the limits of human understanding. The representative significance of the critical philosophy was clearly recognized by Friedrich Schlegel when he said that people are wrong when they look upon it "as though it had fallen from the skies. It would have had to originate in Germany even without Kant, and it could have done that in many ways."[9] Ricarda Huch remarked once[10] that "it is very strange how little influence, on the whole, a philosophic system exerts, how it is rather exposed to transforming influences in all the individual minds that take hold of it." This observation, which is doubtless correct, may be explained by the fact that a philosophic system can be alive only to the extent to which it represents contemporary living thought.

The deep influence of Kant's critical philosophy must thus be interpreted as proving that its definite formulations corresponded to a general trend of the age. Indeed, the motif of "the vanity of confidence in opinions," of "the brevity and uncertainty of our knowledge," of "the falseness of human powers," of "the weak-

---

even if he had not written anything but the one phrase: 'The new gospel will come.' " In 1799, in a review, *Jugendschriften*, II, 308, of Schleiermacher's *Reden über die Religion*, F. Schlegel complained that "religion is something our age has lost," but on second thought he added a footnote which refers to the "misunderstood hint" in Lessing's "remarkable words: 'The new gospel will come.' " These passages suffice to show that the faith in human perfectibility, which is so very characteristic of the Eighteenth Century, did not disappear during the romantic era.

[9] F. Schlegel, "Athenäums-Fragmente," 387. It reads: "Man betrachtet die kritische Philosophie immer so, als ob sie vom Himmel gefallen wäre. Sie hätte auch ohne Kant in Deutschland entstehen müssen, und es auf viele Weisen können. Doch ist's so besser."

[10] Richarda Huch, *Blütezeit der Romantik*, p. 155.

ness of the human mind"—to put it in phrases gleaned from titles of works in eighteenth- and seventeenth-century literature[11]—can be pursued throughout the Eighteenth Century until it crystallizes in Kant's criticism. By this time, however, another trend was well under way. Eucken[12] describes it as "a new wave of life which urged to seek and see in reality something entirely new," a wave which surged up "in the rise of German humanism, with its demand for a more immediate contact with life, for a more intimate relationship with nature, for a totalitarian conception" of the universe. The men who represent this trend could not heed the Kantian warning. In them "worry about the riddles of the universe"[13] was too acutely alive. Haym[14] characterizes this situation when he states that the endeavor to overcome the Kantian limits of the world of reason and imagination through aesthetic visualization (*Anschauung*)

is the identical problem which occupied—in various forms—Schiller and Wilhelm von Humboldt, Friedrich Schlegel and Schelling and the entire period, the same problem which finally led to an aesthetization of logic, physics, and ethics through Hegel's universal system.

With respect to all the post-Kantian systems of thought it was said at about the time of Goethe's death[15] "that the impossibility of a knowledge of an extrasensual world had led them into the necessity of some other sort of acquaintance with it. This cannot or should not be called knowledge, but it is very hard to find another name for it." Nevertheless, Eucken's characterization of this trend as a surging wave is sadly correct. It rises and falls and disappears before long in the old resignation. When Tieck concluded that the only result of his endeavor "to understand the

---

[11] Cf. p. 87, n. 49, and *The Vanity of Dogmatizing: or Confidence in Opinions Manifested in a Discourse of the Shortness and Uncertainty of our Knowledge, and its Causes,* etc. by Jos. Glanvill, M. A., London, 1661.

[12] Rudolf Eucken, *Geistige Strömungen der Gegenwart* (Leipzig, 1916⁵), p. 129.

[13] C. G. Carus, *Organon der Erkenntnis,* p. V: "Wenn noch vor einem halben Jahrhundert E. Platner im höheren Grade berechtigt war, zu sagen: 'Voraussetzen möchte man, daß der Mensch lebe in stets wachsendem Kummer um das Räthsel der Welt und des menschlichen Daseins,' so hat dagegen das Interesse der Jetztwelt großentheils von diesen höchsten Aufgaben ganz und gar sich abgewendet."

[14] R. Haym, *Romantische Schule,* p. 345.

[15] H. Cysarz, *Erfahrung und Idee,* p. 173, quotes this passage from August Wilhelm Rehberg, *Sämtliche Schriften* (Hannover, 1828-31), I, 149.

plants and metals and stones" had been that he "had lost his own self,"[16] there was already something in the air which later on received its classical form in the wisdom of Du Bois-Reymond's *ignoramus, ignorabimus.*

The rise and fall of this wave of epistemological optimism can be surveyed in sharp relief through a study of one literary motif. This is the motif of the "veil of truth" or more specifically, of the veil of the goddess at Sais. The interest of such a survey centers, naturally, in Hardenberg's fragments of a novel, *The Apprentices at Sais.* Thus it is perhaps best to present the material as though it were our task to trace a connection from Schiller to Hardenberg. These two men were united in a beautiful relationship of teacher and student,[17] a fact which can only serve to make their separation by a world of thought the more striking. All the later material can be gleaned along a considerable detour in between. Schiller's poem "The Veiled Statue at Sais" of 1795 preaches eighteenth-century resignation. Its ethos is basically different from, say, Goethe's seeming resignation in "Grenzen der Menschheit."[18] In Schiller we find merely a traditional reference to human weakness, for the "law" which, together with the veil, separates the apprentice from truth impresses us as a senseless decree which has no personal significance for those who are to obey it. There is no reason why; there is nothing but the categorical and yet timid warning "Presume not Truth to scan," if Pope may be thus paraphrased.[19] It recalls in a way Plato's cave parable, or more directly

---

[16] Ludwig Tieck, *Gedichte* (Dresden 1821-23), p. 243:
> Natur hab ich ergründen wollen
> da kam ich gar auf seltsam Schrollen,
> verlor mich in ein steinern Reich;
> ich glaubte alles, nichts doch zugleich,
> wollt' Pflanz, Metall und Stein verstehn,
> mußt mir doch selbst verloren gehn.

[17] Cf. Hardenberg's letter to Professor Reinhold of October 5, 1791, *Novalis Schriften,* IV, 24ff. Schiller is called here the "Erzieher des künftigen Jahrhunderts." In the next sentence his name appears in what seems to be a list of all the great men known to young Hardenberg at the time. It includes among others Galileo and Spinoza, Michelangelo and Machiavelli. The relations of Hardenberg to Schiller have been discussed more fully by P. Kluckhohn, *Novalis Schriften,* I, 14*f.

[18] Cf. p. 87, n. 49.

[19] A. Pope, "Essay on Man," IV, 47: "Presume not God to scan." On Milton's

Brockes' good-natured sermon: "God does not want us to know and understand Him. Our duty is admiration, and any attitude toward God not based exclusively on such humble submission is wicked."[20] Furthermore, it is not even possible to interpret the moral of Schiller's poem as accidentally contained in a fable for which the poet cannot be held responsible and which he accepted because he wanted to write an impressive ballad. Schiller's poems were not conceived in this fashion. Besides, he used the same metaphoric interpretation of the veil of truth in several other places, which are perhaps less conspicuous but certainly even more representative for the general direction of his thought. In the first of the *Letters on Aesthetic Education* Schiller laments the fact that science and philosophy try to tear the veil of truth to pieces. This means for him that they try to abandon what is immaculate and naïve to a crudely rationalistic mechanization. Their search for truth, Schiller seems to hold, signifies their endeavor to expand their realm at the expense of that of the arts.

This same attitude can be pursued throughout the entire period of Schiller's final maturity. In 1799 he virtually quoted Haller when he stated in "The Words of Illusion" that "no mortal hand will lift the veil of truth."[21] It is strange, indeed, that this did not bring Goethe's wrath upon him as a similar expression of renunciation brought it upon Haller.[22] Schiller's poem "Kassandra" of

---

parallel phrase "Be lowly wise," cf. Grant McColley, "Milton's Dialogue on Astronomy," *PMLA,* LII (1937), 756ff.

[20] Barthold Heinrich Brockes, *Gegner der zweiten schlesischen Schule,* edited by Ludwig Fulda, "DNL," vol. 39 (Berlin and Stuttgart, 1884), p. 355. The passage is a free translation. The original reads:

> Er will sich hier von uns nicht fassen
> Und nur allein bewundern lassen;
> Dahin nur gehet unsre Pflicht
> Und weiter nicht.

[21] Schiller, "Die Worte des Wahns." There can be no enjoyment of life as long as man seeks satisfaction in the pursuit of illusory values:

> Solang er glaubt an die goldene Zeit . . .
> Solang er glaubt, daß das buhlende Glück
> Sich dem Edeln vereinigen werde . . .
> Solang er glaubt, daß dem ird'schen Verstand
> Die Wahrheit je wird erscheinen;
> Ihren Schleier hebt keine sterbliche Hand
> Wir können nur raten und meinen.

[22] Cf. p. 43, n. 36.

1802, finally, repeats the warning that the veil should not be lifted and bases this statement on the assertion that "error alone is life while knowledge means death."

> Frommt's, den Schleier aufzuheben,
> Wo das nahe Schrecknis droht?
> Nur der Irrtum ist das Leben,
> Und das Wissen ist der Tod.[23]

It is, to be sure, not quite just to interrupt the discussion of Schiller's attitude at this point. A psychological interpretation of it might well be able to demonstrate as its underlying cause the poet's own subconscious endeavor to stem the tide of an excessive faith in the power of philosophical reason.

This observation is inspired by a passage in Wackenroder. It states that a laudable zeal has misled the seekers after truth. "They have endeavored to unveil the secrets of Heaven and to place them amongst the objects of this earth." This is a more poetic restatement of Schiller's clearer reference to a "rational mechanization of the immaculate and naïve" as the main objective of science and philosophy. However, Wackenroder continues:

The wise of the world[24] have ejected obscure sensations from their bosoms. Is man in his weakness able to illuminate the secrets of Heaven? Does he consider himself capable of the intrepidity of bringing to light what God keeps covered with His hand? Can his pride be tolerated when he rejects the dark sensations which descend and visit us as veiled angels?[25]

The interest of this passage is twofold. On the one hand it demonstrates why Wackenroder might be called "the discovered missing link" between the Storm-and-Stress and Romanticism. He does not state that man is incapable of superior understanding, but he does maintain that such an understanding can reach us only in the divine form of obscure sensations. This is precisely the conception on the basis of which the Storm-and-Stress developed its

---

[23] Schiller, "Kassandra," VIII, 1ff.

[24] Wackenroder's expression is "Die Weltweisen." The context lends to this synonym for "Philosophen" a connotation of "the worldly-wise."

[25] Wilhelm Heinrich Wackenroder, "Herzensergießungen eines kunstliebenden Klosterbruders," *Kunstanschauung der Frühromantik,* edited by Andreas Müller, "Deutsche Literatur, Reihe Romantik," III (Leipzig: Reclam, 1931), 58f.

"inspirational sciences."[26] It refers to that "fullness of the heart"[27] which alone was thought capable of inspiring the sciences to do more than collect "dead treasures." "Without the warm sympathies of the heart," said Stolberg,[28] "the sciences are almost nothing." This leads to the other interesting aspect of Wackenroder's remark. The attitude which it represents would have shocked the clear mind of Schiller as sentimental muddle-headedness. It was something which even the most fervent emotionalism of his own Storm-and-Stress had been adamant in condemning. The idea that the lifting of the veil of truth might be achieved as an experience of dark sensations could not fail to strike a mind like Schiller's as self-contradictory nonsense. Truth is the object of clear thinking or it is no truth. Clear thinking alone can aspire after truth. Yet human thought is not absolute, and absolute truth will thus forever keep out of human sight behind the veil of its goddess.

As far as the problem of cognition is concerned Schiller remained to the very end a faithful disciple of Kant. It is one of the most amazing phenomena in the history of German thought that he could do so although he lived throughout all those years in closest contact with the veritable antipode of Kant.

It was," says Stefansky,[29] "even before the *Critique of Judgment* drew the distinction between human and divine reason and ascribed to the latter alone the power to proceed in thought from the whole to its parts, that Goethe disproved this limitation through the artistic and human results of his Italian journey . . . That which, according to Kant, God alone should be able to achieve, had thus been attained by Goethe's own blessed humanity.

This skillful summary seems to be based on Goethe's own account, which was significantly inserted into a discussion of the poet's scientific method of configurative visualization.[30] He quotes Kant

---

[26] Cf. H. Cysarz, *Erfahrung und Idee*, p. 70, where the term "Inspirationswissenschaft" seems to occur for the first time; also p. 215, where Cysarz coins the synonymous term "Genialitätsdisziplin." Bonnet, Lavater, and Robinet are mentioned as representatives of this sort of science.

[27] The very phrase "Fülle des Herzens" seems to have been characteristic of the Storm-and-Stress. It occurs as the title of an essay by F. L. Stolberg. Cf. p. 125, n. 11. It is used in "Werther." Cf. Goethe, *Sämmtliche Werke*, XIV, 87.

[28] Cf. p. 125, n. 11.

[29] Georg Stefansky, *Das hellenisch-deutsche Weltbild* (Bonn, 1925), pp. 78ff.

[30] "Anschauende Urteilskraft," *Werke* (Sophienausgabe), second series, XI, 54.

to the effect that the human intellect, i.e., the *intellectus ectypus*, is bound to proceed from the particular to the general, while it is the exclusive privilege of God's archetypal intellect to be capable of proceeding intuitively from the whole to its parts. The passage concludes with delightful irony which reminds us of Lessing's assertion that he was the nobody who could deny the incontestable merits of Gottsched: "And so there was nothing that could prevent me from succeeding in the adventure of reason, as the old man from Mt. Royal has called it himself."[31] All of this may explain at the same time why the motif of the veil of truth in Goethe's works could all by itself be made the theme of a rich and penetrating essay. Its occurrences are significant by sheer force of numbers.[32] Their essence, however, is always the same: What human eyes are able to see, what the human intellect is capable of comprehending must doubtless be called a poetic veil, for it is a privilege of human eyes and minds that they can visualize their objects as beautiful and poetic. However, this veil of poetry is given us by the hand of Truth. Beholding it, we are beholding Truth: "Am goldenen Abglanz haben wir das Leben."[33]

Schiller's and Goethe's attitudes appear to be mutually exclusive. There is nothing that can bridge the gulf between them, except that paradoxical power of friendship which can synthesize two opposites into a new and richer whole, or that love of which Goethe said that it is the only effective defense against the greatness of others. The early Romanticists, on the other hand, display an attitude which characterizes them as followers, if not as actual disciples, of Goethe, whom they called occasionally "Mahadöh,

[31] ". . . wie es der Alte vom Königsberge selbst nennt . . ."

[32] Cf., e.g., *Faust*, I, lines 319f.:
> Geheimnisvoll am lichten Tag,
> Läßt sich Natur des Schleiers nicht berauben.

The first of these lines belongs in the group of basic paradoxes which could be gathered from Goethe's writings under the general key phrase of "offenes Geheimnis." It is only in such paradoxes that description is possible in the sphere of the "Urphänomene" which inspire amazement and veneration. Thus the second line does not state that nature *will not,* it rather states that nature *cannot* drop her veil. Cf. also Goethe's poem "Zueignung." Its phrase "der Dichtung Schleier aus der Hand der Wahrheit" has been paraphrased in the text. This juxtaposition of "Dichtung" and "Wahrheit" must be used by the way to explain the deeper significance of the title of Goethe's autobiography.

[33] Cf. also p. 18, n. 14.

the Lord of Things." As he had opened the doors of nature to enter quietly into the realm of her truths, so they, the younger generation, clamored impetuously that the doors be unlocked, for the time had come. "It is time," exclaimed Friedrich Schlegel in the first of his "Ideas,"[34] "that the veil of Isis be torn, that the secrets be made public. He who cannot endure the sight of the goddess must flee or perish." Even Hardenberg, unwittingly perhaps, expressed the idea with an unmistakable turn against Schiller: "He who does not wish to lift the veil is no worthy disciple of Sais."[35]

The so-called younger Romanticists do not continue this tradition. The categorical demands of Hardenberg and the younger Schlegel would have impressed them as stupidly arrogant or sacrilegious. Nor was it their merit if the chaste and quiet confidence of Goethe's attitude toward nature did not entirely disappear. Nevertheless, the idea that "nature is ready to give abundantly," that she reveals her secrets gladly "to him who has carefully examined and prepared himself,"[36] must always have been characteristic of "the quiet in the land." Eschenmayer spoke for them when he wrote as late as 1817:[37]

The customary form of observation of nature is thoughtless and seems to expect that she will reveal her secrets all by herself. That is impossible, for the veil, the robe, is essential to her. Only the naïve (*unbefangen*) and chaste mind is granted the privilege of being allowed to lift the veil of Isis and to throw a glance into the mysteries. For the crude and unchaste mind it remains an eternal secret.[38]

---

[34] "Die Foderungen und Spuren einer Moral, die mehr wäre als der praktische Teil der Philosophie, werden immer lauter und deutlicher. Sogar von Religion ist schon die Rede. Es ist Zeit den Schleier der Isis zu zerreißen, und das Geheime zu offenbaren. Wer den Anblick der Göttin nicht ertragen kann fliehe oder verderbe."

[35] *Novalis Schriften*, I, 14.

[36] Goethe, "Allerdings. Dem Physiker," 13ff.:

> Sage mir tausend tausendmale:
> Alles giebt sie reichlich und gern;
> Natur hat weder Kern
> Noch Schale,
> Alles ist sie mit einemmale;
> Dich prüfe du nur allermeist
> Ob du Kern oder Schale seyst.

[37] Carl August Eschenmayer, *Psychologie in drei Theilen als empirische, reine und angewandte* (Stuttgart and Tübingen, 1817), p. 567, §510.

[38] Cf. also Goethe to Eckermann, February 13, 1829: "Die Natur versteht gar

Such questions, however, seem to have had no meaning whatever for minds like that of Arnim, for instance.

It is obvious, on the other hand, that the simple and beautiful certainty of Eichendorff's Catholicism was on its guard not to be disturbed by the man-made black magic of the problem of cognition.

> Du sollst mich doch nicht fangen,
> Duftschwüle Zaubernacht!
> Es ruhn mit goldnem Prangen
> Die Stern' auf stiller Wacht,
> Und machen überm Grunde,
> Wo du verirret bist,
> Getreu die alte Runde—
> Gelobt sei Jesus Christ![39]

Eichendorff's parks are full of white marble statues, especially at night. While it would certainly be absurd to ascribe to them an intended allegorical significance, yet there is something symbolically suggestive in the wickedness of their naked beauty. At times they appear again on the morrow; but then they are harmless and fully veiled. A particularly striking instance of this occurs in the third book of Eichendorff's narrative poem "Julian." The hero says to the statue, "I often saw you in my dreams," and gives her a ring. The following day she appears as his faithful human companion, and Julian begins to be the Apostate. Here the statue is clearly to be taken as the symbol of the unchristian and wicked sensuality of paganism which is lurking in the hearts of all of us.

> Du aber hüt' den Dämon, der in der Brust dir gleißt,
> Daß er nicht plötzlich ausbricht und wild dich selbst zerreißt.[40]

The endeavor to rob the goddess of her veil is not, in Eichendorff's views, a sign of Promethean courage; it is wicked and ugly. It is the sincerity of this attitude which saves this poet from the accusation of superficiality when he insists that we should be satisfied with the surface of things. "Take gladly the flowers of life," he

---

keinen Spaß, sie ist immer wahr, immer ernst, immer strenge; sie hat immer recht, und die Fehler und Irrtümer sind immer des Menschen. Den Unzulänglichen verschmäht sie und nur dem Zulänglichen, Wahren und Reinen ergibt sie sich und offenbart ihm ihre Geheimnisse."

[39] J. v. Eichendorff, "Der Umkehrende II."

[40] J. v. Eichendorff, "Julian," XVII, 43f.

says,[41] "as the moment may offer them, and do not dig for the roots in the ground, for down there it is joyless and still."

Further it must be mentioned that the motif of the veil of Isis was used in an illustration for Alexander von Humboldt's *Ideas on the Geography of Plants*.[42] The frontispiece of this book shows Thorwaldsen's genius of poetry lifting the veil of the goddess of truth. At her feet lies a book which can be recognized as Goethe's *Metamorphosis of Plants*.[43] Finally there are Brentano's brutal lines:

> Euch steht nur das Haar zu Berge,
> Und dies nennt ihr reines Wissen,
> Nennt's der Isis Schleier heben,
> Hebt ihr schamlos euren Kittel.[44]

[41] J. v. Eichendorff, "Das Marmorbild," "DNL," vol. 146[2], p. 188: "Nehmt die Blumen des Lebens fröhlich, wie sie der Augenblick gibt, und forscht nicht nach den Wurzeln im Grunde, denn unten ist es freudlos und still."

[42] Alexander von Humboldt, *Ideen zu einer Geographie der Pflanzen, nebst einem Naturgemälde der Tropenländer,* Tübingen and Paris, 1807. This is the introductory volume of section I, *Allgemeine Physik und historischer Teil,* of Alexander von Humboldt's and Aimé Bonpland's voyage. Cf. also F. Strich, *Mythologie,* I, 331.

[43] F. Strich, *Klassik und Romantik,* p. 136, refers to a novel by Hardenberg's brother Rostorf, *Die Pilgrimschaft nach Eleusis.* It may contain material to be discussed at this point, but copies of it do not seem to be readily accessible. To explain the absence of Tieck's name from the present survey, reference may be made to Fritz Brüggemann, *Die Ironie als entwicklungsgeschichtliches Moment,* Jena, 1909. This study discusses Tieck's romantic irony as the pseudosolution of an epistemological despair. Cf., especially, p. 9: "Für William Lovell wird die einzige Rettung, zu der er sich flüchtet, die Ironie. Er verzichtet auf die letzten Wahrheiten um den Preis gesunden Geistes . . . denn dies ist der Sinn der Worte: 'Er wirft sich zur Erde, um sich zu retten.' Die Ironie beruht also hier auf einer Verzichtleistung einer wahren Erkenntnis der Dinge. Die Welt, wie sie uns erscheint, wird gar nicht als Wirklichkeit genommen, sondern nur als eine dargestellte Wirklichkeit, dargestellt durch das Mittelglied der Funktionen unseres Verstandes." With regard to our concerns, the significance of this is twofold. First, the discussion of the problem of cognition makes it necessary to group Tieck together with Schiller. On a common basis the two display fundamentally different attitudes. Schiller is a man of heroic decision; Tieck an escapist. Second, Tieck's irony cannot have anything to do with the irony of F. Schlegel or Hardenberg. A further analysis of this fact might start from Hardenberg's observation, "Blütenstaub," 29, that Friedrich's irony impressed him as genuine humor.

[44] Clemens Maria Brentano, "Romanzen vom Rosenkranz," *Sämtliche Werke,* edited by Carl Schüddekopf (Munich and Leipzig, 1909-1917), IV, fifth *Romanze,* lines 105ff., spoken by Meliore-Brentano. Michels suggests in his introduction, p. XXXVI, that this passage is a direct slur upon Hardenberg's distich "Einem gelang es . . ." as quoted below. Cf. also "Romanzen," IX, 11, where philosophy is called "des Lichts unehl'che Tochter," and V, 84, where Guido says:

> Wißt, ich war in tiefster Seele
> Lang' ob dieser Zeit ergrimmet,
> Welche zu entblößen strebet,
> Was Gott keusch verhüllt will wissen.

The bitterness of these words is directed against the cardinal sin of romantic poetry, i.e., the exhibitionism *à la* Schlegel's *Lucinde*. In this respect Brentano himself did not feel free from guilt, and the silence which he chose later on to impose upon his muse may well be explained as the result of a desperate decision on his part to stop the self-abuse of continually unveiling his innermost soul.[45] The passage just quoted is thus to be interpreted as an instance of cruel self-castigation. Its conscious purpose, however, seems to have been a direct attack on the early romantic endeavor to achieve an identification of world-cognition with self-cognition. This, indeed, as Brentano hinted correctly, was the essence of Schlegel's[46] and Hardenberg's epistemological optimism. It was, at any rate, the essence of Hardenberg's deepest wisdom as he tried to formulate it in his elaboration of the motif of the goddess at Sais.

A remarkable "allusion" to this early romantic attitude can be found in Wieland's novel *Agathon*.[47] In the course of its events the hero, Agathon, reaches a state where he is completely disillusioned. He has lost faith in the mysteries, for he feels that they cannot teach him how to lift the veil of nature. At this time Archytas teaches him that we have within us a complete world which is invisible but nevertheless accessible to us. In its center our spiritual ego holds court and legislates like a god in the midst of chaos. If we penetrate into this sacred sphere we find in it the revelation of truth, for here there is no possibility of deception.

The most concentrated expression of Hardenberg's wisdom relative to the problem of cognition is found in a distich which makes symbolic use of the Sais fable for a restatement in less pedagogical terms of the essence of Wieland's idea:

[45] As early as 1810 Brentano wrote to Ph. O. Runge: "Das Talent, was ich liebe und verstehe, zu dichten, würde ich gewiß lauter vor der Welt ausgesprochen haben, wenn nicht alles, was ich dichten mochte, zu sehr die heilige Geschichte meines Innern gewesen wäre, als daß ich es ohne Frechheit in das laute, unteilnehmende Tagewerk der Welt hätte fügen dürfen." Cf. "Deutsche Literatur, Reihe Romantik," XVI, 255.

[46] This problem, it is true, was no direct preoccupation of Friedrich Schlegel. His anthropocentrism, however, may be inferred from his intelligent utterances about the idea of an organic coherence in the world of things. His later career, it is true, can be used by those who wish to prove that his earlier views were mere literature and intellectualism. The emphasis in the text rests on Hardenberg.

[47] This reference is taken from F. Strich, *Mythologie*, I, 99. Cf. Chr. M. Wieland, *Sämmtliche Werke*, V, 296ff.

Einem gelang es—er hob den Schleier der Göttin zu Sais.
Aber was sah er? Er sah—Wunder des Wunders—sich selbst.[48]

This version differs strikingly from the tale of Hyazinth and
Rosenblüth as it was incorporated in the novel *Die Lehrlinge zu
Sais*.[49] Hyazinth reaches the temple of the goddess, lifts the veil
and finds Rosenblüth. This second version is extant in a brief
summary which the poet may have jotted down as a first sketch
of his tale:[50]

A minion of Fortune longed to embrace ineffable nature. He sought the
mysterious see of Isis. He left his fatherland and those he loved, and in
his passion he did not heed the grief of his betrothed. Long lasted the
journey. Its hardships were great. Finally he came upon a spring and
flowers. These were preparing a path for a family of spirits. They disclosed to him the road to the sanctuary. Delighted with joy he came
to the gate. He entered and saw—his betrothed, who welcomed him with
a smile. As he looked around, he found himself in his bedroom, and a
lovely serenade accompanied from below his windows the sweet solution
of the secret.

It is only by a combination of these two seemingly incompatible
forms of the Sais story that the bases of Hardenberg's conception
of the problem of cognition can be understood. A common element
in both versions can be detected through a modified approach.
Among the notes pertaining to *Heinrich von Ofterdingen* there is
one which seems to suggest that Hardenberg planned at one time
to prepare for the conclusion of this novel by the introduction of
Jesus as a pilgrim to Sais.[51] The Son of God attains truth. The
personification of our religion unveils for us the goddess of truth.
Then there is among the outlines of works which Hardenberg did
not find time to execute a note which refers to a novel built around
the central conception that the hero's beloved and the religion he
seeks prove in the end to be one and the same thing.[52] The road

[48] *Novalis Schriften*, I, 41.
[49] *Novalis Schriften*, I, 11ff.
[50] *Novalis Schriften*, I, 41.
[51] *Novalis Schriften*, III, 333. A secondary interest of this point lies in the
fact that it indicates more clearly than Hardenberg's own epistolary utterances why
the poet interrupted his work on *Die Lehrlinge zu Sais*. The framework of this
novel was recognized as too narrow. It represented but one incident in a larger
conception. Of this the *Ofterdingen* is merely the first and less important part.
[52] *Novalis Schriften*, I, 396f. Cf. also II, 307; "Ich habe zu Söphchen Religion—
nicht Liebe."

to knowledge is the road to love.[53] As an idea this is not new at all, but Hardenberg does not take it as an idea which can be thought, written, read, and admired as a beautiful product of human reason. With him it is a personal, real, and almost brutal experience. In one of his diaries he poses the question why Luther used the word *erkennen* with reference to woman as the object.[54] There is no answer and none seemed needed. For Hardenberg it was self-evident that a loving soul has the power to assimilate its object,[55] to become one with it as we are one with our religion or some other field of experience of similar depth. This leads to the touching creed: "If I believe that Sophie can come to me, she will finally come in the most unexpected place: in my soul."[56] One loves in one's soul, not in the world without. If it is love which alone can lift the veil of truth, then it is in the soul of the seeker after truth that the revelation of truth can be found.

> Einem gelang es—er hob den Schleier der Göttin zu Sais.
> Aber was sah er? Er sah—Wunder des Wunders—sich selbst.

One final bold conclusion remains to be drawn. Love is not a present which may be handed to some one individual whose per-

---

[53] Cf. chapter IX, "Totality," where the idea of love as a means of cognition will be discussed in connection with Hemsterhuis' importance for German Romanticism.

[54] *Novalis Schriften*, II, 216. The complete entry reads: "Erkennen—dessen Gebrauch bei Luther." The same idea is found in F. v. Baader: "Es gibt kein affektloses, kein eitles, das heißt kein anderes Erkennen als das in der Stelle 'Adam erkannte sein Weib und sie gebar' ausgedrückte." Cf. J. Nohl, "Baader," p. 625. The connection between woman and cognition seems to be a simple mythical truth. Cf. Padraic Colum, *Anthology of Irish Verse* (New York, 1922), p. 13, where one of the most exquisitely beautiful passages of the world's poetry seems to present knowledge under the guise of a woman. It is a prose rendering of a "Love Song of Connacht," which the editor quotes as an example of how Douglas Hyde "used the idiom and rhythm used by the Irish peasant" when he attempted to put Irish songs into English. The passage reads: "If you were to see the Star of Knowledge and she coming in the mouth of the road, you would say that it was a jewel at a distance from you, who would disperse fog and enchantment, her countenance red like the roses, and her eye like the dew of the harvest, her thin little mouth very pretty, and her neck of the color of lime." Cf. also p. 58, "Ringleted Youth of My Love," also by Douglas Hyde, especially stanza 3.

[55] This is Hardenberg's "Urinfinitismus" which made it impossible for him to understand Schelling's polar "Urduplizität." Cf. Paul Kluckhohn, [Introduction to] *Weltanschauung der Frühromantik*, "Deutsche Literatur, Reihe Romantik," V (Leipzig: Reclam, 1932), 7.

[56] *Novalis Schriften*, III, 218.

sonal property it becomes. It rather is that which makes of us adherents to life, to God, to the world. To them it belongs. If it is concentrated on one single object, then only because this object has been accepted as the representative of life, of God, of the world. "The beloved," says Hardenberg[57] "is an abbreviation of the universe." His statement that Sophie can appear to him in his soul continues logically: "—and thus in the outside world. The truly exterior can act upon me only through me and in me." The seeker after universal truth can find it only in his soul. When Hardenberg decided that *gnothi seauton* should be his motto,[58] he knew that this would make him a disciple at Sais, that it would initiate him into the mysteries and finally allow him to see the goddess of universal truth without her veil.[59]

Hardenberg's anthropocentrism is doubtless a highly personal contribution. Yet, to paraphrase Friedrich Schlegel,[60] people are wrong when they look upon it "as though it had fallen from the skies. It would have had to originate in Germany even without Hardenberg, and it could have done that in many ways." As a matter of fact, it did originate in many ways of which Hardenberg's is but one, although perhaps the most extreme and poetically the most appealing. On whatever basis one may rethink these romantic thoughts, it is impossible not to be struck by their affinity with the deepest convictions of Herder, the "father of German Romanticism."

[57] *Novalis Schriften,* II, 47. Cf. also II, 393 : "Der Mensch ist eine Analogienquelle für das Weltall."

[58] Cf. *Novalis Schriften,* IV, letter to Professor Reinhold of October 5, 1791.

[59] A connection between the symbolism of the motif of the goddess at Sais and the problem of time and eternity discussed above seems to be established by Henry David Thoreau, *Walden,* at the beginning of the chapter on "Reading": "With a little more deliberation in the choice of their pursuits, all men would perhaps become essentially students and observers, for certainly their nature and destiny are interesting to all alike. In accumulating property for ourselves or our posterity, in founding a family or a state, or acquiring fame even, we are mortal; but in dealing with truth we are immortal, and need fear no change nor accident. The oldest Egyptian or Hindoo philosopher raised a corner of the veil from the statue of the divinity; and still the trembling robe remains raised, and I gaze upon as fresh a glory as he did, since it was I in him that was then so bold, and it is he in me that now reviews the vision. No dust has settled on that robe; no time has elapsed since that divinity was revealed. That time which we really improve, or which is improvable, is neither past, present, nor future."

[60] Cf. p. 95, n. 9.

It is necessary to pause at this point in order to restate the principle of "romantic" anthropomorphism in terms of Herder's philosophically more mature ideas. In an attempt to detect a common element in all those widely divergent utterances of Herder's which refer to the question of a palingenetic interconnection among all living things, Unger[61] comes to the conclusion that there is "in their deepest depth yet one uniform and autochthonous urge, which might perhaps be defined most precisely as an endeavor to understand the universe *on the basis of the human soul*." There is in this something that might be called a panpsychic biocentrism. A living principle unites the universe into one coherent whole and permits man, as its most highly organized configuration, to think of all the rest as *his* creation. Herder himself presents this thought much more subjectively:

The quiet resemblance which I perceive and feel in the whole of *my* creation, of *my* soul, and of *my* life, that great spirit which shows itself in the visible world and in that which is invisible, this one identical progression and homogeneity of laws: that is my seal of truth.[62]

The Sais of this truth is in the soul of man, and the pilgrimage to the goddess leads to the fountains of the seeker's own life. In Herder's prophetic style this reads: "Thou seekest the great law which moves the worlds? Mortal, look into thyself. There thou wilt find the higher rule which not only moves the worlds but which also moves itself." Further we find these words: "Feel thyself and thou feelest God within thee. In thee God feels Himself as sun and animal do not feel Him but as He achieves Himself within Him."[63]

We have here Herder's characteristic insistence on an unbridgeable difference between man and the members of all the lower realms of nature. Man can feel God as sun and animal cannot. More important, however, is the fact that this break is dissolved, as it were, in one great general law which rules over and within man, sun, and animal alike. It is the law of life. This is the founda-

[61] R. Unger, *Herder, Novalis und Kleist*, p. 4. Italics mine.
[62] J. G. Herder, *Vom Erkennen und Empfinden* (1778), p. 6, *Sämmtliche Werke*, VIII. Italics in the translation mine.
[63] J. G. Herder, "Das Gesetz der Welten im Menschen," *Sämmtliche Werke*, XXIX, 161. "Die Schöpfung. Ein Morgengesang," *ibid.*, XXIX, 444.

tion on which the structure of Herder's universe is based. "The first word was life," he wrote in 1769 in his *Travel Diary*,[64] which must be read, in this as in so many other respects, as a prophetic abstract of all his later endeavors. This remained forever the center of Herder's wisdom: The first thing and the last thing is life. The Most High "could not give His creatures anything higher than life. The Godhead in whom there is only one essential force . . . could not produce anything which was not a living imprint of its power and wisdom and goodness."[65] God's essence is in everything created, and the essence of every created thing must thus be in everything else. As human beings we know at least that we have the essence of God and His entire creation in our own souls. Thus Herder could say to each and all of us:[66]

Of everything which the Spirit of the world[67] moves and nurtures He pressed the meaning into your heart. Meaning is the element of the spirits. A living word which is not known to any language, your inner word, your longing for this trace, calls you, O man, the interpreter of nature. Only an interpreter? No! The force of your urges reveals in you the higher quality. You alone can be the motive power in nature, you alone, who are its masterpiece, can at the same time be its creator.

[64] J. G. Herder, "Journal meiner Reise im Jahre 1769," 2, *Ideen,* edited by Friedrich von der Leyen, Jena, 1904.

[65] J. G. Herder, "Gott," *Sämmtliche Werke,* XVI, 541, 543f., and 569ff. Here the essence of these conversations is summarized in ten major conclusions. The first two read: "Das höchste Daseyn hat seinen Geschöpfen nichts Höheres zu geben gewußt, als Daseyn. Die Gottheit, in der nur eine wesentliche Kraft ist, die wir Macht, Weisheit und Güte nennen, konnte nichts hervorbringen als was ein lebendiger Abdruck derselben, mithin selbst Kraft, Weisheit und Güte sei, die ebenso untrennbar das Wesen jedes in der Welt erscheinenden Daseyns bilden."

[66] J. G. Herder, "Bilder, Allegorien" (1801), *Sämmtliche Werke,* XXIII, 310:

> 6. Von Allem, was der Weltgeist regt und pflegt,
> Hat er Bedeutung Dir ins Herz geprägt.
> Bedeutung ist der Geister Element,
> Ein lebend Wort, das keine Sprache nennt;
> Dein inn'res Wort, Dein Ahnen dieser Spur,
> Nennt Dich, o Mensch, Ausleger der Natur.
>
> 7. Ausleger nur? Nein! Deiner Regung Kraft
> Enthüllt in Dir die höhre Eigenschaft.
> Das Triebwerk der Natur kannst Du allein,
> Ihr Meisterwerk, der Schöpfung Schöpfer sein.
> Voll Mitgefühl in Freuden wie im Schmerz
> Schlägt in Dir ihr, der Schöpfung großes Herz.

[67] Schelling's "Weltseele" in his "Hypothese der höhern Physik" and also the "Riesengeist," of which he has his Heinz Widerporst say that it is everywhere in the universe, are hardly more than prose translations of Herder's "Weltgeist."

This is again the basis for the exhortation: Know thyself! It is only in self-knowledge that world-knowledge can be attained, for "the truly external can act upon thee only through and within thee."[68]

The Eighteenth Century, too, had had a way of appreciating the value of the old imperative "Know thyself!" Self-knowledge had been considered an important science, and the way to attain it deserved serious study. Acquaintance with its nature had been held to yield worth-while reflections and observations on the character of man.[69] The importance of such reflections and observations is self-evident. To know man, it is true, does not amount to a great deal, but since "The only Science of Mankind is Man,"[70] one should try to do one's very best in that narrow and inexpansible sphere. A world separates this conception from that of Herder, of Hardenberg, and of most of their contemporaries. For them the wisdom of *gnothi seauton* meant an achieved identification of the Platonic idea that God is the measure of all things with its Protagorean counterclaim that the measure of all things is man.[71] "Know thyself," said Troxler,[72] is not just a wise inscription on a divine temple of antiquity. It is a voice calling in every human heart; in some, a delicate breathing from hidden depths; in others, a wild noise from without which can hardly be understood." Self-knowledge is here represented as the final goal as well of a quiet *nisus formativus* as of the most violent lust for life. The essence of all existence is life, and a knowledge of life is the essence of self-knowledge. "We shall understand the world when

---

[68] *Novalis Schriften* III, 218.

[69] The last two sentences are adapted from the title of a book which otherwise has no direct interest for our concerns. Cf. John Mason, *Self-Knowledge. A Treatise shewing the Nature and Benefit of that Important Science, and the Way to attain it. Intermixed with various Reflections and Observations on Human Nature*, London, 1784.

[70] A. Pope, "Essay on Man," II, 2.

[71] Cf. Friedrich Gundolf, "Hölderlins Archipelagus," *Dichter und Helden* (Heidelberg, 1921), p. 15, who seems to speak of a merging of Protagoras' πάντων χρημάτων μέτρον ἄνθρωπος with Plato's πάντων χρημάτων μέτρον θεός. A further important item for a study of the motif of *gnothi seauton* is Karl Philipp Moritz' *Magazin zur Erfahrungsseelenkunde*, 1783-1793. This descriptive name appeared on its title page below the more conspicuous words ΓΝΩΘΙ ΣΑΥΤΟΝ. It experienced a second edition in 1805, which indicates that it met with considerable interest.

[72] I. P. V. Troxler, "Blicke in das Wesen des Menschen," p. 239.

we understand ourselves," said Hardenberg.[73] Where does the road to knowledge lead? he asked, and the answer was: Always within!—*"Immer nach Hause."*[74] "Happy is he who no longer seeks throughout the world but demands from himself the stone of eternal wisdom. The man of reason is the only adept, and the king is within him."[75] "If we are searching for the plan of the universe, we may learn that we ourselves are that plan."[76] For "man is merely a metaphor of the universe."[77]

In this connection it seems important to draw attention to Hardenberg's literary habit of introducing absolutely new and unexpected elements, persons, events, etc., by designating them as "mysteriously familiar." This is a very convenient device, for it justifies the most extravagant romantic leaps and bounds. Yet, however annoying it may be if taken as a mere stylistic mannerism, it does succeed in shaping the romantic chaos into an ordered and organic whole as soon as it is understood as a plausible consequence of Hardenberg's anthropocentric views. Adam Müller[78] said of the higher natural sciences that their purpose is "not to discover (*Erfinden*) but to recover (*Wiederfinden*)." This must, obviously, be also the sole significance of all the "new" experiences of our lives: they bring us face to face with things we had for-

---

[73] *Novalis Schriften,* II, 238: "Wir werden die Welt verstehn, wenn wir uns selbst verstehn." F. Schlegel, "Ideen," 100, said: "Wir werden den Menschen kennen, wenn wir das Centrum der Erde kennen." This amazing contrast characterizes both these thinkers fully.

[74] *Novalis Schriften,* I, 229: "Wo gehen wir denn hin? Immer nach Hause." The romantic motif of going home is the motif of finding one's real self. When Heinrich von Ofterdingen, *Novalis Schriften,* I, 111, is only about to leave home, he has the strange feeling that he is really going home. The true Romanticists are always going home, and some of them find their way. This motif was given its most sensitive form by Eichendorff in one of the poems written after the death of his child:

> Wir armen, armen Toren,
> *Wir irren* ja im Graus
> Des Dunkels noch verloren,—
> Du fand'st dich längst nach Haus.

A less restful pathos rings in Caroline von Günderode's lines:
> Doch schau hinab in Deiner Seele Gründen,
> Was Du hier suchest, wirst Du dorten finden,
> Des Weltalls seh'nder Spiegel bist Du nur.

[75] *Novalis Schriften,* I, 353.
[76] *Novalis Schriften,* II, 331.
[77] *Novalis Schriften,* II, 350.
[78] A. Müller, *Vorlesungen,* p. 119.

gotten but which are part of the universe of our souls. To learn
to know is merely to recognize, and soon the "new" is felt to be
"strangely familiar." Thus Hardenberg relates of the teacher at
Sais[79] that he found on his journeys "everywhere things which
he knew." This caused him to combine the most different fields
of human knowledge, exactly as the poet himself was planning
to do in his great *Enzyklopädistik:* stars were recognized as people, stones were animals, and the clouds were plants. Of the earliest
men, Hardenberg says in chapter II of the *Lehrlinge*[80] that everything impressed them necessarily as "human, known, and familiar"
because the nature of an impression must needs correspond to
the nature of the sense organ. When Hyazinth reaches the temple
of the goddess,[81] he falls asleep because only a dream can bring
him into the realm of truth. Then he feels that everything is "so
familiar although of an unheard-of splendor." Heinrich in *Ofterdingen* from the time when he received the image of the blue
flower into his soul,[82] has felt that everything is "so much more
familiar." The strange news about poets which the traders bring
to his notice he receives with the remark: "I feel of a sudden as
though I had heard about it somewhere, somewhen in my deepest
youth." The song of the old miner[83] makes him feel "as though
he had heard it before somewhere." When he thumbs the old
book in the hermit's cave,[84] he sees a number of illustrations which
impress him "as marvelously familiar," just as the traits of old
Master Böhme[85] when he appears to greet the child who is reading
his works. Mathilde, finally, says to Heinrich: "I think I have
known you since immemorial times."[86]

This list of phenomena of the *déjà vu* in Hardenberg's works
could easily be lengthened. The material adduced suffices, however, to prove that the poet's identification of world-cognition with
self-cognition was not merely an ideological construction. If it

[79] *Novalis Schriften,* I, 15.
[80] *Novalis Schriften,* I, 15.
[81] *Novalis Schriften,* I, 27.
[82] *Novalis Schriften,* I, 101.
[83] *Novalis Schriften,* I, 155.
[84] *Novalis Schriften,* I, 169.
[85] *Novalis Schriften,* I, 360.
[86] *Novalis Schriften,* I, 191.

were, we should have to suppose that all the instances of the *déjà vu* cited above were consciously devised, which is not likely on any grounds. There is not even the slightest evidence that Hardenberg was aware of any connection between his conception of the problem of cognition and the stylistic peculiarities of his poetic presentation. His epistemological ideas had either arisen from the subconscious depths of his psychic existence or had descended thither through complete assimilation. They were, at any rate, in the most absolute sense his personal property. This does not mean that these ideas had never been conceived before the time of early German Romanticism. On the contrary, their history[87] can

[87] On Hardenberg's contact with Plotinus, cf. Paul Friedrich Reiff, "Plotin und die deutsche Romantik," *Euphorion*, XIX (1912), 591: "Will man die Bezeichnung eines Schlüssels der älteren Romantik überhaupt anwenden, so gebührt sie einem Denker des Altertums, Plotin . . . [Er] inspiriert das ganze System des Novalis und manchen Gedanken des mittleren Schelling . . . Durch Novalis und Schelling, wenn nicht direkt, wirkt er auch auf die beiden Schlegel ein." Édouard Spenlé, *Novalis* (Paris, 1904), p. 18, said of Hardenberg, "C'était un de ces esprits qui subissent moins des influences que des fascinations." The poet's own account of his connections with Plotinus agrees with Spenlé and not with Reiff. He wrote to F. Schlegel in December, 1798, *Novalis Schriften*, IV: "Ich weiß nicht, ob ich Dir schon von meinem lieben Plotin schrieb. Aus Tiedemann lernt ich diesen für mich geborenen Philosophen kennen—und erschrak beinah über seine Ähnlichkeit mit Fichte und Kant." In a letter to Caroline of January 20, 1799, *Novalis Schriften*, IV, he stated that no one else had advanced again as far as Plotinus had. This passage was copied from his notes and thus thought twice, as it were. Cf. *Novalis Schriften*, III, 266. A second series extends from Böhme by way of St. Martin to Baader. When Baader wrote, *Werke*, XI, 72: "Der Mensch [soll], was um ihn ist, durch sich und nicht sich durch das, was um ihn ist, erklären," he merely translated St. Martin's exhortation: "Expliquer les choses par l'homme et non l'homme par les choses." Cf. Louis Claude de St. Martin, *des Erreurs et de la vérité* (1775), p. 9. On Baader's share in Schubert's translation of this work, cf. p. 119, n. 104. St. Martin's general importance for Baader is discussed by F. Lieb, *Baader*, pp. 145ff. On Böhme and St. Martin, cf. Lieb, p. 157. This German-French contact had been established during St. Martin's stay in Strasbourg from 1788 to 1791. Lieb's conclusion, p. 172, reads: "Die Wiederaufnahme dieser Gedankenwelt in St. Martin's Schriften hat, wie wir gerade an Baader sehen, nicht wenig zur Renaissance des Neuplatonismus und der sich daran anschließenden theosophischen und naturphilosophischen Spekulation im Zeitalter der Romantik beigetragen." Several of St. Martin's works were translated by Matthias Claudius. Particular importance seems to have been assigned to the *Tableau naturel des rapports qui existent entre dieu, l'homme et l'univers*, Lyon, 1782. The German translation was by Freudenfeld, *Über das natürliche Verhältnis zwischen Gott, dem Menschen und der Welt*, Reval and Leipzig, 1783 and 1785. The French text was reprinted as late as 1901. An abridged German edition appeared even in 1919, Konstanz and Leipzig. For a summary of St. Martin's thought, cf. Max Dessoir, *Vom Jenseits der Seele* (Stuttgart, 1920[4-5]), p. 291: "Im Lehrgebäude des Martinismus gibt es zwei Grundpfeiler: der eine ist der Satz, daß in der Materie eine Weltseele lebt, der andere ist die

be pursued into a very distant past. Yet, when Hardenberg came
in contact with books which contained them and which might thus
be taken as his source, he seems to have felt that they were
"strangely familiar," as though "he had known them since immemorial times."

If it is true, however, that Hardenberg's ideas on the problem
of cognition were not developed in direct dependence on older
sources, it is equally true that they were developed by him as a
typical representative of his age. They may be considered as a
characteristic property of Romanticism in general. There is, for
instance, the devout Catholic Franz von Baader, whose spiritual
background was certainly quite different from that of Hardenberg.
His conception of the problem of cognition depends on the central
idea that the universe is the product of God's thinking. Human
ideas, as part of Creation, originate thus ultimately, not in our
brain but in the mind of the Creator. That I think, is due to the
fact that I and my thoughts have been thought by God. As a
thought of God, my thinking contains the product of God's thinking. It contains the world, and world-cognition means self-cognition. This reasoning Baader concentrates in the phrase: "Cogito
quia cogitor."[88] This conception and Hardenberg's are doubtless

---

Behauptung, daß des Menschen Seele als Gedanke Gottes das göttliche Wesen
widerspiegelt. Daher sieht der Mensch so aus wie Gott, daher sind die Einzeldinge
im eigentlichen Wortverstand Nachahmungen geistiger Vorbilder." A third connection comes again from Plotinus and reaches the romantic era by way of Giordano Bruno. Regarding its first leg, cf. Julie Sarauw, *Der Einfluß Plotins auf Giordano Brunos* Degli Eroici Furori (Jena, 1916), especially pp. 52ff., with parallels under
rubricks like I. Begriff der Gottheit, II. Die Weltseele, III. Die Seele,
VII. Materie. On Bruno's importance for the romantic era, cf. Werner Saenger,
Goethe und Giordano Bruno, "Germanische Studien," vol. 91 (Berlin, 1930), especially pp. 116ff., where Gothe's so-called Spinozism is disclosed to actually have been
a Brunonianism. On Goethe's Spinozism and the possibility that it was really a
Bonnetism, cf., p. 63, n. 31.

[88] Hans Wilhelmsmeyer, "Der Totalitätsgedanke als Erkenntnisgrundsatz und als
Menschheitsideal von Herder zu den Romantikern," *Euphorion,* XXXIV (1933), 232.
The same thought is found in Schelling's 44th aphorism in the *Jahrbücher der
Medizin als Wissenschaft* (1806): "Das Ich denke, Ich bin, ist, seit Cartesius, der
Grundirrtum in aller Erkenntnis; das Denken ist nicht mein Denken, und das
Sein nicht mein Sein, denn alles ist nur Gottes oder des Alls." This is the "proud
humility" of Luther's "Ich kann nicht anders . . ." It is what Blake had in mind
when he said of his songs, "They are not mine." It is, finally, the idea which
Hardenberg, *Novalis Schriften,* III, 360, elaborated in his statement that mankind
represents a sort of ganglion in which the universe thinks. This extreme *irrationalism*

related. They are mutations[89] of one basic idea. Yet Baader's version reminds us more directly of Herder, particularly of his statement quoted above[90] that God impressed His essence into the soul of man and made him thus a recapitulation of the world below. In view of this affinity it is not surprising that Baader felt bound to Herder in sincere veneration and deep gratitude. The same holds true for a number of other thinkers of the younger generation of Romanticists. Indeed, it is possible to limit the discussion of their conception of the present problem to a few brief references to their attitude toward Herder.

There remains but little to be said with respect to Baader. He, the psychologist of the "macroanthropos,"[91] wrote in his diary[92] that he had chosen Herder as his genius and that he felt him to be an apparition of a higher order before whom he had to bow in due respect. It would scarcely be unjust to Baader to consider him in a great many respects as the scientific continuator of Herder. Of Baader's science it has been said[93] that it rested on two axioms. The first is the claim that an intuitively organological or religiously symbolical interpretation of nature should replace the mathematically exact and "irreligious" physics; the second, the endeavor to get hold of the higher and real nature in its immateriality through parapsychic experiments and experience. This latter point is merely a question of method. The former is basic,

---

can be reached in an unbroken series of stages from the extreme opposite represented by Descartes' *rationalism*. The *Cogito ergo sum* appears in Brockes, "DNL," vol. 39, p. 355: "Ich weiß, ich bin. Warum? Ich denke." It is slowly modified into *Dubito ergo sum*. An emotional quest for more than rational certainty finds a less limited basis: "Je sens ainsi je suis." Cf. F. Bulle, *Franziskus Hemsterhuis*, p. 16. The emotional basis expands and reaches the center of feeling in God. I feel because God makes me feel, I think because God makes me think, and finally, I am because God thought me. *Cogito quia cogitor* or *Cogitor a Deo ergo sum*.

[89] Cf. p. 74, n. 3.

[90] Cf. p. 110, n. 66.

[91] Cf. *Novalis Schriften*, III, 124: "Die Welt ist der Makroanthropos." This expression was also used by Baader. Cf. K. Joël, *Der Ursprung der Naturphilosophie*, p. 34. Hardenberg, *Novalis Schriften*, II, 378, called Baader a "Realpsychologe." This must mean a psychologist of the "macroanthropos." Concerning the long continued misinterpretation of Hardenberg's phrase, cf. W. Olshausen, *Friedrich von Hardenberg*, pp. 19f. and J. Nohl, "Baader," p. 613.

[92] Cf. F. Lieb, *Baader*, p. 36, also F. v. Baader, "Tagebücher," *Werke*, XI, 52ff. ("Nach Lesung der zerstreuten Blätter von Herder") and 139.

[93] D. Baumgardt, *Franz von Baader*, pp. 327f.

and in it there is nothing which could be in disagreement with Herder's views. It was not Baader, as one might feel inclined to guess, but Herder who wrote:[94] "That which is physically united, why should it not be united mentally and morally also? Mind (*Geist*) and morality are also physics and serve the same laws, which depend lastly on the whole planetary system, only in a higher order."

Of Johann Wilhelm Ritter it has been said, though with some exaggeration, that he was the only Romanticist whose attitude toward Herder was cordial in a deeper sense.[95] His *Fragments of a Young Physicist* may be considered as a monument in memory of this friendship. Four years earlier, in 1806, he said in his address *On Physics as an Art*[96] that "the condition under which man is alone capable of attaining knowledge of nature, is that the two be alike." There is consequently no science of nature which is not, at the same time, a science of man. However, in Ritter's identification of world-knowledge with self-knowledge a highly personal note can be discerned. It results from an attempt to fathom the metaphysical causes of man's fateful quest for truth. Why should we have to worry "about the riddles of the universe?"[97] The other animals do not seem to know an urge of this sort. In this we are different[98] and separated from the rest of Creation. Nevertheless, man is longing for a reunion with nature,[99] and the sciences are the means which he employs in his endeavor to bridge the gulf. It is bridgeable. The life in man and the life in nature are identical. This is the metaphysical conviction which alone makes our scientific efforts meaningful and possible. Yet, the fact that such efforts are necessary indicates again that the identity of all life is true only if taken *sub specie aeternitatis*. In terms of time the

[94] Cf. Oskar Loerke, "Herders Weltgebäude," *Die neue Rundschau* (1935), p. 579.
[95] O. Walzel, *Romantik*, p. 15.
[96] J. W. Ritter, *Die Physik als Kunst*, p. 24. This essay deserves more attention than it is generally given. G. Stefansky, *Das hellenisch-deutsche Weltbild*, p. 217, says correctly: "Schellings, Novalis', Schleiermachers Gedanken sind hier in dem tausendfarbigen Licht von Ritters Phantasie und Sehnsucht auseinander gefaltet: insofern ist diese Schrift das merkwürdigste Zeugnis aus der Zeit der deutschen Romantik."
[97] Cf. p. 96, n. 13.
[98] Cf. p. 53, n. 2.
[99] Cf. chapter IX, "Totality," especially p. 170f.; also p. 118, n. 101.

oneness of all life is but a task, precisely the task of the sciences of nature. At present there is a break between the life of man and that in nature. To put it crudely and in more modern terms, the dual personality of Life is a case of schizophrenia. Sanity shall be restored. On a higher level of consciousness man will achieve a union with nature as perfect as the simpler one which characterizes plant and animal life. At that time the sciences will cease to be sciences. They will have attained their goal and deserve the name of arts.

It is, however, a peculiar aspect of Ritter's ideology that it does not lead to the familiar conception of a triadic progression from an unconscious to a conscious union of man and nature which must pass through an intermediate stage of painful separation.[100] According to Ritter there was no golden age in the past. Man's endeavor to establish one in the future does not signify that there is in him a vague recollection of the paradise which he lost. It rather indicates that we are darkly aware of the unique intentions which nature pursued in creating us.

She completed all her other creatures," Ritter explains,[101] "but not her last and highest, not man. In his case she interrupted her work in a state of imperfection and intended this to motivate man's urge to attain perfection all by himself. For this task she equipped him with the prerequisite powers, and everything he did or does must be interpreted as serving his purpose to overcome his imperfection by means of self-perfection.

[100] Cf., e.g., Schiller's distich "Das Höchste" of 1795:
  Suchst du das Höchste, das Größte? Die Pflanze kann es dich lehren.
  Was sie willenlos ist, sei du es wollend—das ist's.
[101] This rendering is very free, for Ritter's style resists translation. Cf. *Die Physik als Kunst,* p. 2: "Alle Übrigen hat sie [die Natur] vollendet, nur ihr Letztes [den Menschen] nicht . . . Zwischen den so eben erwähnten Zustand seiner Unvollendung, bey welchem die Natur abbrach, und den mit ihm begründeten andern seiner Selbstvollendung, den herbeyzuführen sie ihm überließ, und das Vermögen dazu mitgab, fällt Alles, was wir je von seinem Thun und Streben vorgefunden haben, und noch finden." On the possibility of a reunion of man and nature, cf. *ibid.,* pp. 56f.: "Ist Wiedervereinigung mit einer getrennten Natur, Zurückgang in die vorige Harmonie mit ihr, das, was den Menschen überall zunächst beschäftigte, nach welchem all sein Sinnen und Trachten, von jeher jeden Morgen neu sich richtete,— und diese Wiedervereinigung mit ihr, die Folge einer Einsicht und Gewalt in die Natur, die aus Allem Willen gleichsam Einen nur, aus Allem Leben nur Ein Leben, aus aller Sorge um dasselbe nur Eine Einzige macht, deren Lenker und Führer der Mensch allein, die Zahl des mit ihm zugleich Beglückten aber unendlich ist—: so wird daraus eine Vollkommenheit des Lebens und seines Genießers entstehen, die eben so, und in Aller Hinsicht, unendlich seyn muß, als die Menschen früher nicht wirklich schon Eigne, es in Einiger erst war." On physics as about to become an

Finally there is Gotthilf Heinrich Schubert who also approached the problem of the "nature of things" through the identity of nature and the inner world of man. "The rhythm," he said, "which we recognize in the solar system, must be discovered also in the life of each human individual."[102] In 1811 he translated Saint Martin's book *On Errors and Truth*. In it he found the demand "that the nature of things be explained by man and not man by the nature of things."[103] The basic importance of this passage impressed him deeply. He even used it in reformulating the title of the entire work which he called *On the Spirit and Essence of Things or Philosophical Views of the Nature of Things and the Purpose of their Existence*, [an essay] *wherein Man is everywhere considered as the Solution of the Riddle.*[104]

Of Schubert it has been said[105] that he "belonged to the few who recognized Herder as the father of German Romanticism." The personal acquaintance of the two dated back to 1796, when Schubert, then sixteen years of age, had attended the Gymnasium in Weimar and formed a lasting friendship with Herder's son Emil. In 1804, shortly after Herder's death, he wrote to this friend:

O my dear Emil, he no longer is with us, the greatest man of this age . . . The day will come when all who know him will recognize most sincerely what he meant to his age as long as he lived. Then the Spirit of God will come over them as in the ages of Life, and they all shall speak with tongues, mightily before all the nations; for he was the prophet of God.[106]

---

art, cf. p. 59: "Daß aber diese höchste Aller Künste [die Physik] bis jetzt noch immer mehr den Namen einer bloßen Wissenschaft getragen . . . hilft bloß die Ahnung dessen, was sie, einst am Ziele angekommen, seyn muß, gans vollenden."

[102] Cf. Gotthilf Heinrich von Schubert, *Der Erwerb aus einem vergangenen und die Erwartungen von einem zukünftigen Leben* (Erlangen, 1853-56), I, 405, where the author states that his first plan for a dissertation concerned the analogy of the solar system and man. Cf. also Franz Rudolf Merkel, *Der Naturphilosoph Gotthilf Heinrich Schubert und die deutsche Romantik* (Strasbourg, 1912), p. 26.

[103] Louis Claude de St. Martin, *des Erreurs et de la vérité* (1775), p. 9. Cf. also p. 114, n. 87.

[104] *Vom Geist und Wesen der Dinge oder philosophische Blicke auf die Natur der Dinge und den Zweck ihres Daseyns, wobei der Mensch überall als die Lösung des Räthsels betrachtet wird.* The preface was contributed by Baader.

[105] Cf. Arthur Eloesser, *Die Deutsche Literatur von der Romantik bis zur Gegenwart* (Berlin, 1931), p. 15: "Schubert wenigstens hat Herders Mitvaterschaft an der Romantik anerkannt."

[106] January 23, 1804. Cf. F. R. Merkel, *Der Naturphilosoph G. H. Schubert*, p. 10.

What Herder meant to his age, or better, what he could have meant to his age, may be summarized in the simple term "organic anthropocentrism." The universe is an organized whole, and its essence has been impressed by the Most High into the soul of man. We have developed this idea as the general property of all German Romanticism and shall conclude by asserting that it was, at the same time, Romanticism's most vital contribution to nineteenth-century thought. The most influential preoccupation of the era of industrialism has not been, it will be agreed, a problem propounded by any of the technological sciences. It was rather the biological question of evolution. This has affected our outlook on life; it has influenced our religion and has changed our attitude toward the rest of Creation. In this connection evolution must not, of course, be identified with any particular theory. It merely stands for the idea that all the species of the animal realm are connected in genetic interdependence, that they constitute one living chain of which man is the last and most highly developed link. The factual observation on which this idea rests may best be stated in the form of the basic law of biogenetics as it was formulated by Haeckel in 1866: "Ontogeny, the development of an individual animal, is a shortened recapitulation of phylogeny, the evolutionary history of the species to which it belongs." This contains, to be sure, the elements of a descent-theoretical interpretation which must be disregarded if the law is to become the basis of all the various conceptions of evolution. The actually observational contents of Haeckel's law may be stated in terms adapted from Carus' memoirs: "There is an unmistakable parallel between the history of human development from the ovum to the mature individual and the successive stages from the infusoria to the anthropoid animals."[107] In this form *the basic law of biogenetics describes a fact which can be observed only by a mind trained in anthropocentric thought* of the kind which we have seen to be characteristic of German Romanticism. If it is metaphysically true that man is an epitome of the universe, then it must also be physically true, for *one* law rules throughout all the realms of existence. If it is metaphysically necessary to conceive of man as

---

[107] Adapted from C. G. Carus. Cf. p. 122, n. 114.

the last and most perfect link in the chain of the animal kingdom, then it must also be physically observable that he repeats its various stages. Thus we know *a priori* that the basic law of biogenetics was part of the intellectual equipment of every good romantic thinker. This fact may be given an empirical basis by a few concluding quotations.

Of the younger Herder it has been observed by J. Petersen[108] that it was a favorite axiom of his cultural philosophy to parallel the stages in the history of mankind with the periods in the development of the individual.[109] Indeed, expressions like "childhood of mankind" etc., which came into vogue with Herder, have never disappeared from the technical vocabulary of the history of civilization. It seems that the earliest categorical formulation of the basic law of biogenetics was given by Kielmeyer in 1793;[110] but it is very characteristic that Schelling, who claimed to see in Kielmeyer's work the morning star of an entirely new era in the natural sciences,[111] nevertheless felt obliged to trace its basic thoughts to an origin in Herder's *Ideen* and Spinoza dialogues

[108] J. Petersen, "Das goldene Zeitalter bei den deutschen Romantikern," p. 142: ". . . [der] Lieblingsgedanke, mit dem der junge Herder an die Kulturphilosophie herangetreten war."

[109] This idea is, naturally, no invention of Herder's. A genetic conception of history can hardly fail to make use of its metaphoric expressiveness. One may thus expect to find it in Voltaire, in Montesquieu, and certainly in Vico. On Voltaire, cf. Gustave Lanson, *Voltaire*, "les grands Écrivains français" (Paris: Hachette, n.d.), p. 131: "Herder et Michelet, Thierry et Guizot ne l'ont remplacé [Voltaire comme historien] qu'en le continuant." On Vico, cf. B. Croce, *Storiografia*, p. 248: "Una ricchissima ed organica anticipazione del pensiero romantico si era avuto nella Scienza nuova del Vico." Also Benedetto Croce, *la Filosofia di Giambattista Vico*, Bari, 1911; and Goethe's entry in his diary under date of March 5, 1787, *Werke* (Sophienausgabe), XXXI, 28: "Es ist gar schön wenn ein Volk solch einen Ältervater [wie Vico] besitzt; den Deutschen wird einst Hamann ein ähnlicher Codex werden." It seems, finally, plausible to interpret the interest of thinkers in the Seventeenth Century in exotic and primitive peoples as vaguely conditioned by an interest in the prehistoric past of their own race. J. F. Lafitteau, who had been active as a missionary in Canada, was apparently the first to interpret modern ethnological observations as significant for our conception of the early stages in the development of our own civilization. Cf. L. Darmstaedter, *Handbuch zur Geschichte der Naturwissenschaften*.

[110] Karl Friedrich von Kielmeyer, *Über die Verhältnisse der organischen Kräfte untereinander in der Reihe der verschiedenen Organisationen, die Gesetze und Folgen dieser Verhältnisse*, 1793. This essay had resulted from a lecture delivered at the Karlsschule in Stuttgart. Kielmeyer was a student under Blumenbach and a friend of Cuvier.

[111] F. W. Schelling, *Weltseele*, p. 298: ". . . eine Rede, von welcher an das künftige Zeitalter ohne Zweifel die Epoche einer ganz neuen Naturgeschichte rechnen wird."

Gott.[112] Oken gave in 1809 the formulation:[113] "The animal passes in the course of its development through all the classes of the animal kingdom. The foetus is a representation in time of all the species of animals." This he condensed further into the statement: "Animals are merely foetal stages of man." Referring to Oken's early work, Carus wrote by the middle of the century,[114] at a time when it was already necessary to take sides in preparatory controversies[115] about what we should call descendentalism:

Through Oken the amazing fact became known that there is an unmistakable parallel, which should not be extended too far into details, between the history of human development from the microscopic ovum by way of the tender and soft embryo to a final formation in the mature individual on the one hand and the successive stages on the other from the microscopic infusoria by way of the tender and soft mollusc to the anthropoid animals.

[112] Cf. O. Walzel, *Romantik*, p. 14.

[113] L. Oken, "Naturphilosophie," §198: "Das Tier durchläuft während seiner Entwicklung alle Stufen des Tierreiches. Der Fötus ist eine Darstellung aller Tierklassen in der Zeit." *Ibid.*, §212: "Die Tiere sind nur Fötuszustände des Menschen."

[114] Carl Gustav Carus, *Lebenserinnerungen und Denkwürdigkeiten* (Leipzig, 1856-1866), I, 72.

[115] Such controversies came, on the whole, in the wake of Lamarck's theory. A very amusing illustration can be found in the American edition of Matthias Jacob Schleiden, *Poetry of the Vegetable World*, Cincinnati, 1853. On p. 292 the author expresses his conviction "that the whole fulness of the vegetable world has been gradually developed out of a single cell and its descendants, by gradual formation of varieties, which became stereotyped into species, and then, in like manner, became the producers of new forms." To this Alphonso Wood, the editor, adds a note in which he calls Schleiden's view a wild hypothesis. It is, Wood says, "a modification of the famous development theory of Lamarck, which has been so often refuted by the ablest writers." That which holds true for plants, Wood's reasoning goes on, must also be true for beasts. "And we must hence regard the primitive Monad as our great grand progenitor, and thence trace our descent down through shellfish, Saurians, Dolphins and lastly, Monkeys! And all this absurdity for what? It is merely to relieve the Almighty Creator from the fatigue of having created so many species,—nay, from creating at all! Since that simple primogenitive cell might easily have been struck out of the sea-foam by electricity! Alas for the darkness of German Theology!—A. W."

VII

THE INFINITY OF NATURE

ROMANTICISM is an attempt to conquer infinity.[1] The romantic conquest of infinity is doomed to fail, and this accounts for what is commonly called a lack of structure in romantic thought, the romantic disregard for limits, the inability to impose a concise form. These traits are not primary. They follow as necessary consequences of one basic failure. However, the "urge to conquer infinity," if taken as an essential characteristic of romanticism, widens the scope of this term far beyond its traditional connotations. The following paragraphs are concerned with man's experi-

[1] The idea of distance as suggesting infinity has been treated strikingly by Lascelles Abercrombie in his book *Romanticism*, London, 1926. Cf. especially p. 42, with the following progression: 1.) ". . . we are there pleased most,/Where something keeps the eye from being lost . . ." (Sir John Suckling, *Against Fruition*, before 1646); 2.) ". . . Distance presents the object fair . . . But when we come to seize th' inviting prey,/Like a shy ghost, it vanishes away . . ." (John Norris of Bemerton, *The Infidel*, before 1678); 3.) ". . . Why to yon mountain turns the musing eye? . . . 'Tis distance lends enchantment to the view,/And robes the mountain in its azure hue . . ." (Thomas Campbell, *The Pleasures of Hope*, 1799). Still more striking is the juxtaposition of the opening paragraphs of Hardenberg's first "Hymn to Night" and W. Heinse's "Hildegard von Hohenthal." The latter reads: "Die Sonne löscht alle Freuden der Nacht aus! wie die schönen Sterne, so die süßen Melodien und Harmonien der Phantasie . . . Die Nacht hat etwas Zauberisches, was kein Tag hat; so etwas Grenzenloses, Inniges, Seliges. Das Mechanische der Zeitlichkeit, das einen spannt und festhält, weicht so sanft zurück, und man schwimmt und schwebt, ohne Anstoß, auf Momente im ewigen Leben." It would be hard to find a more typically romantic characterization of the lure of the infinite as revealed by the veil of darkness. Heinse, however, uses the passage only by way of contrast and introduction. In the passage just quoted the hero, Lockmann, voices his disapproval of the coming of dawn, but then he looks out of the window, perceives the beautiful Hildegard, and the rest of the novel sings a song of life in body and of light on form, and, at least throughout its poetically most successful portions, the reader, like Lockmann occasionally (*Werke*, V, 123), is entirely "lüsternes Auge." Hardenberg, on the other hand, begins (*Novalis Schriften*, I, 55) with a hymn to light: "Welcher Lebendige, Sinnbegabte, liebt nicht vor allen Wundererscheinungen des verbreiteten Raums um ihn, das allerfreuliche Licht . . ." Yet this, too, is but contrast and introduction. The pathos of this passage exhausts itself without achieving any convincing plasticity. "Abwärts wend' ich mich zu der heiligen, unaussprechlichen, geheimnisvollen Nacht." Now only, in what he calls the bridal union with night's infinity, does the poet reach the highest peaks of inspiration, and what follows is the most sublime of all the works of German romantic literature. Cf. also F. Strich, *Klassik und Romantik*, especially p. 75.

ence of infinity and with his endeavor to assimilate that experience. They deal thus with romanticism only in the widest and vaguest sense, and the term "romantic" will appear as practically synonymous with "modern."

Previous chapters have discussed man's "worry about the riddle of the universe"[2] and the climactic re-elaboration of the idea that man is an epitome of the world of phenomena. This was a re-iteration of the old conception of the human microcosm as a repetition in outline of the universal macrocosm. It had been a fairly simple idea as long as the world could be conceived as finite. However, when this world came to be regarded or experienced as infinite, the task became, in Blake's beautiful words,[3] to "Hold Infinity in the palm of your hand/And Eternity in an hour." In these two simple lines we grasp the identity of the problems of Werther and of Faust, and it is but natural that young Goethe's Prometheus defies the gods in strikingly similar words:

> Könnt Ihr den weiten Raum
> Des Himmels und der Erde
> Mir ballen in meine Faust? . . .
> Vermögt Ihr mich auszudehnen,
> Zu erweitern zu einer Welt?[4]

The strong "expansionist" trend behind these expressions is not something new that appeared suddenly in the last quarter of the Eighteenth Century. Professor Lovejoy[5] remarks justly that "it has usually been post-dated by historians"; that "it was no invention of Goethe, nor of the German Romanticists, nor even of Lessing, but had been expressed repeatedly throughout the century, both by eminent philosophers and universally read men of letters." It may be described more concretely as an endeavor to reduce the infinite universe to a humanly surveyable structure. As such it found a particularly revealing expression in the idea of the plurality of worlds. Unger, who treats this question at length, observes that "such thoughts, or rather fantasies, are current throughout the entire century." He believes that they were

---

[2] Cf. p. 96, n. 13.
[3] Cf. p. 138, n. 12.
[4] 1773, first act, lines 37ff.
[5] A. O. Lovejoy, *The Great Chain of Being*, p. 250.

prepared by, and radiated from, the monadology of Leibnitz.[6]

It is, however, to be noted that Fontenelle's *Conversations on the Plurality of Worlds*[7] presented the idea as early as 1686 as a perfectly plausible one. The first German translation of this book—by Gottsched—appeared, by the way, as early as 1727. Also Pope spoke casually about the inhabitants of other stars and based thereon the interesting suggestion that we would understand more fully why God made us as we are if we could watch our astral fellow creatures.[8] Wieland charges the idea with an enthusiasm that announces the coming Storm-and-Stress:

> O wie erstaunt mein Geist, und hört fast auf zu denken,
> Da seine Blicke sich in jene Tiefen senken,
> Die kein Geschöpf ermißt, wo in gewohnten Höhn
> Sich Sterne ohne Zahl mit ihren Bürgern drehn.[9]

It was obviously no knowledge of astronomy that moved these authors to populate the stars. It was rather "an ardent personal experience,"[10] a "fullness of the heart" which flowed out beyond the confines of factual knowledge. Stolberg's rhapsodic essay "Fülle des Herzens" of 1777 shows the emotional background upon which astronomy appears as an "inspirational science."

Who would fail to recognize the value of the sciences?" asked Stolberg rhetorically and rather vaguely.[11] "They feed and form the mind. But

[6] R. Unger, *Herder, Novalis und Kleist*, p. 112.

[7] Unger does not fail to mention this work. A "nouvelle édition" of the *Entretiens sur la pluralité des mondes* appeared in Marseilles in 1780. The same year brought also a second German edition: Bernhard von Fontenelle, *Dialogen über die Mehrheit der Welten*, mit Anmerkungen . . . von Elert Bode . . . Berlin, 1780. Huygens' *Kosmotheoros* belongs in the same continuity. It appeared in 1698 at the Hague. An English edition followed immediately: *Christiani Hugenii* Κοσμοθεωρος *sive de terris coelestibus earumque ornatu conjecturae.* Hagae Comitum 1698. *The celestial worlds discovered: or, conjectures concerning the inhabitants, plants and productions of the worlds in the planets.* Written in Latin by Christianus Huygens, and inscrib'd to his brother Constantine Huygens . . . London, 1698. In spite of Voltaire's mocking *Micromégas* the question remained alluring. Kant's *Allgemeine Naturgeschichte* of 1755 was followed by J. H. Lambert's *Kosmologische Briefe über die Einrichtung des Weltbaus* in 1761 and Christian Ernst Wünsch's *Kosmologische Unterhaltungen für die Jugend* in 1780.

[8] A. Pope, "Essay on Man," I, 33.

[9] Chr. M. Wieland, "Die Natur der Dinge," IV, 653, *Werke*, I[1].

[10] H. Cysarz, *Erfahrung und Idee*, p. 70.

[11] Friedrich Leopold Graf zu Stolberg-Stolberg, "Fülle des Herzens," *Deutsches Museum* (July, 1777), and *Der Göttinger Dichterbund*, edited by August Sauer, III, "DNL," vol. 50 (Berlin and Stuttgart, 1893), p. 24.

most scientists are satisfied to know what they need; and when they revel in an abundance of knowledge, they do so either to satisfy their vanity or as a sort of hobby which leaves their hearts cold. They do not collect honey in the garden of the muses but feed themselves as lazy bumblebees. What benefit will they derive after their death from all their accumulated knowledge? As little as they did during their lives from the coins they brought together in order to have a collection of them in their cases. To him who is without feeling the knowledge he possesses is like a dead treasure; to him who has that feeling his knowledge is a source of pure joys, of elevating emotions, of noble thoughts, which form his character, widen his heart, and work on into eternity. Or do you think any feeling can die without affecting on and on into eternity him who felt it? Without the warm participation of the heart the sciences are almost nothing. It is only through this participation that astronomy delights us in revealing to us the sparks of the heavens as thousands of suns, each one probably surrounded by terrestrial globes and each one of these inhabited by sentient and immortal beings.

When Wieland and Stolberg fill the universe with a multiplicity of inhabited worlds, it is in response to an uncontrollable urge to project an infinite life into the infinite spaces. The starry heavens above become for them a field of human sensation. The earth-bound individual draws other worlds into his emotional realm, for relatives of his inhabit those other worlds and their home is in a way also his.

Infinity escapes sense perception. It is its very essence that it cannot be measured by human thoughts and finite senses. Yet the clear and resplendent firmament as viewed from a mountain top or simply from a narrow attic window does succeed in making the impossible come true: in it infinity speaks directly to the senses, as Schiller says in "Die Künstler":

> Eh vor des Denkers Geist der kühne
> Begriff des ew'gen Raumes stand,
> Wer sah hinauf zur Sternenbühne,
> Der ihn nicht ahnend schon empfand?[12]

To be sure, not everybody is prepared for such an experience. It takes a "romantic" soul, and that means in the present context a soul that longs for or demands a living contact with life's infinity, with the infinity of all that exists. This closes the circle: Roman-

---

[12] Schiller, "Die Künstler," lines 5off.

ticism is an attempt to conquer infinity, and the urge to conquer infinity characterizes the romanticist.

A detailed study of the literary motif of the starry heavens would yield a beautiful epitome of the history of human thought. In lieu of it, the following series of quotations may serve to set in relief what was meant by the vague but convenient expression a "romantic" soul.

"If one were to reach the limits of the atmosphere," says Plato,[13] "or if one had wings and flew aloft, he would then know what the real heavens, the real light, and the real earth are. He would look down with contempt on the weatherworn cliffs and chasms and gaze in admiration at the glory of the heavens." Earthly necessities, this seems to be Plato's feeling, interfere tragically with an appreciation of the real beauty of the worlds above. We are nevertheless able to gain at least some vague first notion, a "forefeeling,"[14] of what the immaculate brightness of light must be when we view it in the freer realm of pure ideas. Plato speculates here on the effect it would have on us if we could rise and emancipate our view from the dimness of the earth's atmosphere.

Aristotle speaks of a similar elevation and emancipation, but the characteristic difference is that he is not concerned with creatures such as we may long to be at some time in the future. He imagines a race of beings who inhabit the interior of the earth and long for emancipation and elevation to our human level. Aristotle speculates on what their sensations would be upon perceiving the beauty of the starry heavens which we are wont and privileged to see whenever we wish. "They would be convinced that there are gods and that all these splendors can only be the work of gods."[15]

[13] Alfred Biese, *Das Naturgefühl im Wandel der Zeiten* (Leipzig: Quelle & Meyer, 1926), p. 25, quotes from "Phaidon," 109E: "Wenn jemand zur Grenze der Luft gelangte oder Flügel bekäme und hinaufflöge, so würde er den wahren Himmel, das wahre Licht und die wahre Erde erkennen; verächtlich würde er herabsehen auf die verwitterte, zerklüftete und anstaunen die wunderbare Herrlichkeit der Himmlischen . . . wo die prächtigsten Bäume und Blumen und Früchte und Steine in bunterer Farben als Karneole, Jaspisse und Smaragden, prangen und ein reiner Äther glückliche, mit den Göttern traulich verkehrende Menschen umfängt."

[14] The expression comes from Bayard Taylor's translation of *Faust* II, 6972.

[15] Cicero, *De natura deorum*, II, 37, has Aristotle make this statement. It is quoted by A. Biese, *Naturgefühl*, p. 25. Cf. also Thassilo von Scheffer, *Die Legenden der Sterne im Umkreis der antiken Welt*, Stuttgart: Rowohlt, 1939.

Post-Hellenic pessimism adds a sort of inferiority complex[16] which insists on the smallness of man in the face of the grandeur of the firmament above and escapes into Neoplatonic admiration of the beauties of the world beyond. The early Christian observer then brings the wonders of the stars into his dualistic ideology. "If the visible temporal and perishable world is so beautiful, what must the invisible and eternal one be?"[17]

The starry heavens have become witnesses to the omnipotence of God. In this form the theme is to be taken up again in the Eighteenth Century when proofs of the power or mere existence of God assumed particular importance. The farther deistic trends succeeded in pushing God into the background, the more important it became to find reliable demonstrations that "the hand that made us is divine."[18]

The idea that the beauties of nature are proof of the benevolence of a supreme being may of course be a sincere expression of the childlike faith of a simple and beautiful soul. A touching illustration of this is to be found in the story of Fräulein Paradis, a patient of Mesmer's, which the *Vossische Zeitung* published in 1777. Fräulein Paradis had been blind since early childhood.

[16] A. Biese, *Naturgefühl,* p. 30, quotes from Ptolemaios:
    Staub bin ich—ich weiß es—ein Sterblicher, aber betracht' ich,
    Sterne, den kreisenden Lauf eurer verschlungenen Bahn,
    Dann, o glaub ich die Erde nicht mehr mit dem Fuß zu berühren,
    Sondern am Tische des Zeus kost' ich ambrosische Kost.
It is probably a sacrilege to recall in this connection the gentleman from Hamburg who accompanies Thomas Mann's Tonio Kröger to Denmark. When he stands on the deck and watches the starry heavens, he exclaims: "Wir Menschen haben den Telegraphen erfunden und das Telephon und so viele Errungenschaften der Neuzeit, ja, das haben wir. Aber wenn wir da hinaufsehen, so müssen wir doch erkennen und versdehen, daß wir im Grunde Gewürm sind, elendes Gewürm und nichts weiter." A short while later he is overtaken by a desperate fit of seasickness. Cf. Thomas Mann, *Tonio Kröger,* chapter VII.

[17] St. Basil the Great (329-379), *Hexaëmeron,* quoted in A. Biese, *Naturgefühl,* p. 54: "Wenn du je in einer heitern Nacht die bewundernswerte Schönheit der Sterne mit gespanntem Blick betrachtet hast und du plötzlich in dem Gedanken an den Künstler des Universums nachdachtest, wer er denn sei, der mit diesen ewigen Blumen den Himmel so wunderbar gezeichnet und geschmückt hat und der bewirkte, daß die Schönheit dieses Schauspiels nicht minder groß ist als die Gesetzmäßigkeit . . . Wenn nun aber die sichtbare Welt, diese zeitliche, vergängliche, so schön ist, wie muß erst die ewige, unsichtbare sein."

[18] Joseph Addison's paraphrase of the 19th Psalm. The Psalm itself may also be referred to in the present connection in so far as it is a treatment of the motif of the *Herrlichkeit Gottes in der Natur.*

Mesmer finally succeeded in restoring her eyesight, thus opening up for her a world of new experiences. The published account relates then a series of psychologically interesting details, but the most fascinating incident occurred when the patient saw for the first time the firmament of resplendent stars.

She quietly raised her hands toward the gloriously shining sky, no doubt to send up to it an ardent prayer of thanks which came from the depth of her soul. After a few moments she exclaimed: "O how solemnly these stars look down upon me! Nothing could possibly be more glorious in all nature. If one experiences an ardent desire for true worship of the supreme Being, then it must be here, here beneath this ceiling of brilliance where I am now standing."[19]

This simple quietism which loves the Creator in His creation is not entirely unrelated to the simplest deism which admires the Almighty as "the great mechanic of the creation."[20] In this view

[19] *Vossische Zeitung,* 1777, Nos. 55ff.; reprinted by Eberhard Buchner, *Ärzte und Kurpfuscher* (Munich: Albert Langen, 1922), No. 253a. The story of Fräulein Paradis had a strange sequel, which does not belong in this context. She became blind again, Mesmer was arrested and had to leave Austria. There remain a number of details which have not been cleared up.

It is, naturally, not to be implied that this peculiar pathos was confined to the Eighteenth Century. Cf., e.g., Robert Bridges, *Poetical Works* (1936), p. 512:

It is a deeper thrill, the joy that lovers learn
taking divine instruction from each other's eyes
the Truth that all men feel gazing upon the skies
in constellated Night—*O God the Father of Heaven!*
When I arose and saw the dawn, I sighed for Thee!

In passing it must be pointed out that eighteenth-century quietism might well represent the soundest basis for a further pursuit of the motif of the starry heavens into the harmonious pantheism of Jean Paul. Cf., e.g., "Quintus Fixlein" (1796), *Sämmtliche Werke* (1840-42), III, 230: "Ich schaue auf zum Sternenhimmel, und eine ewige Reihe zieht sich hinauf und hinüber, und alles ist Leben und Glut und Licht, und alles ist göttlich oder Gott." Also "Titan" (1800ff.), *Sämmtliche Werke* (1840-42), XV, 298: "Als er den heiligen unsterblichen Himmel . . . sah . . . da fragte der Geist sich selber: 'Wer kann mich ergreifen, ich bin ein Geist unter Geistern.'" Both these passages have also been adduced by Clifford Lee Hornaday, *Nature in the German Novel of the Late Eighteenth Century* (New York, 1940), pp. 61f.

From Jean Paul's *Titan* the transition would be natural to Goethe, whose naturalistic wisdom (to judge subjectively) attained its most mature formulation in an organic, metamorphic variant of the motif of the starry heavens. Cf. *Wilhelm Meisters Wanderjahre, Sämmtliche Werke,* XVIII, 141ff. The passage is related to the idea that Makarie is a repetition of the stellar system, but its further implications are virtually inexhaustible.

[20] Thomas Paine, *Age of Reason* (1794) (New York: Wiley, n.d.), p. 254. The quotation below, *ibid.,* p. 53.

God is the designer of the supermotor which we call the world. Over it He spread the tent of the firmament, which must have a practical function like everything else, although it may seem that God presented us with it simply as a sample of what He is really capable of doing. The insipidity of such superrationalism may become downright amusing, as in Paine's passage:

It is only by contemplating what he calls the starry heavens as the book and school of science that man discovers any use in their being visible to him, or any advantage resulting from his immensity of vision. But when he contemplates the subject in this light, he sees an additional motive for saying that nothing was made in vain; for in vain would be this power of vision if it taught man nothing.

Behind this proud assertion of a basic rationality of all that exists is hidden the great fear that all of it is possibly quite without meaning and sense. It is this fear which trembled in young Tieck's questions: "Why do the innumerable worlds dance their clumsy dance around their suns? Why did the Creator issue from His hand the creation? Why did He project the host of stars through the heavenly spheres?"[21]

Indeed, what matters in these questions cannot be their answer but rather the reason why they could be asked. A soul that fills the infinite spaces above, a microcosm that knows it is one with the macrocosm, cannot be troubled by them. This is the only solution: As the outer world expanded into infinities, so the inner microcosmic world had to expand to infinite depths. When Johann Christian Günther wished to describe the splendor of the starry heavens, he knew of no better means of conveying the impression of their immensity than to allude to the equal or greater immensity of his amazement:

> Ich zieh den Mond- und Sternenschimmer
> Dem angenehmsten Tage vor;
> Da heb ich oft aus meinem Zimmer
> Haupt, Augen, Herz und Geist empor,
> Da findet mein Erstaunen kaum
> In diesem weiten Raume Raum.[22]

[21] Ludwig Tieck, *Almansur,* 1790. The hero addresses these questions to a hermit.
[22] Johann Christian Günther, "Lob des Winters," *Die Gegner der zweiten schlesischen Schule* (cf. "Bibliography," s.v. *Brockes*), p. 75.

This double expansion finds characteristic illustrations in Kant. In him the synthesis of rational proof or external evidence of the existence of God and subjective experience is achieved, for with him the meaning of "proof" in such a context is definitely clarified:

If among other things I consider the microscopic observations of Dr. Hill and the numerous species of animals in one single drop of water, beasts of prey with tools of destruction but overcome by still mightier tyrants of this world of water while they are busy in the pursuit of others; if I view the tricks, the power, the scene of rioting in one single drop of matter and lift my eyes from there to see the immeasurable space swarm with worlds as though of dust, then no human language can express the feeling engendered by such a thought, and the subtlest metaphysical analysis is by far inferior to the sublimity and dignity which is characteristic of such a view.[23]

A still more outspoken but generally familiar parallelization of the depths of the inner and the heights of the outer world is the famous phrase toward the end of the *Critique of Practical Reason* where the starry heavens above and the moral law within us are cited as the most sublime objects of our admiration and reverence.[24]

Much romantic thinking could be interpreted simply as a translation of this passage from Kant. So for instance Beethoven's note:[25]

When in the evening I look astounded up at the sky and see moving eternally in their worlds the host of bodies of light which are called

[23] Immanuel Kant, *Der einzig mögliche Beweisgrund zu einer Demonstration des Daseins Gottes* (1763), p. 124n. John Hill, 1716-1775. Kant refers to the *Hamburger Magazin*.

For a modern version of the same thought, cf. Burton Rascoe, *Prometheans* (New York, 1933), p. 66: "I have only to look at a slide under a microscope or glance at the heavens at night or to listen to a program coming in over the radio, to know that there are mysteries I shall never fathom and that may never be explained to the very last of my descendants."

[24] The passage introduces the conclusion of Kant's *Critique of Practical Reason:* "Zwei Dinge erfüllen das Gemüt mit immer neuer und zunehmender Bewunderung und Ehrfurcht, je öfter und anhaltender sich das Nachdenken damit beschäftigt: der bestirnte Himmel über mir und das moralische Gesetz in mir." Rudolf Unger discusses it in connection with his treatment of the idea of a plurality of worlds, *Aufsätze zur Literatur- und Geistesgeschichte* (Berlin, 1929), pp. 40-66: " 'Der bestirnte Himmel über mir . . .' Zur geistesgeschichtlichen Deutung eines Kantwortes (1924)."

[25] *Beethovens Denkmal im Wort,* edited by Richard Benz (Offenbach-on-Main: Gerstung, 1924), pp. 77f.

suns and earths, then my mind soars beyond these many millions of distant stars to the one source from which all things created stream and from which new creations will eternally continue to stream.

In the eternal flux of ever-new creations, in the eternal revolution and evolution of galaxies around one central source, one central sun,[26] the smallest particle has its all-pervading function. This is what gives the romantic soul the strength to fill the infinite spaces with its exuberance and to reach the center in a feeling of affinity. "When the sky above swarms with innumerable stars," writes Runge in 1802 in a letter to his brother Daniel, "then my soul jubilates and flies about in the immeasurable space surrounding me; there is no longer an above or below, there is no time, no beginning and no end; I hear and feel the living breath of God, who holds the world and carries it, and in whom everything lives and works."[27]

[26] F. Schlegel wrote on November 27, 1798, to Caroline about August Ludwig Hülsen's intention of writing "eine Abhandlung über die Zentralsonne." He thinks that Hülsen is "der rechte Mann dazu, die Astronomie zu einer schönen Wissenschaft zu bilden." Cf. R. Haym, *Romantische Schule*, p. 512. The essay by Hülsen does not seem to exist.

[27] Letter of March 9, 1802. Cf. W. Koch, *Briefe deutscher Romantiker*, p. 266. The passage is strangely reminiscent of one in Goethe's *Werther*, second letter, May 10. There is not only a parallelism in thought and progressive sentence structure, but even in individual expressions. Goethe wrote: "Wenn das liebe Thal um mich dampft, und die hohe Sonne an der Oberfläche der undurchdringlichen Finsterniß meines Waldes ruht, und nur einzelne Strahlen sich in das innere Heiligthum stehlen, ich dann im hohen Grase am fallenden Bache liege, und näher an der Erde tausend mannigfaltige Gräschen mir merkwürdig werden; wenn ich das Wimmeln der kleinen Welt zwischen Halmen, die unzähligen unergründlichen Gestalten der Würmchen, der Mückchen, näher an meinem Herzen fühle, und fühle die Gegenwart des Allmächtigen der uns nach seinem Bilde schuf, das Wehen des Alliebenden der uns in ewiger Wonne schwebend trägt und erhält—mein Freund . . ." The parallel sentence in Runge reads: "Wenn der Himmel über mir von unzähligen Sternen wimmelt, der Wind saust durch den weiten Raum, die Woge bricht sich brausend in der weiten Nacht, über dem Walde rötet sich der Äther, und die Sonne erleuchtet die Welt; das Tal dampft, und ich werfe mich im Grase unter funkelnden Tautropfen hin, jedes Blatt und jeder Grashalm wimmelt von Leben, die Erde lebt und regt sich unter mir, alles tönt in einem Akkord zusammen, da jauchzet die Seele laut auf und fliegt umher in dem unermeßlichen Raum um mich, es ist kein Unten und kein Oben mehr, keine Zeit, kein Anfang und kein Ende, ich höre und fühle den lebendigen Odem Gottes, der die Welt hält und trägt, in dem alles lebt und wirkt: hier ist das Höchste was wir ahnen—Gott!" The differences between these two sentences are perhaps even more revealing than their similarities. The contrast between the almost stammering emotionalism of Werther's experience which leads up to a desperate longing for an adequate artistic form of expression and Runge's quietistic certainty regarding the significance of the experience could be bridged by something which

Hardenberg's fourth hymn to Night[28] evolved from basically the same experience. Here, however, the poet's longing for rest merges with the stillness of an eternal night which is disturbed by the brightness of the stars as his own eternal slumber is temporarily disturbed by his duties of action in life and light.

> Ich lebe bei Tage
> Voll Glauben und Mut
> Und sterbe die Nächte
> In heiliger Glut.

Yet, infinity and infinite rest must and will come in eternal darkness. Love is the road, and thus the first hymn can call the beloved "a sun of night," which means the center of darkness as the other sun is the center of light. The reunion with the beloved, the dissolution of light in darkness, will be an eternal bridal night.[29] The experience of infinity in a vision of the starry heavens has brought about the individual's longing for dissolution. Self-expansion has come close to being self-annihilation. For Hardenberg it is a religious trust in the coherence of all light in one central darkness

---

would have to be called a fusion of religion and art. This is to be found in Wackenroder, "Phantasien über die Kunst," *Kunstanschauung der Frühromantik,* edited by Andreas Müller, "Deutsche Literatur, Reihe Romantik," III (Leipzig: Reclam, 1931), 114, in a passage which shows, like that from Runge, unconscious indebtedness to Goethe: "Wenn ich in meiner Einfalt unter freiem Himmel vor Gott glückselig bin,—indes die goldnen Strahlen der Sonne das hohe blaue Zelt über mir ausspannen und die grüne Erde rings um mich lacht,—da ist's am rechten Ort, daß ich mich auf den Boden werfe, und in vollen Freuden dem Himmel lautjauchzend für alle Herrlichkeit danke. Was aber tut alsdann der sogenannte Künstler unter den Menschen? Er hat mir zugesehen, geht, innerlich erwärmt, stillschweigend daheim, läßt sein sympathetisches Entzücken auf leblosem Saitenspiel weit herrlicher daherrauschen, und bewahrt es auf, in einer Sprache, die kein Mensch je geredet hat, deren Heimat niemand kennt, und die jeden bis in die innersten Nerven ergreift."

[28] *Novalis Schriften,* I, 57f.

[29] Hardenberg's turning away from light is of course partly a turning away from the Enlightenment. Cf. *Novalis Schriften,* II, 76, where it is said of light: "Es ließ sich eher zerbrechen, als daß es mit Farben gespielt hätte." The idea of a black light is fully explained in Klingsor's tale, *ibid.* I, 206, where the black lamp tips over when the clerk (*der Schreiber*) comes into the cave. As soon as the black lamp has been extinguished the room becomes bright again. Somewhere in modern poetry I have read the expression: "Mein liebes schwarzes Licht." The idea is not simply a playful inversion of that which is normal. Its importance for Jan van Ruusbroec and other medieval mystics is discussed under the key phrase "het licht, dat in duister verkeert" by J. Huizinga, *Herfsttij der Middeleeuwen* (Haarlem: Tjeenk Willink & Zoon, 1928³), p. 320.

which keeps the experience from being self-destructive. If this
trust disappears, horror and fear must emerge.

They resound, indeed, in a letter of Kleist to his friend Rühle
written in August 1806: "What may be the name of that little
star which can be seen on Sirius when the sky is clear?" It is
desperate and not religious amazement that dictates such a question. Yet Kleist insists still more clearly on the insignificance of
our world and of human individualities: "And this entire enormous
firmament is but a speck of dust compared with infinity . . . richer
in possibilities than thoughts can grasp . . ."[30] For Kleist there is
something oppressive in the grandeur of the starry heavens. His
reaction was essentially that of the later Nineteenth Century, for
which the order in the universe, as the Eighteenth Century had
established it by faith and by knowledge, had disappeared again.[31]
"When Tennyson wrote: 'The stars,' she whispered, 'blindly run,'
he was not only representing the current pessimism of nineteenth-
century philosophy but was also reflecting the outlook of nineteenth-century astronomy."[32] Hebbel voiced the same feeling,
when he said:[33] "I cannot understand how the sight of the starry
heavens should widen man's breast: in me it dissolves the feeling
of personality, and I cannot imagine that nature should bother to
maintain my miserable self in its futility."

The difference between this passage from Hebbel and the various quotations from writers of the preceding age is a striking one,
but it is easily understood. For Hebbel and his time the problem
was the relation of the individual to the totality of nature from
which it knew it had broken away: the tragedy of individuation!
For the earlier age the problem was still that of the individual's

[30] August 31, 1806.
[31] In 1782 Fr. Wilh. Herschel accepted definitely the idea that the sun has a
movement of its own. In 1784 he published his book *On the Construction of
Heavens*. In 1786 came his first catalogue of nebulae. One year later it was already
time for a second catalogue. Up to 1802 Herschel listed 2302 nebulae. Yet this dizzy
number was only the beginning of those which became known as "astronomical."
[32] G. W. Gray, "Our Greater Galaxy." The passage leads up to an appreciation
of the work of J. C. Kapteyn of Groningen who, in 1904, announced his discovery
of star streaming. From that hour on, as another astronomer quoted by Gray put
it, "the stellar system ceased to be a collection of individuals, and became an organic
whole!" It became again what it had been toward the end of the Eighteenth Century.
[33] Cf. A. Biese, *Naturgefühl*, p. 214.

rank and position in the self-evident continuity of the entire universe: the longing for organic integration. In Hebbel's age there were not many who, like Carus,[34] could quote in kindred spirit this passage from Goethe: "What is the good of all this display of suns and planets and moons, of stars and galaxies and nebulae, of worlds a-growing and of worlds complete, if finally a happy human being does not enjoy life in their midst?" For this is the positive essence of Goethe's rhetorical question: the happiness of man, in all his miserable smallness, is not—to put it paradoxically —devoid of interest from the point of view of the infinite display of suns and planets, of moons and stars and nebulae and galaxies. There is a definite interdependence between the infinitely small represented by a human individual and the infinite greatness of the universe. At first sight it may seem that this is merely one of those doctrines which the human mind may devise and to which it may cling in desperate self-protection against the fatal recognition of its absolute insignificance. That it is considerably more remains to be demonstrated by a new approach.

[34] Carl Gustav Carus, *Physis* (Stuttgart, 1851), concluding paragraph. Dr. Thijs Jolles traced this quotation for me. It comes from *Winckelmann und sein Jahrhundert*, second paragraph of the chapter "Antikes." Its last words are: ". . . wenn sich nicht zuletzt ein glücklicher Mensch unbewußt seines Daseyns erfreut?" Carus has the curious substitution "in ihrer Mitte" for Goethe's "unbewußt."

VIII

TYPE AND ORGANISM

THE UNIVERSE, as its name indicates, is a unit.[1] The idea that it must be conceived as infinite, represents for us an inheritance from the philosophy of the Renaissance.[2]

Infinity as a problematic experience has affected, successively and in ever expanding circles, all the various fields of human thought. Its first tangible product may be seen in modern astronomy, although a Copernicus and a Kepler—just as their contemporaries in the natural sciences—could not admit it into their systems as a definite axiom.[3] It conquered mathematical thought, manifesting itself in the guise of differential and integral calculus.[4]

[1] It is possible, it seems, to consider that unity as not so obvious after all. Will Durand in his short *Story of Philosophy* (New York, 1926), p. 561, quotes from William James' *Pragmatism: A New Name for Old Ways of Thinking* (1907), p. 312. " 'The world is one!'—the formula may become a sort of number-worship. 'Three' and 'seven' have, it is true, been reckoned as sacred numbers; but abstractly taken, why is 'one' more excellent than 'forty-three,' or than 'two million and ten'?" Instead of discussing James' answer, Durand explains in a footnote: "The answer, of course, is that unity, or one system of laws holding throughout the universe, facilitates explanation, prediction, and control!" This may be an answer, but it leaves the question unsolved.

[2] K. Joël, *Der Ursprung der Naturphilosophie*, p. 29: "Die Unendlichkeit wie die Einheit der Welt, diese Erträgnisse der Renaissancephilosophie, sind nicht aus Induktionsschlüssen gewonnen. Das Gefühl ist's, das die Tendenz zur Einheit und Unendlichkeit in sich trägt."

[3] Cf. K. Joël, *Der Ursprung der Naturphilosophie*, p. 29: "Aus der Unendlichkeit Gottes beweist Bruno die Unendlichkeit der Welt. Nur der tiefmystische Cusaner ist ihm darin vorangegangen; die Naturforscher, selbst Kopernikus und Kepler wollen von der Unendlichkeit der Welt noch nichts wissen, und doch haben auch sie die unsichtbare Ordnung der Welt gesucht und gefunden."

[4] The following dates from the history of mathematics seem to belong here. They are presented without comment on their significance for the history of thought. The interpretation of this aspect of our problem must be left to a competent mathematician. In 1635 Buonaventura Cavalieri touches the principle of differentiation. Pierre Fermat does the same in 1636. Newton's fluxions of 1671 are basically identical with the system which Leibnitz developed in 1676. Differential calculus is definitely established in 1686 by Leibnitz, *De geometria recondita et analysi indivisibilium atque infinitorum*. In 1739 Bernard Forrest de Bélidor is the first to apply the new system to a technological problem. In 1797 Joseph Louis Lagrange establishes the theory of analytical functions, which make it possible to base differentiation on finite quantities in contrast to Leibnitz who had to work with the infinitely small. In 1822 Fourier elaborates his mathematical theory of heat.

At about the same time it appeared in baroque art as an insatiable urge for expansion. Its literary history is that "of romanticism in all its forms and shades and of all times."[5] Better still, it is the experience of infinity which conditioned that Faustian restlessness, which Friedrich Schlegel worded so strikingly: "Wer etwas Unendliches will, der weiß nicht was er will. Aber umkehren läßt sich dieser Satz nicht."[6]

He who strives for the infinite cannot know what he wants. His goal is a basic paradox. When Cusanus[7] conceived of the universe as an unlimited unit, he postulated as a basic truth a mystic *contradictio in adjecto,* "the world is an unlimited limitation." Young Goethe's exclamation, "Wo faß ich dich, unendliche Natur?",[8] represents an impetuous demand for a direct and sensual experience of a *coincidentia oppositorum,* of the coincidence of infinity with a tangible reality. Romantic thought postulates such a coincidence as what might be called the *Urphänomen* of the ego. This is what Schelling had in mind when he stated: "That which we call the ego, is only a reunion [coincidence] of the ideal and the real,[9] of the finite and infinity."[10] Schleiermacher's *Discourses on Religion* represent the demand, which reminds us of Herder,[11] that infinity be visualized, not only in the ego, but in all finite phenomena. The idea that it is possible to "view infinity in a grain of sand," is not only the basis of romantic solipsism

---

[5] A. Meyer, "Goethes Naturerkenntnis," n. 8: "In andern Geistesgebieten gelangte der Durchbruch des Unendlichen z.T. viel später zur Reife. In der bildenden Kunst brachte er den Barock, in der Literatur die Romantik aller Formen, Zeiten und Schattierungen, deren vollendetste Formen im Grunde die Klassiker sind, und in der Politik die heute noch nicht zur Reife gelangte Idee der Nationalstaaten hervor."

[6] F. Schlegel, "Kritische Fragmente," 47.

[7] Cf. especially Ernst Cassirer, *Individuum und Kosmos in der Philosophie der Renaissance,* "Studien der Bibliothek Warburg," vol. 10, Leipzig and Berlin, 1927.

[8] Goethe, *Urfaust,* line 102.

[9] This is the problem of Schiller, "Das Ideal und das Leben." On March 25, 1785, Schiller wrote to Huber: ". . . bei ökonomischen Berechnungen [wird] meine Seele geteilt, beunruhigt, ich stürze aus meinen idealischen Welten, sobald mich ein zerrissener Strumpf an die wirkliche mahnt." It is obvious that the worlds of ideals and torn stockings coincide artificially only and with bad grace.

[10] Friedrich Wilhelm Schelling, "Bruno *oder* Über das göttliche und natürliche Prinzip der Dinge," *Werke,* edited by Otto Weiß (Leipzig, 1907), II, 492, Lucian: "Was wir Ich nennen, ist nur jene Einheit des Idealen mit dem Realen, des Endlichen mit dem Unendlichen."

[11] Cf. p. 110, n. 66.

in all its various forms, it is all in itself the foundation and very essence of early romantic aesthetics.[12] "Saturate your emotional experience of life with the idea of infinity," says Friedrich Schlegel,[13] and when he continues, "then you shall understand the ancients and poetry" he sacrifices his beloved Winckelmann and all of antiquity to the un-Hellenic cult of modern boundlessness. Elsewhere[14] he explains that the essential difference between antiquity and modern times must be seen in the fact that the Greeks had a mythology while we are still striving to develop one.[15] The idea that a symbol is for the individual what a myth is for the race,[16] is a romantic idea. Both symbolism and mythology are a throwing together (*syn* and *bolos*) of an infinite truth with its finite representation. Schelling defined Greek mythology as "the representation of infinity as such in something finite."[17] Hardenberg[18] had generalized this idea long before in his statement that it is the task of a reader "to find the universe in every book" which, we may qualify, can claim to be a work of art.

The simple conception that genuine art is a finite representation of infinity, is generally romantic.[19] Implicit as well as explicit references to it as a dogmatic principle of general validity abound in the literature before and shortly after the year 1800. A few random illustrations may indicate their characteristic trend. In 1787 Goethe wrote in his Italian diary[20] with reference to the

---

[12] William Blake, "Auguries of Innocence," first quatrain:
To see a World in a Grain of Sand
And a Heaven in a Wild Flower,
Hold Infinity in the palm of your hand
And Eternity in an hour.

[13] F. Schlegel, "Ideen," 85.

[14] F. Schlegel, "Rede über die Mythologie," *Jugendschriften,* II, 358.

[15] On the idea of a new mythology, cf. F. Strich, *Mythologie,* and chapter XIII, "Cosmic Poetry."

[16] Friedrich Gundolf, *Goethe* (1925[12]), p. 583: "Symbol ist das für die einzelne Person, was der Mythos für eine Gesamtheit ist."

[17] Friedrich Wilhelm Schelling, "Philosophie der Kunst," §42, *Sämtliche Werke,* edited by K. F. A. Schelling (1856ff.), first series, V.

[18] *Novalis Schriften,* III, 336.

[19] It is, characteristically enough, also the essence of classical aesthetics. Cf. Paul Ernst, *Der Weg zur Form* (1928), p. 332: "Ein Künstler ist ein Mensch, der in seiner ganzen Persönlichkeit und mit ihr verbunden ein besonderes Weltbild hat, das er mit bestimmten, ihm eigentümlichen Mitteln zu gestalten und . . . aus sich herauszustellen sucht." Written in 1910.

[20] Goethe, *Italienische Reise,* September 6, 1787.

works of Greek sculpture that they were, "produced by men according to true and natural laws, the highest works of nature. Everything arbitrary and unreal crumbles away: here is necessity, here there is God." It is a familiar thought that God is represented by His Creation. If, however, an individual work of art is said to contain the essence of God, then it must be concluded that such a work of art contains also the essence of the universe, its basic laws, the necessity of its existence. That this was actually Goethe's thought may be inferred from the fact that he wrote the passage just quoted clearly in response to Herder's Spinoza-dialogues with their central teaching that God created nothing which is not an imprint of His power and wisdom.[21] August Wilhelm Schlegel justified his admiration for Dante by asserting that no other poet had succeeded as fully in a "direct presentation of infinity" as the author of the *Divina Commedia*.[22] In a bold generalization Friedrich Schlegel stated that "all the sacred plays of art are merely remote imitations of the infinite play of the universe which is itself a work of art eternally in progress."[23] It is highly significant that this idea attained a final and, as it were, dogmatic codification in Bernhardi's review of the "mythological almanac"[24] by Schlegel and Tieck for the year 1802:[25]

All art is visualization of the universe, and this conception implies the solution of a contradiction and contrast. The universe is something infinite, but visualization implies reduction to the most limited confines of existence. Art consists thus in representing the infinite in limitation, and this cannot be done except through a transformation into images and symbols.

The romantic endeavor to achieve in art the *coincidentia* of infinity and reality, is obviously more than a corollary of an ab-

[21] Cf. p. 110, n. 65, and Goethe's letters, *Italienische Reise*, October 5 and 8, 1787.
[22] Cf. p. 79, n. 18.
[23] F. Schlegel, "Rede über die Mythologie," *Jugendschriften*, II, 364.
[24] Cf. "DNL," vol. 135³, and F. Strich, *Mythologie*, II, 91.
[25] August Ferdinand Bernhardi, reprinted from his journal *Kynosarges* in *Kunstanschauung der Frühromantik*, edited by Andreas Müller, "Deutsche Literatur, Reihe Romantik," III (Leipzig: Reclam, 1931), 285: "Alle Kunst ist Anschauung des Universums, und in diesem Begriff liegt schon eine Aussöhnung eines Widerspruches und Gegensatzes. Denn das Universum ist etwas Unendliches, Anschauung aber führt auf die engste Grenze des Daseins, es wird daher die Kunst darin bestehen, das Unendliche in dem Begrenzten darzustellen, und dies kann nicht anders geschehen, als durch die Verwandelung in das Bild und Symbol."

stract mathematical idea or of an insatiable urge for expansion.
Wielding "the magic rod of analogy,"[26] Schelling seems to allude
to its real basis. "The way," he says,[27] "in which the finite is
linked up with the infinite, is most nearly paralleled in the world
of known and visible things by the way in which the parts are
linked up with the whole in an organic body." Here we have *in
nuce* the complete result of the present analysis, but for the time
being Schelling's statement must serve merely as the basis of one
important observation. It is a statement which conceives of infinity, albeit only in a simile, as an organic whole. This is possible only if infinity is a concept which has its place in man's
experience of the world of finite organisms, or more generally,
of the world of reality. Indeed, it seems possible to discern in all
romantic references to the idea of infinity this common and peculiar element, that it is a concept directly inspired by an experience of visible nature. In this, "romantic" infinity differs
from "mathematical" or "emotional" infinity. With Schelling and
his contemporaries the problematic experience of infinity, which
Joël[28] calls our inheritance from the philosophy of the Renaissance, has finally attained its widest scope. It has established
itself in the sphere of phenomenal existences.

This last expansion of the idea of infinity seems to have occurred in the course of the Eighteenth Century. The problems
which appeared in its wake were, obviously, more than problems
in abstract philosophical thinking. Indeed, it is not surprising
that they should have become a major concern of the natural
sciences. A clear survey of their significance in that field can be
given in the form of an analysis of certain aspects of Robinet's
work *On Nature*,[29] which was published between 1761 and 1768.

---

[26] Who coined the expression "Zauberstab der Analogie"? Historians of Romanticism
use it frequently. Cf., e.g., Ricarda Huch, *Ausbreitung und Verfall der Romantik*,
p. 269, and Chr. Bernouilli and H. Kern, *Romantische Naturphilosophie*, p 399, in
a note referring to G. H. Schubert. It occurs in Hardenberg, *Novalis Schriften*, II, 78:
"Lernt aus der Geschichte und gebraucht den Zauberstab der Analogie."

[27] F. W. Schelling, "Bruno," p. 454.

[28] Cf. p. 136, n. 2.

[29] J. B. Robinet, *de la Nature*. The first volume appeared in 1761, the second in
1763. A second edition of both appeared together with volumes III and IV in 1766.
Volume V followed in 1768 bearing the subtitle, "Vue philosophique de la gradation
naturelle des formes de l'être. Les Essais de la Nature qui apprend à faire l'homme."

Such an analysis can serve at the same time as the basis for further conclusions regarding the romantic conception of infinite organization. The metaphysical basis of Robinet's work is the conviction that nature is an infinite continuity, an endless chain of finite links. There can be no gaps; and as far and as fast as thought can travel, it will never reach the end of the chain of actually existing forms. From the point of view of man there must be an infinite and uninterrupted continuity of animate beings extending upward to the final, i.e., the infinitely perfect existence of God; and an equally infinite and uninterrupted continuity must extend downward to the last infinitesimal of matter. Now it is obvious that only a very short section of Robinet's infinite chain can be covered by things and beings which human eyes have actually observed. There must be many others. Indeed, those which remain to be discovered are considerably more numerous than those which have already come to our attention. Robinet became thus one of the most daring explorers of the entire Eighteenth Century. He stayed behind his desk, but the "scientific" yield of his flights of fancy was much richer than that of travels undertaken by men like William Dampier, Vitus Bering, and Karsten Niebuhr.[30] It may be suggested with absolute seriousness that much more than a queer coincidence should be seen in the fact that Robinet wrote his fantastic work *On Nature* at precisely the time when the major scientific expeditions of the Eighteenth Century were under way. The years from 1761 to 1768 are the period of Bougainville's first trip around the globe (1766), of that of Wallis-Carteret (1766), of Cook's first journey (1768), of James Bruce's travels to discover the source of the Nile (1768), and of Pallas' expedition to Siberia (1768). Robinet's chain of beings had a place for all the newly discovered species and varieties of beings and things. Its boundless receptivity forced

---

The following discussion depends on A. O. Lovejoy, *The Great Chain of Being*, pp. 269ff. Quotations from Robinet are given, as far as possible, in Lovejoy's translation.

[30] These explorers precede Robinet. William Dampier published the account of his journey in 1707; Veit Bering undertook his last trip together with Chirikov in 1740 and died before its completion on December 8, 1741; in 1761 Karsten Niebuhr was sent by the Danish Government to Arabia, Persia, Palestine, and Asia Minor.

this author into an amazing credulity with regard to the tallest stories about fanciful creatures found in supposedly authentic reports or even in legend and fiction. It further induced him to undertake speculative expeditions to other celestial globes,[31] where he collected hypothetical material on all sorts of creatures which happen not to exist on our little planet. Nevertheless, Robinet's speculation about individual links in the chain of being, as for instance his discussion of mermaids and mermen, which alone seems to have preserved his name in the larger handbooks of literary history, is merely a logical consequence of his literal interpretation of the idea of an unbroken continuity in nature. This interpretation it is which constitutes Robinet's basic contribution and claim to immortality.

The idea that all the realms of nature with all their individual members belong together because they constitute one continuous chain was not an invention of Robinet's. It had been formulated, e.g., in Bonnet's palingenetic doctrine.[32] However, its application by this thinker had not, according to Robinet,[33] been either consistent or logical. In Bonnet's conception it is possible to distinguish a number of definite stages in the continuity of natural things. There is first the inorganic realm. It is followed by that which is organic but inanimate. Then comes the organic, which is animate but devoid of reason. Only the last stage is rational in addition to being organic and animate. This system implies that a transition is possible from a negative, the inanimate, inorganic, etc., to a positive, the animate, organic, etc. Yet, Robinet maintains, it is obvious that the negative is always at an infinite distance from the positive.[34] It is impossible to connect the two

[31] Cf. p. 125, n. 6.
[32] Cf. p. 64, n. 33.
[33] J. B. Robinet, de la Nature, IV, 1f.; A. O. Lovejoy, The Great Chain of Being, p. 275.
[34] From here it would be possible to reach the conclusions of the present discussion by a different road. A romantic philosopher like Schelling would hold that it is absurd to speak of an infinite distance separating the positive from the negative. The relation between these two is a question of polarity and not of distance. Cf. p. 150, n. 61. Polarity as a universal principle leads directly to the idea of a universal organism. Cf. p. 150, n. 59. Of this it can be said that it was destined to replace the old concept of a chain of being as the guarantor of continuity and unity in nature. It was destined to do so in full consideration of the axiom that nature is infinite. Its superiority over the idea of a chain is precisely that the latter must conflict with

in a smooth continuity, and thus he concludes: "If we wish to allow nature to pass insensibly from one of her productions to another without compelling her to make leaps, we must not admit the existence of any inorganic beings, or any inanimate or any nonrational."[35] All the differences in nature must be differences in degree. Her most extreme productions must be recognized as mere exaggerations of something normal. All possible beings are held together by the fact that each one contains but variants of all the elements which might be found in any of the others. On

the condition of infinite extension. All of this means that Robinet could have constructed a doctrine of a universal organism quite similar to that of Schelling, that he could thus have overcome the notion of a two-dimensional continuity of nature along a *chain* of beings, if instead of stating that the negative is always at an infinite distance from the positive, he had been able to see that the relation between the negative and the positive is a question of polarity. This, however, was impossible. The polar idea developed parallel to the theory of electricity. The two seem to have been functionally interdependent. With reference to Schelling and the idea of polarity, Theobald Ziegler, *Die geistigen und sozialen Strömungen Deutschlands im 19. und 20. Jahrhundert bis zum Beginn des Weltkrieges* (Berlin, 1927), p. 61, states bluntly: "Diesen Begriff entnahm er der Lehre vom Magnetismus, wie er ihn nach dem damaligen Stande des Wissens als Galvanismus oder tierische Elektrizität kennen gelernt hat." Now, the terms "negative" and "positive" as we use them currently to designate electric tension were introduced by Lichtenberg as late as 1778. At the time when Robinet wrote it was thus hardly possible to conceive of polarity as a philosophical concept overcoming the idea of an infinite distance between the positive and the negative. Indeed, Robinet could not even distinguish between the logical and the real negation, of which only the former implies an actual contradiction. This discrimination, clearly defined in the terms *nihil repraesentabile* and *nihil negativum* or *irrepraesentabile*, was introduced still later by Kant, *Versuch, den Begriff der negativen Größen in die Weltweisheit einzuführen*, Grätz (counterfeit edition), 1797. The importance of Kant for the polar idea may be gathered from the following quotations. Hardenberg, *Novalis Schriften*, II, 120, wrote: "Negation [ist] mehr als Mangel. Setzen des Entgegengesetzten." A. Müller, *Lehre vom Gegensatz*, p. 228, refers explicitly to Kant's essay and admits his direct indebtedness. It is a work, he says, on which "wir uns mit unsrer gegenwärtigen Arbeit gewissermaßen stützen. Bei der großen Klarheit, mit der dort schon das Wesen des Gegensatzes und sein Verhältnis zum Widerspruche, der Unterschied zwischen dem Negativen und der Negation auseinandergesetzt wird, wäre es unbegreiflich, wie nicht die sämtlichen nachherigen Untersuchungen dieses Philosophen eine ganz andre Richtung nahmen als sie wirklich genommen haben, wenn es ihm nicht vielmehr um den Begriff der negativen Größen, als um den reinen Begriff des Negativen selbst zu tun gewesen wäre." This passage gains in interest if we agree with Wilhelm Metzger, *Gesellschaft, Recht und Staat in der Ethik des deutschen Idealismus* (Heidelberg, 1917), p. 260, who calls Müller's book "die Programmschrift der romantischen Weltanschauung." Cf., finally, F. Schlegel, "Athenäums-Fragmente," 3: "Kant hat den Begriff des negativen in die Weltweisheit eingeführt. Sollte es nicht ein nützlicher Versuch sein, nun auch den Begriff des Positiven in die Philosophie einzuführen?"

[35] J. B. Robinet, *de la Nature*, IV, 4f.; A. O. Lovejoy, *The Great Chain of Being*, p. 276.

this basis it seems impossible not to conclude that every existent must be considered as a finite representation of the infinite number of all the others. In simpler words, all of nature's children must have been modeled upon one basic pattern, which might be called the prototype.[36]

The task to conceive of a finite and tangible representation of nature's infinity would thus have induced Robinet to anticipate the Goethean idea that individuality is always a metamorphic variation of an original type or interindividual pattern. This is not altogether wrong. Indeed, in a discussion of Robinet's work Professor Lovejoy comes to the following conclusion:[37] "Robinet, though not the originator, was (as far as I know) the first elaborator and enthusiastic champion of that notion of an *Urbild,* upon which all organic and perhaps all natural forms are variations, which was to be taken up by Herder[38] and to become almost an obsession of Goethe at one period."[39] Between Robinet's and Goethe's conceptions of the prototype there remains, nevertheless, an important difference, which seems to deserve further investigation. Robinet's reasoning is about as follows: The principle of continuity in nature forces us to assume that all natural phenomena have something in common. They all must be derived from one single type form, which is capable of an infinite number of variations.

When I compare," Robinet continues,[40] "the stone with the plant, the plant with the insect, the insect with the reptile, the reptile with the quadruped, I perceive, through all the differences which characterize each of them, relations of analogy which persuade me that they have been conceived and formed in accordance with a single model of which they are variations graduated *ad infinitum.* They exhibit all the salient traits

---

[36] Cf. p. 56, n. 18 for Diderot's reference to something like a prototype of the vertebrates.

[37] A. O. Lovejoy, *The Great Chain of Being,* p. 279.

[38] Cf. Johann Gottfried Herder, *Ideen zur Philosophie der Geschichte der Menschheit* (1784-1791), first chapter of book V. The idea is characteristically limited to the animal kingdom.

[39] The qualification "at one period" seems superfluous. There is no safe approach to any aspect of Goethe's work except through the idea of the prototype. However, when F. Cassirer, *Beethoven,* p. IX, says, "Fast wissen es nun schon die Kinder: Goethe lehrt Metamorphose," he is, unfortunately, too optimistic. Cf. also p. 3, n. 1.

[40] J. B. Robinet, *de la Nature,* IV, 17; A. O. Lovejoy, *The Great Chain of Being,* p. 278.

of this original exemplar, which in realizing itself has taken on successively the infinitely numerous and diverse forms under which Being
manifests itself to our eyes.

In all of this there is nothing which might not refer to Goethe's
conception as well. The basic difference between the two thinkers
appears, however, when Robinet defines his prototype as "a particular form distinct from all other forms" which must be regarded as "the element generative of all beings."[41] The prototype, in other words, is the element which stones, plants, insects,
reptiles, and quadrupeds have in common. It is the ultimate unit
out of which all existents are built. To prevent it from becoming
a mere atom, Robinet offers the further definition that "the prototype is an intellectual principle which does not change except
in its realization in matter."[42] This spiritualization of the prototype presents it as a sort of monad but does not change the fact
that it is the lowest and simplest element from which all the
higher forms of existence can be derived. It is potentially a stone,
a plant, an insect, a reptile, or a human being. When it is actually
realized in matter, unfathomable reasons force it to settle on one
of these levels, although it is potentially quite ready to take its
place in the highest realm.[43] The identity of man and beast is due
to the fact that the latter's prototype had human ambitions which,
however, were somehow thwarted. Similar ambitions in the proto-
types of lower organisms manifest themselves by forcing their
material representation to assume a shape which reminds us of
what they were striving to attain: trees look like animals, rocks
like plants, roots and branches like legs or arms, etc.[44] Every
link in the chain of being may feel sure that it is envied by all

[41] *Id., ibid.*
[42] J. B. Robinet, *de la Nature,* IV, 17: ". . . le prototype est un principe intel-
lectuel qui ne s'altère qu'en se réalisant dans la matière . . ."
[43] The highest realm is for our purposes that of man. Robinet, as a matter of fact,
conceives of higher ones. The willingness on the part of the prototype to take its
place higher up when it undergoes realization in matter, is naturally engendered
by a force which makes for unlimited perfectibility. The prototype may be enslaved
by matter. On a higher level of perfection it uses matter as its tool. On the highest
level it may be able to rid itself entirely of all materiality. Then it belongs to the
realm of immaterial spirits. Cf. J. B. Robinet, *de la Nature,* V, 12f.
[44] Cf. J. B. Robinet, *de la Nature,* IV. In this volume there are drawings of semi-
human radishes and the like.

the lower ones which long to attain its superior level. From the human point of view Robinet can formulate as follows: "All the varieties intermediate between the prototype and man I regard as so many essays of Nature, aiming at the most perfect, yet unable to attain it. I think we may call the collection of the preliminary studies the apprenticeship of Nature in learning to make man."[45] The prototype disposes thus of a certain vitality which is at times sufficient to attain the level of man. Generally, however, it is exhausted before it gets that far. It is a principle which reminds us of Avicenna's *vis plastica*, the force which this medieval thinker used to explain what we should call petrified fossils as organisms the generative element of which ran dry before they attained animation.[46]

Goethe, on the other hand, did not conceive of the prototype as either a monad or the simplest unit of nature's construction material.[47] His early idea, it is true, had also been that "the proto-

[45] J. B. Robinet, *de la Nature*, V. For the full title of this volume, cf. p. 140, n. 29. Cf. also J. B. Robinet, *Parallèle de la condition et des facultés de l'homme avec la condition et les facultés des autres animaux* (1770), which is claimed to be a translation from the English. A. O. Lovejoy, *The Great Chain of Being*, p. 368, doubts the existence of an English original.

[46] This idea that a moulding and animating force which fails at times to achieve its purpose is active everywhere in nature represents a peculiar variety of vitalism. With Robinet the purpose is always at least to attain material realization in a human shape. In this form Schleiermacher used the idea metaphorically. Cf. F. Schlegel, *Jugendschriften*, II, 264, "Athenäums-Fragmente," 352, ascribed to Schleiermacher by Minor: "Es ist eine Dichtung der Geschichtsschreiber der Natur, daß ihre plastischen Kräfte lange in vergeblichen Anstrengungen gearbeitet, und nachdem sie sich in Formen erschöpft hatten, die kein dauerndes Leben haben konnten, noch viele andre erzeugt worden wären, die zwar lebten, aber untergehen mußten, weil es ihnen an der Kraft fehlte sich fortzupflanzen." A moral is then drawn with reference to a parallel situation in the spiritual life of humanity. A related metaphor is that which speaks of animals as the dreams of nature whose awakening is achieved in man. Mme. de Staël found this in a certain poet whose name she does not mention. Cf. *de l'Allemagne*, III, 333. F. Hufeland, "Über Sympathie," p. 36, has an almost literal parallel: "Das Pflanzenleben [ist] einem bewußtlosen Schlafe, das Leben der Tiere aber einem Traume zu vergleichen, aus welchem erst der Mensch zu vollem Bewußtsein erwacht."

[47] Attention must be drawn to one isolated instance where Goethe used a compound with *Ur-* for the smallest unit of matter. In Diderot's *Neveu de Rameau* the hero is asked how he explains the fact that he, who has such a fine musical ear, is absolutely devoid of any feeling of moral responsibility. He replies in Goethe's translation, *Sämmtliche Werke*, XXIX, 295: "Wahrscheinlich weil es für diese [Tugend] einen Sinn gibt, den ich nicht habe, eine Fiber, die mir nicht gegeben ist." Goethe's "Fiber" translates the French "fibre." Cf. Denis Diderot, *Œuvres complètes*, edited by J. Assézat (Paris, 1875), V, 468. Then the question arises how he, the

type must be a particular form distinct from all other possible forms."[48] It had been, for Goethe, too, the universal form from which all the others might be derived. However, instead of being elemental and primitive, it had presented itself in Goethe's conception as highly complex because it had to be all-inclusive.[49] Later on Goethe discarded the idea that it should be possible to discover actual specimens of the prototype for which, in the more limited sphere of botany, he had searched the flora of Sicily.[50] It no longer was a theme which existed apart from its variations, but rather the interindividual type form which manifests itself only in a multiplicity of individual modulations.[51] To be sure, these modulations vary in perfection. It is possible to visualize the prototype in all its representations, even the most primitive; but the more highly developed a given individual is, the stronger is also its claim to be taken as the fullest realization of its model. We may translate Goethe's thought into more speculative terms, for in thus transgressing the limits of his phenomenological science we obtain a much clearer perspective of his basic principles. If it is possible to arrange all the realizations of the prototype in matter in a scale of perfection, then it must be permissible to

---

hero, is going to influence his son's development, and he expresses his attitude of *laissez-faire* determinism in these words, again in Goethe's translation: "Ist er bestimmt ein rechtlicher Mann zu werden, so würde ich nicht schaden; aber wollte die Urfaser, daß er ein Taugenichts würde, wie der Vater, so wäre sämmtliche Mühe . . . etc." The word "Urfaser" renders a French "la molécule" which refers to a previous "la maudite molécule paternelle."

[48] Cf. p. 145, n. 41.

[49] Cf. Goethe, *Italienische Reise*, April 17, 1787, and May 17, 1787.

[50] This change in Goethe's conception of the "Urpflanze" can already be perceived in a comparison of the two entries in the Italian diary mentioned in note 49 above. In April 1787 Goethe wrote in Palermo with respect to the "Urpflanze": "Eine solche muß es denn doch geben." One month later he wrote in Naples: "Die Urpflanze wird das wunderlichste Geschöpf von der Welt, um welches mich die Natur selbst beneiden soll." He calls it a "Modell" by means of which plants can be invented which really do not exist. Nature would not have to envy Goethe if she had this "Modell" among her actually existing plants.

[51] Edgar Dacqué, *Urwelt, Sage und Menschheit* (Munich, 1925[3]), p. 56, is fully justified in identifying his conception of the prototype with that of Goethe. He writes: "Wir verstehen unter Urform . . . die in allen zu einem Typus gehörigen Arten und Gattungen, auch in den anfänglichsten, schon vollständig vorhandene typenhaft konstitutionelle Gebundenheit und Bestimmtheit, die Potenz, die bei allem äußeren evolutionistischen Formenwechsel als das Lebendig-Beständige da ist—eine Entelechie wie auch Goethe wohl den Begriff Urform faßte."

conceive of each one as the prototype of all those which are inferior to it. The most perfect link is the prototype of the chain
of being. Man is the prototype of the animal kingdom and God
of the entire creation. All the animals are variations of man, and
all existents are representative variations of God. This is a romantic elaboration of the central idea in Goethe's natural philosophy. We find it in Hardenberg. "The unattainable," he says,[52]
"is, as it were, the ideal representative of the sum total of the
entire series. Thus it seems to be the last link, the type of every
link, and is indicated by every link."

It is necessary to return once again to Robinet. The difference
between his and Goethe's conceptions of the prototype can now
be given a very sharp formulation. The Frenchman conceived of
it as the first and most primitive link in the chain of being, the
German as the last and most perfect. Both thinkers needed the
prototype as a limited, finite representation of the unlimited, infinite fullness of nature. Robinet tried, as it were, to derive infinity
from its basic element, to which he assigned infinite potentialities.
Goethe, on the other hand, viewed the infinite whole in all of its
parts. This difference can be strikingly demonstrated by a play
on words. Robinet conceived of the prototype as the first *Glied*
(link) of a chain; Goethe saw it in every *Glied* (member) of an
organism. If Robinet had achieved the impossible, if he had attained infinity and had substituted the last and most perfect
Glied of his chain for the first, his views would have coincided
with those of Goethe. The infinite, as Hardenberg put it, is the
last *Glied* and, at the same time, the type of every other. The two
meanings of the word *Glied* coincide in infinity. There the series,
the scale, the chain, becomes an entity, a totality, an organic
whole. *Glied* may be taken as link, grade, stage, or as limb, organ,
member; it remains "a variation of the whole."[53] The whole is
the type on which all of its parts are modeled.[54]

[52] *Novalis Schriften,* III, 143.

[53] *Novalis Schriften,* II, 342.

[54] The prototype, it seems evident, is a concept to be derived directly from that
of the type. It is important to note that this does not seem to hold true for Robinet.
His conception of types was essentially like that of Goethe and even of modern
biology, but it had no connection with his views of the prototype. Robinet's *type*
appears when he limits perfectibility in nature in such a way that no creatures

The problematic experience of the universe as infinite and yet as one finds thus its biological solution in the conception of a total organism. This statement is convertible. The organic[55] idea depends on the experience of the paradox that the world as a unit is yet infinite. No other basis can possibly support the pan-organic views of Herder, Goethe, and the early Romanticists. The philosophical confirmation of this statement is found in Schelling. He wrote in 1798:[56] "The contrast between mechanism and organism, which has impeded the progress of the natural sciences for so long, will disappear as soon as our investigation attains the conception of nature as one whole." When the world is recognized as an organization, it will be apparent that "a general organism is the prerequisite for everything mechanical."[57] This is the core of Schelling's natural philosophy. It necessitates the supposition that one general principle "combines all of nature," i.e., as Schelling puts it,[58] a principle in which "we recognize anew that Being which the oldest philosophy welcomed as the common soul of all nature." Universal organization admits

"have the power to transcend their natural state; they are held within it by bonds not to be broken. If some have the power to modify their existence, this liberty does not pass beyond the limits of their species." Cf. de la Nature, I, 25; A. O. Lovejoy, The Great Chain of Being, p. 273. E. Barthels, Goethes Wissenschaftslehre, p. 32, summarizes Goethe's conception in a modern terminology: "Experience teaches the careful observer that there is in the world of organisms a dual principle of constancy and variability. Constancy characterizes the type as an aesthetic thought of nature. Variability pertains to the species which are formed in their struggle with the surrounding world." Finally, according to Hans Weinert, "Die neuesten Ergebnisse über die Abstammung des Menschen," Forschungen und Fortschritte, XII (1936), 401f., the most recent results in biological research with regard to the theory of descent have established the fact that a change in external conditions cannot lead to anything but the annihilation of a given species unless there be in it the possibility to reappear by mutation in a new form. If this is true, it means that the variability of species is conceived as strictly limited by the rigidity of types in Robinet's sense of the notion.

[55] The word organic has lost its original vigor through its use as a technical term in chemistry. E. Dacqué, "Außen und Innen der organischen Entwicklung," p. 157, proposes to reserve the word entirely for the semantic value which chemistry has assigned to it. For the more general value which the word has through being the adjective pertaining to organism, Dacqué proposes the horrid neologism "organismic" (organismisch). The present essay uses the word "organic" as the adjective pertaining to organisms. The context seems always clear enough to prevent a confusion with its technically chemical sense.

[56] F. W. Schelling, Weltseele, p. VI.

[57] F. W. Schelling, Weltseele, p. X.

[58] F. W. Schelling, Weltseele, p. 305.

of further definition. "Nature," says Schelling,[59] "must be free in blind necessity (*Gesetzmäßigkeit*) and again bound by necessity (*gesetzmäßig*) in perfect freedom. It is only in this combination that the concept of organization can be found." It seems thus that organization must be understood as the product of a basic paradox, or in Schelling's terminology, of a polar tension. This, however, is only one special manifestation of the principle of polarity which Schelling pursued in all its metamorphic appearances from the lowest to the highest realm of nature.[60] Polarity cannot be explained. It is given through the protophenomenon of motion. Motion, however, can be described in these terms:[61] It presupposes the action of a positive force and the counteraction of a negative one. The positive force as such would be infinite and transcend the limits of the possibility of observation. "It is limited through its counterpart and becomes thus a finite quantity. It begins to be the object of perception or in other words, reveals itself in the phenomena of nature."[62] All these ideas may be summarized in the statement that an infinite principle forced into finite limitation manifests itself in the universal organism which we call nature. This, it will be observed, reformulates at the same time the conclusions of the entire foregoing discussion.

The organic idea has justly been called "the dominating principle in the spiritual world, which has its dawn in the rise of Storm-and-Stress against the age of Enlightenment."[63] It is impossible to survey all its manifestations in that world of classic-romantic idealism. A representative illustration of its basic significance can, however, be presented in the form of an analysis of one aspect of the ideology and aesthetic doctrine of the younger Friedrich Schlegel. What did this disciple of classical antiquity mean by the term *romantic* after he had decided that we have a right to be as we are and to act as we must, and that it is only on this basis that the Greeks can be our teachers?

Friedrich Schlegel's "Athenäums-Fragment" No. 116 has de-

---

[59] F. W. Schelling, *Weltseele*, p. 234.
[60] Cf. p. 76, n. 9.
[61] This is a summary of F. W. Schelling, *Weltseele*, pp. 3f.
[62] F. W. Schelling, *Weltseele*, p. 4.
[63] H. Wilhelmsmeyer, "Der Totalitätsgedanke," p. 212.

servedly been made the basis for a great many attempts to define romanticism as a critical concept. Indeed, it is in itself precisely such an attempt. A clear analysis of it can be achieved only by constant reference to Schlegel's "Discourse on Poetry." There[64] he asserts that a novel (*Roman*) is a romantic book (*romantisches Buch*), and seems to attribute great importance to this statement. It is perhaps nothing but a witty tautology, but as such it still implies that every really romantic book must also be a novel. Indeed, the argument of "Fragment 116" with its description of romantic poetry as "progressively universal" can be used to deepen our understanding of romanticism only in so far as romantic poetry depends on the novel. Elsewhere[65] Schlegel describes the novel as an encyclopedic survey of the life of a given individual. This again explains the phrase in the fragment that some authors, attempting to write a novel, produced merely an autobiography, i.e., a mechanical enumeration of the events of their own lives. A real novel, if we may read between the lines, does not enumerate facts. It reproduces a living life in all its ramifications and dependences.[66] Now, Friedrich Schlegel used the term *romantic* for his own tendencies because he saw in the romance period, i.e., in the world of medieval fairies, knights, and epics, an early realization of what he felt to be the task of modern literature. This, however, means at the same time that he saw no possibility of a renewed, modern realization of his literary ideals except in a form which, in the last analysis, was merely a modern transformation of something inherited from the romance age of romances or novels.[67] The "Athenäums-Fragment" No. 116 states

[64] F. Schlegel, "Brief über den Roman," *Jugendschriften*, II, 372.

[65] F. Schlegel, "Kritische Fragmente," 78.

[66] There is a novel in every life, but only one. Cf. F. Schlegel, "Kritische Fragmente," 78, also 89: "Sollte es nicht überflüssig sein, mehr als einen Roman zu schreiben, wenn der Künstler nicht etwa ein neuer Mensch geworden ist?" Hardenberg said in a letter to Caroline: "Ich habe Lust, mein ganzes Leben an *einen* Roman zu wenden." Cf. *Novalis Schriften*, IV, 277, February 27, 1797.

[67] Both these points, the romance age and the age of romances, are important for the semantic value which the early German Romanticists ascribed to the term "romantic." As far as the second is concerned, i.e., the dependence of the concept romantic on that of romances or novels, cf. Richard Ullmann and Helene Gotthard, *Geschichte des Begriffes Romantisch* (1929), and A. François, "Romantique," *Annales de la Société J.-J. Rousseau*, V, 199-236. The first, i.e., the point which connects the concept "romantic" with the age of chivalry, establishes a contrast to

thus simply that the Schlegel group in their quest for an adequate
literary form knew of none better suited for their all-embracing
ambitions than that of the novel, which had reached an impressive perfection in Goethe's *Wilhelm Meister*.[68]

This novel, Schlegel states in his essay "On Goethe's Meister"
is a perfectly organic work of art. In it the parts repeat the whole,
and a critical mind can visualize the complete conception on the
basis of the fragment (i.e., the edition of 1795) which alone is
now extant. All the elements of the novel are dependent on each
other, for they are metamorphic stages and successive manifestations of one and the same principle. "The stranger," says Schlegel
with reference to the last chapter of the first book,[69] "serves as an
indication of the heights to which the work is intended to rise.
There, perhaps, art will be a science and life an art."[70] This ascen-

---

"classical" as pertaining to Latin and Greek antiquity. This is emphasized by Mme.
de Staël, *de l'Allemagne*, I, 266: "La littérature romantique est la seule qui soit
susceptible encore d'être perfectionnée . . . [Elle a] ses racines dans notre propre
sol . . . elle exprime notre religion; elle rappelle notre histoire: son origine est
ancienne, mais non antique." In this connection the following should be emphasized.
The French word "roman" meant, according to Hatzfeld-Darmesteter-Thomas,
Dictionnaire général de la langue française (Paris: Delagrave, 1924), s.v., "I.
Anciennt. 1° La langue vulgaire (par opposition à la langue savante ou latin) . . .
2° Œuvre littéraire écrite en cette langue (par opposition aux oeuvres écrites en
latin) . . ." Examples for 1° are found as late as in the writings of Voltaire. In other
words, the term "roman" could, in eighteenth-century France, be contrasted with
"latin" in exactly the sense in which "theodisc" was contrasted with "loeden" in
medieval England and later on also in Germany. Cf. Julius Baum, "Aufgaben der
frühchristlichen Kunstforschung in Britannien und Irland," *Forschungen und Fortschritte*, XI (1935), 222f.: "In England wird der Gegensatz zwischen *theodisc*
(deutsch) und *loeden* (latein) zuerst betont." There is consequently no reason why
Germans should not replace the term "romantisch" by the simpler expression
"deutsch." Indeed, "Romantik plus Vorgeschichte" and "Deutsche Bewegung" are
synonyms.

[68] Cf. F. Schlegel, "Athenäums-Fragmente," 216, and "Über die Unverständlichkeit," *Jugendschriften*, II.

[69] F. Schlegel, *Jugendschriften*, II, 167.

[70] This observation would command respect if it were the conclusion of a full-
length analysis of the entire *Wilhelm Meister*. However, it was jotted down as a
random remark and without fear of "Unverständlichkeit." Its full appreciation
presupposes careful study, and its rich implications are an amazing proof of
Friedrich's teasing tendency to drop intellectual pearls amongst the pebbles by the
wayside. The stranger appears casually, but at a critical moment, in Wilhelm's life.
The affair with Marianne is ripe for a catastrophic break which Wilhelm, naturally,
cannot foresee. His talk with the stranger conjures up his earliest youth and alludes
to the rôle which art might have played in his education. His present one-sided appreciation of art shows at the same time how far he is removed from a balanced and
harmonious conception of life. This fact finds expression in a naïve trust in the

sion is conceived as an ever-repeated modulation of the same theme. Thinking apparently of Wilhelm's illness and of how he recalls with sorrow "all the scenes of his past happiness,"[71] Schlegel observes that the second book of Goethe's novel starts out by "repeating musically the results of the first."[72] Further he says: "The innate urge of this entirely organized and organizing work to form one entity, is expressed in larger and in smaller conglomerations, and everything is at the same time means and purpose." He calls this book, quite characteristically, a "poetic system of the physics of poetry." Its "systematic order" exemplifies "the living gradation (*Stufenleiter*) of every natural history and doctrine of formation (*Bildungslehre*)." Its "most delicate traits in even secondary formations seem to exist by themselves

---

benevolence of fate. Here the stranger interferes: "Leider höre ich schon wieder das Wort Schicksal von einem jungen Manne aussprechen . . . Das Gewebe dieser Welt ist aus Notwendigkeit und Zufall gebildet; die Vernunft des Menschen stellt sich zwischen beide, und weiß sie zu beherrschen; sie behandelt das Notwendige als den Grund ihres Daseins, das Zufällige weiß sie zu lenken, zu leiten und zu nutzen, und nur indem sie fest und unerschütterlich steht, verdient der Mensch ein Gott der Erde genannt zu werden . . ." This allusion to the power of human understanding to force the accidental and the necessary into a higher *coincidentia* follows those references to the art gallery of Wilhelm's grandfather and sounds like a one-paragraph summary of Schiller's *Letters on Aesthetic Education*. It is at the same time a programmatic outline of Wilhelm's future education, not only through aesthetics but through life. Its formulation in terms of a coincidence of freedom and necessity establishes a connection with Schelling's definition of the organic concept, cf. p. 150, n. 59, and supports thus Schlegel's expression that *Wilhelm Meister* is an organic work of art. It is further the basis for his allusion to a possible coincidence of art and science and of life and art as the final goal of the novel. It seems, however, that it is not enough to state these ideas. They could have been justified if Schlegel had not been too "divinely lazy" to pursue them throughout *Wilhelm Meister*. It cannot be our task to do this for him. The first metamorphic reappearance of the stranger and the principles he represents may, however, be pointed out in passing. It occurs in book 2, at a time when Wilhelm's naïve trust in the benevolence of fate has given way to complete disillusionment. He no longer trusts, he merely hopes. "Glücklich sind diejenigen," he says toward the end of chapter IX, "deren sich das Schicksal annimmt." Again the stranger interferes: "Das Schicksal ist ein vornehmer, aber teurer Hofmeister. Ich würde mich immer lieber an die Vernunft eines menschlichen Meisters halten. Das Schicksal, für dessen Weisheit ich alle Ehrfurcht trage, mag an dem Zufall, durch den es wirkt, ein sehr ungelenkes Organ haben. Denn selten scheint dieser genau und rein auszuführen, was jenes beschlossen hatte."

[71] *Wilhelm Meister,* end of book 2, chapter I: "Er verachtete sein eigen Herz, und sehnte sich nach dem Labsal des Jammers und der Tränen.

Um diese wieder in sich zu erwecken, brachte er vor sein Andenken alle Szenen des vergangenen Glücks."

[72] F. Schlegel, *Jugendschriften,* II, 168.

and to enjoy independent lives."[73] All of this might be summarized
in the simple statement that Friedrich Schlegel considered
Goethe's *Wilhelm Meister* as an organic work of art, obeying the
laws of nature and repeating in its structure the organization of
other living beings and of the universe as an animated whole.
Quoting Goethe himself, he might have said: *Wilhelm Meister*,
like the works of the ancients, is a man-made product of nature.
In it there is necessity: in it there is God.[74, 75]

Friedrich Schlegel was thus doubtless one of the first to recognize the relation of Goethe's artistic to his scientific forms of
thought. Schelling, as Walzel says,[76] "was introduced by Goethe
himself into these connections, but only long after Schlegel had
grasped the importance of the organic thought with respect to
aesthetics as also with respect to the problems of cognition in
nature." Hardenberg, it is important to note, arrived contempo-
raneously at quite similar conclusions. He speaks repeatedly of
Natalie and "the beautiful soul" as metamorphic variations of
one person.[77] At about the same time, in 1798, he notes his project
to treat the sciences in Goethe's way,[78] for Goethe was, in Hardenberg's own words,[79] "the first physicist of his age," and as such
"his relation to other physicists was like that of the poet Goethe
to other poets." It is on this basis that Goethe's importance for
early German Romanticism would have to be analyzed. At present, however, these connections serve merely to support the general conclusion: Romantic poetry, according to its early doctrine,
is metamorphic poetry, or what is basically the same, it is organic

[74] Cf. p. 139, n. 23.

[73] F. Schlegel, *Jugendschriften*, II, 170.

[75] Similar ideas are expressed in a different terminology in "Kritische Fragmente,"
124: "Auch im Innern und Ganzen der größten modernen Gedichte ist Reim,
symmetrische Wiederkehr des Gleichen. Dies rundet nicht nur vortrefflich, sondern
kann auch höchst tragisch wirken. Zum Beyspiel, die Champagnerflasche und die drey
Gläser, welche die alte Barbara in der Nacht vor Wilhelm auf den Tisch setzt.—Ich
möchte es den gigantischen oder den Shakespearischen Reim nennen: denn Shakespeare ist Meister darin." Handled as a conscious technique, this becomes, by the
way, the *leitmotif* of Wagner and Thomas Mann.

[76] O. Walzel, *Romantik*, p. 44.

[77] *Novalis Schriften*, II, 350. Cf. also II, 352, where the thought concludes the
passage: "Alle Menschen sind Variationen eines vollständigen Individuums, das ist
einer Ehe, wozu jede innig verbundene Gesellschaft zu rechnen ist."

[78] *Novalis Schriften*, III, 251.

[79] *Novalis Schriften*, II, 404.

poetry. This formulation may finally be clarified by Hardenberg's critical remarks,[80] that the best poetry of the past was consciously intended to be only dynamic, that the transcendental poetry of the future will have to be organic, and lastly, that a full understanding of this demand will show that really great poetry complied with it at all times, if not knowingly at least naïvely.

A few concluding remarks may confront the organic idea with that of a universal mechanism. This will at the same time justify the assumption underlying the foregoing discussion, that it is superfluous and even wrong to try to pursue an idea like that of the universal organism to its ultimate origins.[81] It is a striking fact that the word "organization" in modern idiomatic usage implies most frequently an extreme mechanization rather than anything organic. This seeming confusion is not new. Eucken points out,[82] that there are passages in Aristotle where the word ὀργανικός could hardly be translated by anything but "mechanical." This may remind one of the fact that the mechanistic idea was, after all, likewise conceived as a help in man's endeavor to gain an understanding of what we should call the organism of nature. Indeed, it was an inspired idea which one should hesitate to call dead or mechanical. It even seems to have been capable at times of engendering a fairly religious enthusiasm. There is a striking illustration of this in Fontenelle's *Conversations on the Plurality of Worlds*. The author attempts to convey a clear idea of cosmic order to his interlocutor, a certain fictitious Marquise. He com-

---

[80] *Novalis Schriften*, II, 327.

[81] O. Walzel, *Romantik*, p. 16, says, it is true: "Zwei frühromantische Lieblingsgedanken weisen auf Shaftesbury und über ihn auf Platon und auf den Neuplatonismus zurück: der Gedanke des allseitigen Menschen und der Gedanke des Organismus, angewandt auf Natur und Kunst." Discussing the importance of Schelling for the organic idea, Walzel, *ibid.*, p. 44, emphasizes Friedrich Schlegel's priority. He points out that the concept had a long history in eighteenth-century aesthetics and was passed on to Schlegel and Schelling by Goethe, Herder, and also by Moritz. Cf., however, Ernst Troeltsch, *Der Historismus und seine Probleme* (Tübingen, 1922), p. 286, n. 135, whose attack upon Walzel seems justified: "Für die Frage nach dem Ursprung der Organismus-Idee verweist Walzel auf Hamann, Goethe, Herder und K. Ph. Moritz; auch er räumt Schelling (und Schleiermacher) einen festigenden Einfluß ein. Seine Heranziehung des Neuplatonismus für die Romantik ist ein unpsychologischer Einfall, da müßte man schon die christlichen Mystiker heranziehen. Aber gerade für Organismus und Entwicklung bieten diese Einflüsse direkt gar nichts. Das sind elementare neue Entdeckungen."

[82] R. Eucken, *Geistige Strömungen*, p. 122.

pares the universe to a stage and supposes that a number of philosophers are called upon to explain the flight of Phaeton. Descartes is the one who thinks immediately of ropes and counterweights, and Fontenelle agrees that this explanation is the most plausible one. The obvious conclusion is that ropes and counterweights or their equivalent must also be responsible for the movement of celestial bodies. In conclusion Fontenelle asks the Marquise whether such mechanical views are not distasteful to her. Her reply, however, is this:[83] "I venerate the universe only the more since I know now that it works like a watch. It is amazing that the order of nature in all its admirable precision depends on nothing but such simple things."

It is important to note that Cartesius did not attribute any metaphysical significance to the mechanistic idea. For him it was a principle of the man-made science of physics and served to explain the formations of nature within the limits of reason.[84] His disciple, Robert Boyle, seems to have been guided by something like the enthusiasm of Fontenelle's Marquise. He expanded the sphere of application of the mechanistic idea and would have preferred to replace the word "nature" by the term *mechanismus universalis*.[85] The process which widened the scope of the notion of mechanical functioning continued for a considerable time. Its metaphoric application to psychic phenomena passed over into a doctrine of the mechanism of the soul.[86] At this time and in this view it was no longer possible to conceive of "the influence of one atom or of one individual on another as dependent on qualitative

[83] Bernard le Bovier de Fontenelle, *Entretiens sur la pluralité des mondes* (1686), new edition (Marseilles, 1780), p. 10 .

[84] R. Eucken, *Geistige Strömungen*, p. 119.

[85] R. Eucken, *Geistige Strömungen*, pp. 120 and 127. Robert Boyle, it is true, insisted according to Eucken on the absolute necessity of an acceptance of final causality as a corollary to mechanical causation.

[86] Mechanical terms used to describe psychic phenomena occur in Herder's writings. This may prove their originally "organic" value. Cf., e.g., "Über den Ursprung der Sprache" (1772), p. 23, *Sämmtliche Werke*, V: The origin of language is "nicht blos nicht übermenschlich: sondern offenbar Thierisch: das Naturgesetz einer empfindsamen Maschiene." Also p. 42: "Nicht mehr eine unfehlbare Maschiene in den Händen der Natur, wird er [der Mensch] sich selbst Zweck und Ziel der Bearbeitung." R. Eucken, *Geistige Strömungen*, p. 212, has an example from Lessing, "Literatur-Briefe," No. 7: "Diese Veränderung [ist] durch innere Triebfedern, (mich plump auszudrücken) durch den eigenen Mechanismus einer Seele erfolgt."

differences of an innate power; it had come to be thought of as purely rational and materially mechanical."[87]

When this entire development, which might be called a process of mechanization of the mechanical idea, could finally be surveyed as a matter of the past, it had also become possible to treat and condemn it unjustly as a whole. A thinker like Franz von Baader could indict Descartes as the murderer of all natural life[88] and conceive even of Leibnitz' monadology as an instance of shallow and dead atomism.[89] The injustice of these and similar verdicts is easily explained. They were formulated as a call to arms by men who represented a movement which Poetzsch[90] described as

a new attempt to solve the old problem of individualism and universalism, of personal consciousness and universal causality; i.e., the same problem which, attacked from a metaphysical angle, had moved the preceding age from the *coincidentia oppositorum* of Nicolaus of Cues to the pre-established harmony of Leibnitz, and which led in the deepest minds of the Eighteenth Century to a serious inner disruption not soluble on the basis of the premises of enlightenment.

[87] F. Brüggemann, *Die Ironie,* pp. 29f.

[88] Cf., e.g., F. v. Baader, "Über die Begründung der Ethik durch die Physik," *Werke,* V, 5, referring to the most recent discoveries in galvanism and animal magnetism, "die jener maschinistischen Naturansicht gleichsam den Gnadenstoß gaben, unter welcher die Physik seit des Cartes freilich wie mit bleiernen Fesseln sich gebunden fand, und welche Naturerscheinungen wie absichtlich gewählt schienen, um jener armseligen und geisttödtenden Naturansicht zu spotten, und Physikern, die in und mit ihr grau geworden waren, das öffentliche Bekenntnis ihres Verstandesbankrotts abzunöthigen." Similar passages abound in Baader.

[89] For Baader, Leibnitz' monad was "leer," "unlebendig," "ein flacher Abstractionsbegriff," "ein spirituelles Atom." Cf. *Werke,* II, 160; VIII, 159; IX, 44; also D. Baumgardt, *Franz von Baader,* p. 336.

[90] Albert Poetzsch, *Studien zur frühromantischen Geschichtsauffassung* (Leipzig, 1907), p. 98.

IX

TOTALITY: THE PSYCHIC PROBLEM OF
EGO AND COSMOS

A MODERN SCIENTIST, induced to theorize about one final universal principle, would doubtless discuss the possibility of reducing everything to constellations of electric charges. His speculations might concern not only the realm of matter but also that of
animation. His last conclusion, if he happened to be also a poet,
would possibly state that "life is but a rainbow in a cosmic
storm."[1] Ideas of this sort are not new. Modern science may have
supplied them with new and stronger foundations, but their essence remains today what it was throughout their history: the
endeavor to reduce all mysteries of nature and life to the one
basic mystery of the principle of electricity. Among the earlier
attempts to identify life and matter by interpreting them merely
as different phenomenalizations of an electric protophenomenon,
special importance must be ascribed to the trend which tried to
construe the parallel between psychic and material kinetics manifested in animal and ordinary magnetism as an actual identity.
Animal electricity and animal magnetism owe their significance
in the history of thought precisely to the fact that a scientific and
still more a philosophical interest in them represents generally a
preoccupation with the problem of how the gap between mind
and matter may be bridged. All of this has naturally nothing
whatever to do with the scientific merit or demerit of mesmeristic
or galvanistic theories. If they are wrong, the totalitarianism they
serve remains, nevertheless, an important fact and factor in the
history of thought.

In this connection the case of mesmerism is a very peculiar
one, for the founder of this system of animal magnetism was and
remained convinced that the phenomena he had discovered were
in no way related to the phenomena of inorganic magnetism. The

[1] Cf. p. 18, n. 14.

twentieth point of Mesmer's dissertation of 1766 reads literally:[2]

The magnet, be it artificial or natural, is susceptible to animal magnetism of the same as well as of the opposite potency. Its influence on iron or the magnetic needle undergoes no change in either case. This proves that the principle of animal magnetism is essentially different from that of mineral magnetism.

In this respect the romantic mesmerists disagreed so emphatically with the founder of their doctrine that it was impossible for them to appreciate Mesmer's work as anything but an immature expression of truths which they felt called upon to formulate in fuller comprehension. The physician Kieser wrote in 1817 in a brief survey of the history of medicine[3] that the appearance of Paracelsus in the Sixteenth Century "can be explained only if one relates it synchronistically to the Reformation in religion as also to the expansion of life in politics as well as in art. In the same way," Kieser continued, "the system of Dr. John Brown coincides with the French Revolution. In a deeper sense both have their origin in one common cause." Brown's contemporary Mesmer appeared similarly as an early manifestation of that universal crisis which, as Friedrich Schlegel[4] implied, had produced *Wilhelm Meister,* Fichte's *"Scientiology,"*[5] and the French Revolution. As an individual and historical personage, however, Mesmer had as little kinship with the various revolutions which he lived to witness as the Scotsman Brown, who died one year before the fall of the Bastille. When Mesmer died in 1815, he had spent the last years of his life in Meersburg on Lake Constance as an obscure country doctor hardly aware of the violent struggle which a rather unexpected revival of his doctrines had started. Indeed, there is noth-

---

[2] Friedrich Anton Mesmer, *De planetarum influxu,* 1766. The work is generally quoted as *Über den Einfluß der Planeten auf den menschlichen Körper.* A German translation, however, does not seem to exist. Thesis number 20 is given, e.g., by Ernst Trömmer, *Hypnotismus und Suggestion,* "Aus Natur und Geisteswelt," vol. 199 (Leipzig: Teubner, 1922⁴), p. 13.

[3] Dietrich Georg Kieser, "Entwurf einer philosophischen Geschichte der Medizin," introduction to *System der Medizin,* Halle, 1817.

[4] F. Schlegel, "Athenäums-Fragmente," 216.

[5] This word is taken from Werner Schingnitz, "Die Tatsache Wissenschaft und ihre Geschichte. Zur Grundlegung einer systematischen und historischen Wissenschaftswissenschaft oder Scientiologie," *Archiv für Kulturgeschichte,* XXI (1931), 357-289.

ing romantic about him. He belongs clearly in the psychic structure of eighteenth-century enlightenment.[6]

Mesmer had conceived the perfectly rational idea that the old
observation[7] of an influence of animate organisms upon one another might be made therapeutically more useful if its investigation were put on a systematic and scientific basis. This meant,
first of all, that the influence in question had to be assigned to
a special hypothetical agent. He assumed the existence of a magnetic *fluidum universale,* whose properties he proceeded to exam-
ine. As a general practitioner he made use of his findings but did
not expect them to contribute to a solution of the riddles of life
and nature. Mesmer's cool common sense disappeared quickly,
however, in the inspirationalism of a Lavater and his fellows, in
the totalitarian cravings of the following, romantic generation.
It is true, there remained always a certain "official" mesmerism
which did not permit itself to be swept away by the general trend.
Herder had warned with respect to a related subject[8] that one
should not identify different phenomena merely because they follow the same laws. "Systems of forces," he had written in 1787,
"can be quite different and yet follow one kind of laws, for in
nature everything must depend on everything else, and thus there
can be but one main law according to which the most different
forces are ordered." Something like such prudence was practised
as late as 1816 by a commission which reported to the Prussian
Government its findings concerning the scientific significance of
animal magnetism and the desirability of a special chair for it at
the University of Berlin. Indeed, it had nothing to state which
Mesmer, far back in the Eighteenth Century, could not have said
as well. "There is," we are told,[9] "an influence of one living individual upon another of a kind not heretofore known; through
it peculiar phenomena are produced which have not been known

[6] Cf. also Ricarda Huch, *Ausbreitung und Verfall der Romantik,* p. 270.

[7] Cf. the tradition that Roman emperors and the kings of France, especially
Francis I., could cure diseases, more specifically the scrofula ("King's Evil"), by the
imposition of hands.

[8] J. G. Herder, "Gott," *Sämmtliche Werke,* XVI, 599. Cf. also O. Loerke,
"Herders Weltgebäude."

[9] The report was reprinted in full by Friedrich von Oppeln-Bronikowski, *David
Ferdinand Koreff* (Berlin and Leipzig: Gebrüder Paetel, 1928), pp. 179f.

in this casual nexus before." The report reaches the further conclusion that there must be a special agent responsible for these phenomena. "This agent does not belong to the general physical agents and cannot be sensually produced by general physical and chemical agents. It seems to exist only in the sphere of life. It seems to be the life sphere of the living organism" and, the report continues, may be compared to contagious matter. Nevertheless, the uneven style of this document, which is signed by Hufeland, von Koenen, Hermbstaedt, Mertzdorff, Klaproth, and Klug, shows clearly that it was concocted to satisfy the most divergent views. It states the few obvious facts concerning which six different authorities could not come to a final disagreement. Individually, these men could afford to represent much more characteristic views. This is certainly true in the case of Christoph Wilhelm Hufeland, the best known member of the Prussian Commission on Mesmerism. He was convinced that every organism produces, in addition to warmth, also "a magnetic and still finer vital atmosphere,"[10] and that "this animal magnetism is absolutely analogous to mineral magnetism, only in its living potency."[11]

Hufeland's reference to a "living potency" of the general agent of magnetism is highly important, for it represents a conception in which the dynamism of nature is graded. This stipulates the possibility of a qualitative and perhaps even evaluating differentiation between the various forms in which the basic force of nature is manifested. Indeed, a simple and absolute identification of chemism, magnetism, galvanism, electricity, animation, etc., does not seem to have even been propagated. The identity of these agents was held to develop *in statu nascendi,* as it were, a new ascending structure.[12] In other words, identity, if at all achieved, remained an identity in metamorphic variation. As such it could bridge the gap between animate and inanimate dynamics, and that, it seems, was considered its major task. Eschenmayer, who had begun his career in 1798 with an *Essay on the a priori Deduc-*

[10] Christoph Wilhelm Hufeland, *Journal für praktische Heilkunde* (March, 1817), p. 129.

[11] Cf. Wilhelm Erman, *Der tierische Magnetismus in Preußen vor und nach den Befreiungskriegen,* "Beihefte der historischen Zeitschrift," vol. 4 (Munich and Berlin, 1925), p. 94.

[12] This refers, e.g., to Schelling. Cf. p. 76, no. 9.

tion of the Laws of Magnetic Phenomena,[13] stated in his *Psychology* of 1817 that "he felt called upon as a physician and as a teacher of psychology to devote his attention especially to the gap which has separated for so long psychology from physiology."[14] In 1816 he had published an essay on the explanation of the seeming magic of animal magnetism on the basis of physiological and psychological laws.[15] For ten years, from 1817 to 1827, he edited, together with Kieser and Nasse, an *Archiv* for animal magnetism,[16] which might find many readers today if it were republished as a journal for physio-psychology. In 1852 Eschenmayer crowned his life's work by a book characteristically entitled *Considerations with Regard to the Physical Structure of the World in Relation to the Organic, Moral and Intangible Orders*.[17] Ennemoser taught that "magnetism is the doctrine of the relation of forces, which connect all bodies in the entire universe."[18] His book on *The Spirit of Man in Nature*[19] has the characteristic subtitle "or Psychology in its Harmony with Natural Science." The motto of this work is: "Only he who looks at the whole and looks through it, can find in it the place and significance of the individual."[20]

[13] Carl August Eschenmayer, *Versuch die Gesetze magnetischer Erscheinungen aus Sätzen der Naturmetaphysik, mithin a priori zu entwickeln*, 1798. Not found in American libraries.

[14] C. A. Eschenmayer, *Psychologie*, p. 17, end of introduction.

[15] Carl August Eschenmayer, *Versuch die scheinbare Magie des tierischen Magnetismus aus physiologischen und psychologischen Gesetzen zu erklären*, Stuttgart and Tübingen, 1816. Not found in American libraries. Cf. Karl Goedeke, *Grundriß zur Geschichte der deutschen Dichtung aus den Quellen* (Dresden, 1907-1935³), VI, 2, 263.

[16] Eschenmayer, Kieser, Nasse, *Archiv für den tierischen Magnetismus*, 1817-1827.

[17] Carl August Eschenmayer, *Betrachtungen über den physischen Weltbau, mit Beziehung auf die organischen, moralischen und unsichtbaren Ordnungen*, Heilbronn, 1852.

[18] Quoted in *ADB*, s.v. "Ennemoser."

[19] Joseph Ennemoser, *Der Geist des Menschen in der Natur*, Stuttgart and Tübingen, 1849.

[20] Max Neuburger, *Johann Christian Reil* (Stuttgart, 1913), p. 79, refers to Prochaska as the most extreme defender of the idea that life and electricity are identical potencies. As representatives of various doctrines of animal magnetism Neuburger lists further Pfaff, Humboldt, Ritter, Reinhold, and Hartmann. Ricarda Huch, *Ausbreitung und Verfall der Romantik*, pp. 270ff., adds Wienholt (Bremen), Gmelin (Suabia), Ringseis (Bavaria), Carus, Passavant, Malfatti (Lucca, Vienna), Windischmann (Bonn), Justinus Kerner, Koreff, Eschenmayer, Schelling, Ludwig von Voß, Wolfart, Hufeland. C. A. Eschenmayer, *Psychologie*, §262, duplicates

The most striking manifestation of this tendency to conceive of all the phenomena which are directly or indirectly connected with mesmerism as an organically structured totality is to be seen in the prevalence of discussions about the superiority or inferiority of the magnetic powers in comparison with those which dominate the normal state of human consciousness. Troxler formulated his views concerning this question as early as 1812. Animal magnetism, he said,[21] "transposes man into that dream which is dreamt by the least animate animals, by plants, and even by the inanimate world." The normal state of consciousness in man is "infinitely more dignified." He then goes on to speak of a third state, "in which the middle life sphere rises heavenward" and which marks "a delivery (*Entbindung*) of the immortal life from the immortal-mortal one." This, Troxler fears, has often been confused with its base analogy (*Afterbild*) called "animal magnetism."[22]

A "confusion" of this sort prevails in the views of Christian Wilhelm Hufeland. The report on mesmerism in 1816 of which, it will be remembered, Hufeland was co-author, led to a rather frank correspondence between this physician and his colleague Koreff. The latter felt that the outcome of the entire matter was of the greatest importance for his somewhat compromised reputation. Hufeland, however, could assure Koreff that he agreed with him whole-heartedly:

Magnetism is undoubtedly the development of a higher power in man which stands closer to that of the spirit; it belongs to the higher sphere, to the higher order of things and is a new revelation of that inner life which lies at the basis of external existence.[23]

The correspondence which Hufeland carried on with Koreff in 1816 is an important document in the further history of magnetism. Its interest for the present context, however, is merely

---

Wolfart, Gmelin, Hufeland, and adds, among others, Mesmer, Böckmann, Puységur, Tardy, Heineken, Strombek, Nordhof, Barthels, Kluge, Klein, Renard, Petetin, and more significantly, Reil, Olbers, Schubert, Jean Paul, Arndt. To get a fairly representative list, Ennemoser, Kieser, Troxler, and Nees von Esenbeck ought to be mentioned.

[21] I. P. V. Troxler, "Blicke in das Wesen des Menschen," p. 265.

[22] On Joh. Benjamin Erhard, whose views seem to have been related to Troxler's, cf. Karl August Varnhagen von Ense, *Denkwürdigkeiten*, Neue Folge, II, 144ff.

[23] F. v. Oppeln-Bronikowski, *Koreff*, pp. 198f.

anecdotal and at best delimiting.[24] Hufeland, it seems, did not like the idea that his views coincided with those of the Jewish *uomo universale* or Jack-of-all-trades Koreff. He thus qualified his assent by a carefully worded warning against the use of magnetism for divination and the like. Exorcism, he said, is also a magnetic phenomenon. Koreff's indignant reply is highly diverting. He presents a detailed outline of his career as a magnetist and adds a list of all the men whom he is proud to acknowledge as his teachers. It is a queer list and includes names like Mesmer, Puységur, St. Martin, Laplace, Monge, Biot, Fourcroy, Deleuze, Lagrange, the "madman" Fania, and others. This hodgepodge of "educational" influences characterizes the man. With Koreff, although not through him, mesmerism had reached a stage of perversion in which it could be exploited for commercial fortune telling, table tipping, and other necromantic parlor games designed for the entertainment of lonely spinsters. This development seems to have its roots in Puységur's discovery of somnambulism in 1784. It alone can explain why Shelley thought that his poem "The Magnetic Lady to her Patient," published in 1832, was concerned with magnetism. Complete deterioration is documented by Robert Browning's poem "Mesmerism," published in *Men and Women* in 1855. A note by Elizabeth Barrett Browning summarizes the contents:

With a continuous tension of will, whose unbroken concentration impregnates the very structure of the poem, a mesmerist describes the processes of the act by which he summons shape and soul of the woman he desires, and then reverent perception of the sacredness of the soul awes him from trespassing upon another's individuality.

Charlatanism and lurid sentimentality as aspects of a decadent mesmerism do not enter into our discussion. It must be stated, however, that the later development of magnetism is not devoid of positive by-products such as modern magnetotherapy, especially in Germany, and Christian Science in the United States.

However that may be, Hufeland and Koreff belong to the tradition which is represented by the more generally known case of Friederike Wanner of Prevorst, Justinus Kerner's famous patient. Immermann's rather tactless attempt to ridicule this affair in

[24] Reprinted in F. v. Oppeln-Bronikowski, *Koreff*, pp. 185ff.

Münchhausen had made it more famous than it deserves to be.[25] The case is referred to here because it is indirectly responsible for the most lucid, almost classical statement of the conception of all of nature's phenomena as metamorphic variations of one basic polarity in the Goethean sense. It is a Goethean statement also in the manner in which it defines the subconscious as the realm to which the normally heliotropic human soul strives to return only when in illness or despair.

In 1834 Carus received through a friend the diary of a clergyman which contained the case history of a Saxon peasant girl suffering from somnambulism. Having been asked to criticize this account, Carus developed his views in a long letter,[26] branding as erroneous the tendency "to represent such states [somnambulism and the like] as a veritable intensification of the innermost human life. The only criterion of a true elevation of our existence," he held, "is the intensification of our capacity for genuinely free action." Never have somnambulism, second sight, or other related phenomena been observed to lead to the production of a great work of art or science. When the individuality of man recedes and when he delves into the life of nature, a world of phenomena becomes apparent which a conscious personality does not perceive. "The one bright sun gives us the day, while the host of stars remain hidden. Let the sun retreat, and a thousand stars become visible." He who wants to perceive the direct relation of his existence with the totality of the universal organism must abandon the treasure of his conscious individuality. Sleep must precede somnambulistic phenomena. These are thus closely related to the instincts of animals.

It is for this reason that somnambulistic visions appear often unmistakably as an urge to recover health by the administration of self-prescribed cures. Visions of this sort are consequently nothing but a *vis medicatrix naturae* which rises into dream consciousness.

With explicit reference to the Prevorst case, Carus then proceeds to speak of the frequent and general mistake which consists in

[25] Karl Immermann, *Münchhausen*, II, book 4. Cf. also Carl August Eschenmayer, *Mysterien des inneren Lebens; erläutert aus der Geschichte der Seherin von Prevorst mit Berücksichtigung der bisher erschienenen Kritiken*, Tübingen, 1832.
[26] Carl Gustav Carus, *Mnemosyne* (Pforzheim, 1848), pp. 73-76.

not understanding that a soul cannot manifest (*darleben*) itself unless it be in a body. The writer of the diary criticized in this letter represents a view which tends towards the inevitable conclusion "that the soul should be thought of as a sensually manifested essence, however fine it may be imagined to be, an essence which has been inserted into a body whose growth is then due to energies of an alien order." This conception Carus considers as the root of all confusion in these matters.[27] Anticipating and surpassing modern *Tiefen* psychology, Carus adds that a soul which has encountered obstacles in its normal development manages "to penetrate more deeply into non individualized natural life, so that a more intimate coexistence (*Vereinleben*) in the nonindividual might increase its force until a more successful advance toward a higher goal has become possible." In conclusion Carus refers to the figure of Homunculus in Goethe's *Faust* as clarifying many of these mysteries.

The attitude of Carus might, indeed, be labeled "a romantic humanism of classical clarity." It seems, furthermore, that it was shared by all the more influential representatives of animal magnetism in the romantic era. In this respect Carus must be grouped with men like Eschenmayer, Kieser,[28] Ennemoser, Troxler, and also the great physician Reil.[29] Nevertheless, the opposite view, which conceives of magnetism as a superior power and man's only means to reach out into the sphere of the absolute spirit, cannot be dismissed as a foolish error of immature thought. Quite on the contrary, it must be interpreted as one of the most significant expressions of the romantic longing for the soul's return "to the mothers." One need but think of Hardenberg's hymns to darkness, and one will understand why the Romanticist knew of no horror lurking in those deepest realms. Carus himself said[30] that

[27] Cf., e.g., on Arnim and Jung-Stilling's *Geisterkunde*, p. 71, n. 47.

[28] Cf. Dietrich Georg Kieser, *System des Tellurismus oder thierischen Magnetismus*, Leipzig, 1822.

[29] Johann Christian Reil, *Entwurf einer allgemeinen Pathologie*, I, 53: "Es sind die nämlichen Gesetze, wonach die Natur in der Volta'schen Säule und in dem Organismus wirkt, aber die Form, in der sie wirken, ist hier und dort verschieden. In den lebenden organischen Körpern erscheint der Organismus auf einer höheren Stufe als in der Volta'schen Säule, weil er durch das Substrat, in dem er wirkt, höher potenziert ist." Cf. also M. Neuburger, *Johann Christian Reil*, p. 79.

[30] Carl Gustav Carus, *Natur und Idee* (Vienna, 1861), p. 3. Cf. also *id., Ver-*

it is the beginning of all philosophy to recognize that the vastness
of the unconscious is merely God's consciousness. Through this
one is reminded of Shelley's metaphor[31] which calls the subconscious an ocean

> Whose waves never mark, though they ever impress
> The light sand which paves it, consciousness.

Carus, in Shelley's imagery, knew nothing of the urge to swim
out into the ocean never to return. His endeavor was rather to
build on the shores the brightest possible beacon which might direct the bold sailors in their search far out at sea. That is what he
meant by assigning to all natural philosophy the task "to grasp
the essence of divine growth (*Werden*) in the unconscious, to de-
pict it and to trace it upward to the development of consciousness."[32]

In this conception two elements are clearly to be distinguished.
It interprets consciousness as one peculiar aspect of the unconscious. This is generally romantic. Further, however, it implies
that consciousness is superior to the unconscious. This is not generally romantic. A Hardenberg would ask, why should the cold
light of your beacon be valued more highly than the brilliant expanse of infinite darkness?[33] The clarity of your light is "mathematical slavery" and at best an ugly "impertinence."[34] To be
sure, human consciousness is but a finite variation of nature's—or
God's—unconscious infinity. Yet, this does not mean that we enjoy it as an exclusive privilege of which we may justly be proud.
In this view consciousness seems much rather to be the result of a
tragic catastrophe. We fell into it through the depravity of the
father of our race. The wisdom of our soul may endure and accept
it as a just punishment, but we long for redemption. The fall
into individuation cannot last for ever.

Kleist's essay "On the Marionettes" teaches that infinite con-

---

gleichende Psychologie, p. 1, and two literal repetitions in *Psyche* (Stuttgart, 1851²),
pp. 1 and 57: "Der Schlüssel zur Erkenntnis vom Wesen des bewußten Seelenlebens
liegt in der Region des Unbewußtseyns."

[31] Percy Bysshe Shelley, "The Sensitive Plant," 1820.

[32] C. G. Carus, *Vergleichende Psychologie*, p. 1.

[33] Cf. p. 133, n. 29.

[34] *Novalis Schriften*, II, 76: "Licht . . . mathematischer Gehorsam und Frechheit."

sciousness and the lack of it, that godliness and lifelessness are identical values between which we must choose. Kleist chose what was left when infinite consciousness proved not to be attainable.[35] Hölderlin sang in an early poem, "The Hymn to Freedom," of man as the one in all the world who broke the bonds of universal love and lived a self in independence.

> Unentweiht von selbsterwählten Götzen,
> Unverbrüchlich ihrem Bunde treu,
> Treu der Liebe seligen Gesetzen,
> Lebt die Welt ihr heilig Leben frei;
> Einer, einer nur ist abgefallen . . .[36]

Hölderlin's soul relinquished the "privilege" of rational consciousness. Schopenhauer conceived of individuation as of a collapse of the will,[37] and he endured the punishment to the end. The romantic physician Ringseis knew that all disease is due to the original sin of "individuation through the attainment of consciousness." For him as for a number of his colleagues, especially Windischmann in Bonn, Heinroth in Leipzig, Leupoldt in Erlangen, the redeeming power of the sacraments as administered through the mediation of the Catholic Church was at the same time the only *vis medicatrix naturae Dei*.[38] The underlying idea is to be found in Hardenberg.

There has always been only *one* disease and consequently only *one* universal remedy. Disease comes into nature with sensibility and the nerves as its organs. Thus freedom, arbitrary decisions appear in nature and consequently sin and rebellion against the will of nature, which is the cause of all evil.[39]

It is upon this general basis that the catholicizing tendencies in German Romanticism might find a plausible explanation. Finally, it would not be at all unromantic to suggest that the same connection can serve to elucidate the fact that so many Romanticists died

---

[35] Heinrich von Kleist, "Über das Marionettentheater," *Berliner Abendblätter*, 63 and 66, December 12 and 15, 1810. Reprinted in "Deutsche Literatur, Reihe Romantik," XI, 112-118.

[36] F. Hölderlin, "Hymne an die Freiheit," VIII, 1ff. Cf. p. 66, n. 36.

[37] Formulated in these terms by E. Troeltsch, *Historismus*, pp. 308-10.

[38] Cf. Paul Diepgen, *Deutsche Medizin vor hundert Jahren* (Freiburg i. Br., 1923), pp. 12f. and 40.

[39] *Novalis Schriften*, III, 344.

young. Several of them suffered with tuberculosis, which is a loving and yearning disease of lonely souls.[40]

There remains, however, another highly characteristic aspect
of this romantic longing to return, to find "the way home."[41] It is
perhaps best described in a paradox: the romantic longing to *return* is firmly resolved on *striving ahead*. The concentrated practical activity of a Hardenberg[42] cannot be understood as the expression of one half of his character, which managed somehow not
to interfere when the rest wished to indulge in nocturnal nostalgia.
These seeming opposites belong together. Romantic love of life is
not only compatible with the longing to overcome life, it is its
deepest manifestation. He who fears death, says Hölderlin,[43] does
not love universal life; Hardenberg speaks of death as the emancipation of God in man,[44] and both these statements are convertible. Indeed, this ideology presents itself at times as what
Kindermann, referring as well to Hölty and Lenz as precursors of
Romanticism, called[45] "a flirtation with death by lovers of life."
Yet, there is something more. Hardenberg's decision to die meant

[40] Alfred Heuschke (Klabund) suggests in his *Welt-Literatur* that a "literary history of diseases" might be valuable. This idea is perhaps less fantastic than it
sounds. The assertion that tuberculosis is a romantic disease finds unexpected support in certain historical data. The first description of the eruption of tubercles in the
tissue of the lungs was given in 1794 by Matthew Baillie. The first clinical description
of the disease itself dates, it is true, from 1676 and was a contribution of Richard
Wisemann; but Gaspard Laurent Bayle completed his work on tuberculosis again in
the romantic era, in 1810. Cf. also Lewis T. Moorman, *Tuberculosis and Genius*,
Chicago, 1940.

[41] Cf. p. 112, n. 74.

[42] Cf. Richard Samuel, "Der berufliche Werdegang Friedrich von Hardenbergs,"
Romantik-Forschungen, "Deutsche Vierteljahresschrift, Buchreihe," XVI, 83-112.

[43] F. Hölderlin, "Empedokles," end of first version, *Werke*, p. 387, Panthea speaking
after the death of the hero:

> O die Todesfürchtigen lieben dich nicht,
> Täuschend fesselt ihnen die Sorge
> Das Aug, an deinem Herzen
> Schlägt dann nicht mehr ihr Herz, sie verdorren,
> Verschieden von dir—o heilig All,
> Lebendiges! inniges!

[44] *Novalis Schriften*, IV, letter of October 5, 1791, to Prof. Reinhold. This is the
letter in which Hardenberg wrote: "Γνῶθι σεαυτόν soll mein Memento mori sein."
Cf. p. 108, n. 58.

[45] Heinz Kindermann, *J. M. R. Lenz und die deutsche Romantik* (Vienna,
1925), p. 47: "Lebensfreudige Todeskoketterie."

for him a decision to live life fully.[46] The old idea that we are in the midst of life surrounded by death, appears here in a new interpretation: our life is not surrounded by death but contains it. The infinity of eternal rest is summarized in our finite existence. The infinite vastness of God's and nature's unconscious existence is no longer an ocean into the dark expanse of which the ridiculously weak beacon of human consciousness tries to penetrate. One is contained in the other.

The romantic consciousness, as Ricarda Huch observed strikingly,[47] is filled with the contents of the unconscious. This leads to a conclusion which is again to be presented as a paradox: the romantic longing to return into the realm of the nonindividual may, but need not, imply the dissolution of individual consciousness. It can be taken as a highly conscious process, which coincides, as it were, with a dissolution of the unconscious infinity of nature in the finite consciousness of human life. Further, it follows in this rarefied atmosphere of romantic logic that redemption from individual consciousness can be achieved as a conscious process in which the unconscious infinity of nature will be involved.

A particularly striking illustration of these ideas is to be seen in Ritter's discussion of a *return* to a golden age which *never existed,* of a reunion of man and nature, through which redemption will be attained by both. It will be, he says,[48]

the result of knowledge and of power over nature. These two will unite all volition into one will and all animation into one life. All the worries about life will be one single care, and the guide and director of it will be man; but the number of those who attain happiness with him will be infinite.

Ritter feels the tragic separation of man in his consciousness and individuation from all the rest of universal existence as pain-

---

[46] *Novalis Schriften,* IV, letter of April 14, 1797, to Prof. Woltmann: "Zufrieden bin ich ganz—die Kraft, die über den Tod erhebt, habe ich ganz neu gewonnen—Einheit und Gestalt hat mein Wesen angenommen—es keimt schon ein künftiges Dasein in mir. Diesen Sommer will ich recht genießen, recht tätig sein, mich recht in Liebe und Begeisterung stärken."

[47] Cf. Oskar Walzel, "Wesensfragen deutscher Romantik," *Jahrbuch des Freien Deutschen Hochstifts* (1929), p. 268: "Ricarda Huch [darf] sagen, das Bewußtsein des Romantikers sei mit dem Gehalt des Unbewußten erfüllt." The passage ought to occur in Ricarda Huch's *Romantik.* It may, however, be Walzel's formulation.

[48] Cf. p. 118, n. 101.

fully as any of the other romantic thinkers quoted above. For him, however, it is certain that the light of human consciousness has a redeeming power not only for man but even for those creatures beneath him whose "immaturity" places them on a level preceding that of the Fall, that of separation from nature and that of sin and consciousness. As human beings we are privileged and condemned to achieve redemption: for ourselves from self-consciousness; for the animals from their world-consciousness;[49] for plants from their vegetating but unconscious sensitivity; for minerals and crystals from their insensitive but structuralized existence. If man can reach redemption through that universal consciousness, which Kleist held to be identical with lack of consciousness, then all these forms of lower existence will reach it through him and with him.

The idea of a possible salvation of nature through man seems to be a necessary pendant of the "nihilistic" urge to return into the great unconscious. In an exemplary confrontation of Hardenberg and Hölderlin, Petersen formulates this into a sort of romantic polarity. "Their nature pantheism," he says with reference to the two poets mentioned,[50] "reached fulfillment in diametrically opposed goals. For Hölderlin it was redemption of man through nature; for Hardenberg redemption of nature through man." From a modern point of view one may feel tempted to mock at such thoughts. That is, however, because they have trespassed the limits of the sublime and so, for us, have fallen into the realm of the ridiculous. The Romanticists were not awed by their gigantic dimensions. For a Baader it was quite within the ordinary to suppose that man's longing for salvation was only a clearer form of a parallel urge in all of nature's creatures, from stone and star to plant and animal.[51]

[49] The term *Weltbewußtsein* applied to animals in contrast to man's *Selbstbewußtsein* seems to have been introduced by C. G. Carus in *Psyche*. The thought as such is naturally older. Oken, for instance, has it: "Kein Geschöpf unter dem Menschen kann Selbstbewußtsein haben. Sie haben zwar Bewußtsein von ihren einzelnen Handlungen . . . aber da diese einzelnen Handlungen nur Teile der Welt sind . . ." Cf. Chr. Bernoulli and H. Kern, *Romantische Naturphilosophie*, p. 2.

[50] J. Petersen, "Das goldene Zeitalter bei den deutschen Romantikern," pp. 144f.

[51] Cf. F. Lieb, *Baader*, p. 208: "Die gewaltige Entdeckung Baaders, die er St. Martin zu verdanken hat, besteht nun eben darin, daß an dem Werke der Erlösung das ganze Universum Anteil hat, also auch die Natur." If Baader took this idea

Among the romantic thinkers whose thought tended in this or a similar direction, special attention must again be devoted to Hardenberg. Indeed, nothing can lead us more deeply into his world of ideas than a full grasp of all the implications of his doctrine of a redemption and moralization of nature. "If God became man," he said,[52] "why should He not also be able to appear as stone, plant, animal, element? There is perhaps in this fashion an everlasting redemption in nature." Much more common, however, is the notion that God's redeeming love descends from stage to stage and reaches nature only through man. "Nature must learn morality," we read,[53] and she will, for "we are her teachers."[54] It should be possible, e.g., "to predict the time when the moon will come of age, for we are at present engaged in its education."[55] All of this is not jotted down as the product of an idle fancy. Hardenberg proposes quite seriously as a problem of natural science to determine "whether or not nature has changed under the influence of civilization."[56] That this does not refer to a technological survey of the external changes which man has wrought in the face of the earth becomes evident through Hardenberg's categorical statement that "nature will reach a state of morality when she abandons herself to art from a genuine love for art."[57] That, again, is to be taken literally. Nature can show such a longing. She does it in our sciences, which strive to become arts. When Hardenberg asks, "Can chemistry become an art?" his answer must obviously be: "Through morality!"[58] This is exactly what Ritter meant to say in his address *On Physics as an Art* and Baader in his essay "On Physics as a Foundation of Ethics."[59]

---

from St. Martin, then it is St. Martin's and not Baader's. If Baader experienced it as his personal truth, then St. Martin belongs simply to Baader's church or *vice versa*. This is one of those ideas which can neither be thought nor taught. They must be experienced or they are not true.

[52] *Novalis Schriften,* III, 337.
[53] *Novalis Schriften,* III, 69.
[54] *Novalis Schriften,* III, 72.
[55] *Novalis Schriften,* III, 35.
[56] *Novalis Schriften,* III, 68.
[57] *Novalis Schriften,* III, 73.
[58] *Novalis Schriften,* III, 73.
[59] F. v. Baader, "Über die Begründung der Ethik durch die Physik" (1813), *Werke,* V, 1-42. Cf. especially preface, p. 3.: "Die Absicht und Tendenz dieser . . . Rede ist keine andere, als einerseits die Einstimmigkeit der Schrift- und Naturlehre

A remarkable association of the divining rod with these speculations is established in *Heinrich von Ofterdingen.*[60] The old miner, previously introduced as a disciple of Werner's, has finished his song, "He is the Ruler of this Globe . . ." and is asked to sing another. He is willing to do so and explains that he will repeat a song he once learned from an expert with the divining rod. It tells of the realm of King Gold (the name is not mentioned), in which all the subjects are bound by secret ties. Nevertheless, there are some which are wise enough not to submit. They even try to sap the strong old castle. "If they succeed in laying bare the innermost, the day of freedom will have come." This seems to mean that the divining rod and the inmost significance of mining were associated in Hardenberg's mind, so that mining, like all other attempts of man to penetrate into the mysteries of the earth and of nature in general, must be thought of as attempts to free the spirit of nature from its bonds.[61] The great importance which Hardenberg assigned to these notions would have become much more apparent if *The Apprentices at Sais* had been completed. Then "the child" and his John the Baptist would have returned as "the Messiah of nature, to establish a new testament and a new nature as a new Jerusalem."[62]

---

wieder in Erinnerung zu bringen, andererseits das Unwesen jener neueren Moral zu beleuchten, welche . . . immer unverhohlener sich von Religion und Physik, von Gott und Natur lossagt."

[60] *Novalis Schriften* I, 153-55.

[61] It is interesting to contrast this conception of the spirit of nature with that represented by Heinz Widerporst. Cf. Friedrich Wilhelm Schelling, "Epikurisch Glaubensbekenntnis Heinz Widerporstens" (1799), *Satiren und Parodien*, edited by Andreas Müller, "Deutsche Literatur, Reihe Romantik," IX (Leipzig: Reclam, 1931), especially lines 186ff.:

> [Die Welt] Ist gar ein träg und zahmes Tier,
> Das weder dräuet dir noch mir,
> Muß sich unter Gesetze schmiegen,
> Ruhig zu meinen Füßen liegen.
> Steckt zwar ein Riesengeist darinnen . . .
> Tut nach Bewußtsein mächtig ringen.

Schelling's *Riesengeist* in nature does not long for redemption. There is no allusion anywhere in his poem either to such a need or to such a possibility. This must be connected with Schelling's *Urpolarität* as contrasted with Hardenberg's *Urinfinitismus.* Hardenberg saw Schelling's polarity as "Antinom, Binom," and wanted it to be dissolved, "redeemed" in an "Infinitom." Cf. *Novalis Schriften*, III, 160.

[62] *Novalis Schriften*, I, 541.

It is necessary, however, to combine Hardenberg's idea of nature's redemption through man with his peculiar conception of mediation. The clearest expression of it is to be found in an early solution of the problem of pantheism and polytheism as opposed to monotheism, which gains in significance if contrasted with a famous remark by Goethe. In a letter dated January 6, 1813, Goethe wrote to Jacobi: "As a poet and artist I am a polytheist, but as a scientist I am a pantheist and the one as pronouncedly as the other."[63] This, to be sure, does not imply a sort of double standard in Goethe's world. Yet, there seems to be no verbal synthesis of pantheism and polytheism in Goethe that can be compared with that which Hardenberg achieves by defining pantheism as a religion with an unlimited number of possible mediators, seemingly in contrast to monotheistic religions, which know of but one. These many mediators, however, may, according to Hardenberg, be taken as intermediators, so that a pyramid of mediation results, in which all the various forms of religion, pantheism, monotheism, polytheism, are dissolved in a common religiosity.[64] The logical completion of this reasoning leads to the idea that everything must be the mediator for everything below. Thus man is again the Messiah of nature in so far as it must look up to him in obedience or veneration.

The idea that man is equipped to exert an educational and finally a redeeming influence on nature is but one aspect of Hardenberg's *magic idealism*. Education and redemption in this sense are creative activities which amount to the release or production of things in exactly the same way in which God released or produced the universe. They presuppose, between man and nature as teacher and pupil, as Messiah and disciple, the possibility of perfect identification in an act of loving recognition. Love, which makes cognition possible, says Hardenberg,[65] "is the reason for the possibility of magic."

The clearest view of these dependences, however, can be gained on the basis of Hemsterhuis' *Alexis,* whose catalyzing effect on

[63] Cf. also F. W. Schelling, as quoted by P. Kluckhohn, *Weltanschauung der Frühromantik,* p. 59: "Monotheismus der Vernunft und des Herzens, Polytheismus der Einbildungskraft und der Kunst, dies ist's, was wir bedürfen."
[64] *Novalis Schriften,* II, 28.
[65] *Novalis Schriften,* III, 74.

the formation of Hardenberg's philosophy cannot be questioned. Reference to this work of the Dutch philosopher will serve at the same time to place Hardenberg's magic idealism in a wider perspective. We take up the thread of the conversation between Diokles and Alexis when it has reached the problem of the association of ideas. That such an association is basically important for all forms of man's mental activity, in the arts as well as in the sciences, is patent and need not be discussed. The crucial question is merely: Why and how does it occur? What or who brings it about? The naïve answer that it takes place through the conscious effort of the individual concerned is met by Hemsterhuis with the surprising stratagem of acceptance. Yet, says Diokles,[66] "it cannot be doubted that an association of this sort occurs frequently without the slightest effort [on our part], that it reveals to us things and truths which surpass by far our usual capacities." The He or the It responsible for this must be the same "that taught Homer how to sing, that tells in Dodona or Delphi more or less [clearly] about an uncertain future." This imposes the conclusion that there is a definite parallelism between the world of thought and that of phenomena. Indeed, Hemsterhuis had devoted a previous paragraph to just this question. "Are there," Diokles asks,[67] "between the real things, of which the ideas are the ideas or faithful reproductions, the same relations as between the ideas?" After Alexis has replied with an unqualified affirmative, Diokles continues: "The combination of ideas represents, consequently, that which would actually result from a similar combination of the things themselves, and it represents it with as much truth as that with which each idea represents each thing individually and in isolation." All of this would be purely Platonic reasoning if it were not for the peculiar continuity which Hemsterhuis establishes between the realm of "ideas" and that of things. Interphenomenal relations and also the relations between things and the highest Being are, by definition, as it were, of a moral and ideal order. Yet, Hemsterhuis reasons, we know about them as definitely as about the simple manifestations of the ex-

---

[66] Franziskus Hemsterhuis, *Alexis* oder *Von dem goldenen Zeitalter*, translated by Friedrich Heinrich Jacobi (Riga: Johann Friedrich Hartknoch, 1787), pp. 93f.

[67] F. Hemsterhuis, *Alexis*, pp. 88f.

istence of things, i.e., of light, smell, sound, etc. "Love, hatred, envy, esteem," says Hemsterhuis in his *Letter on Man*,[68] "are words expressing sensations as clear as those expressed by the words tree, star, tower, *do, re, mi,* sweet, bitter, sharp, rose fragrance, jasmin, carnation, cold, warm, hard, soft." If something, whatever it be, corresponds to our sensation of cold, then there must also be something in the realm without which corresponds to our sensation of love or hatred or esteem. The sum total of the relations which produce these sensations, particularly that peculiar relation in which all the others are contained, viz., the relation of finite beings to the Highest One, constitutes the realm of religion. Now, we have sense organs which bring us in contact with "trees, stars, towers, *do, re, mi,* sweet, bitter, etc." Yet we are also in contact with those relations which constitute the realm of religion. It follows that we must have a special religious sense organ. This is what Hemsterhuis calls the *organe moral.*[69]

Dissatisfaction with the traditional system of five senses is, to be sure, no isolated phenomenon in Hemsterhuis. It constitutes rather a highly important philosophical motif which seems to depend on the old conception of a κοινὴ αἴσθησις, a *sensus communis*. Blake[70] raged against a degenerate science which did not rest "till a philosophy of five senses was complete." Hutcheson and Burke[71] insisted similarly on the necessity and actuality of an additional sense. This was to be called the "inner sense" and continued to be thought of as represented by a special organ which perceived relations and registered them as sensations varyingly called enthusiasm, love, intuition, religion, inspiration, etc. Under the name of "common sense" (*Gemeingefühl*) it was introduced into the exact sciences by Reil.[72] In Hardenberg it seems to be connected with the idea that all organs, even the entire organism,

[68] Franziskus Hemsterhuis, *Lettre sur l'homme et ses rapports* (Paris, 1772), pp. 96f.

[69] Franziskus Hemsterhuis, *Über den Menschen und die Beziehungen desselben* (Leipzig, 1782), p. 263: ". . . daß die Religion sich nur aus der Beziehung jedes einzelnen zu dem höchsten Wesen ergibt; und wir haben gesehen, daß diese Beziehung sich nur durch den moralischen Sinn kund macht."

[70] Mona Wilson, *The Life of William Blake* (New York: Ballou, 1932), p. 103.

[71] Cf. F. Bulle, *Franziskus Hemsterhuis*, especially pp. 20ff.

[72] Cf. M. Neuburger, *Johann Christian Reil*, p. 17.

may function vicariously as sense organs.[73] At times it was identified with understanding (*Vernunft*), but as a "universal sense"
(*All-Sinn*) it plays an important rôle throughout the romantic era
as the basis and the sole tool of all super-Kantian cognition.
Thus, Fichte insists,[74] that "the supersensual world is given to
moral man through the inner sense, in which he believes more
than in the outer one, for the latter furnishes only appearances
while the former furnishes the only possible *an sich*." This idea
is basic for all of Fichte's thought, for, without the "inner sense"
there could not be any correct speculative reasoning. The strictest
human logic, Fichte admits, could not possibly avoid all minor
deviations from absolute logic. These would multiply in the
course of a prolonged reasoning and lead to absurd conclusions,
if they were not constantly neutralized by the "inner sense" which
perceives truth directly.[75] Friedrich Schlegel defended in 1801 in
Jena the thesis "Enthusiasmus est principium artis et scientiae,"
and Pasteur liked to recall the etymology of the word "enthusiasm" by speaking of it as of an "inner God." The whole of Baader's world of thought may be deduced from his basic experience
of imagination as that inner sense whose deepest powers cannot
become fully active in this lower form of existence, since, as he
reasons with his characteristic aggressiveness, it is, in this world,
so often stimulated in a fashion that makes of it a sensory organ
for hell instead of one for heaven, which it should be.[76] Herder
spoke of an inner sense for the godly, which is most fully awake
in innocent children,[77] and Ritter, in one of his most beautiful

---

[73] Cf., e.g., *Novalis Schriften,* III, 126.

[74] J. G. Fichte, "Gerichtliche Verantwortungsschrift," *Atheismus-Streit,* p. 230.

[75] Johann Gottlieb Fichte, "Über den Begriff der Wissenschaftslehre," *Werke,*
edited by Immanuel Hermann (1834-1846), I, 78: "Es scheint, daß eine haarkleine
Abweichung von der geraden Linie notwendig zu einer sich ins unendliche ver-
größernden Abweichung führen müsse: und so würde es allerdings sein, wenn der
Mensch alles, was er weiß, durch deutliches Denken zustande bringen müßte;
und nicht vielmehr ohne sein Bewußtsein die Grundanlage der Vernunft in ihm
waltete, und durch neue Verirrungen von der geraden Bahn des formaliter und
logisch richtigen Räsonnements ihn zu dem materialiter einzig wahren Resultate
wieder zurückleitete, zu welchem er durch richtige Folgerung aus den unrichtigen
Zwischensätzen nie wieder hätte gelangen können."

[76] Cf. F. Lieb, *Baader,* p. 50.

[77] J. G. Herder, *Sämmtliche Werke,* XI, 98.

fragments, summarized these ideas and placed them in their proper metaphysical perspective:

We have an inner sense for universal cognition (*Weltkenntnis*), which is far from fully developed. It does not see, it does not hear, etc.; but it knows yet knows not why. It knows for certain, knows about all worlds, and all that just as the eye sees also without knowing why . . . This inner sense should be more highly developed.[78]

One last aspect of the idea of a sense beyond the five senses remains to be noted. This may help to emphasize further the peculiarly romantic structure of the entire problem and will serve at the same time to establish a connection with Hardenberg's *magic idealism*. The inner, common, moral, universal sense was interpreted by some as devoid of any special organ of its own. Others held that such an organ was represented by the totality of man's physical appearance. Yet, all of this was very vague and could not prove that the important sense, on which all genuine cognition seemed to depend, was more than the product of a wishful fancy. Everything one could possibly expect by way of proof, however, presented itself in the form of magnetic, somnambulistic, and related phenomena. These included dreams, myths as dreams of nations,[79] and finally also poetry and religion, all of which, by the way, obtained a deeper significance through their association with the "magnetic" universal sense. The reasoning implied is fairly simple. Let us suppose that we have observed and verified a case of mental television or second-sight. What has happened is

[78] Quoted from Paul Kluckhohn, *Die Auffassung der Liebe in der Literatur des 18. Jahrhunderts und in der deutschen Romantik* (Halle, 1931²), p. 514. On the important possibility that this fragment was contributed to Ritter's collection by Hardenberg, cf. *id., ibid.*

[79] The conception of myths as racial dreams was rediscovered by modern psychoanalysis. Cf. especially C. G. Jung-Zürich, also E. Dacqué, *Urwelt, Sage und Menschheit*. The idea that myths represent the earliest recollections of mankind, not handed down by direct tradition but recovered from a preconscious past, is contained in the romantic conception of myths as a possible historical source. F. Hemsterhuis, *Alexis*, p. 75, may perhaps be construed in support of this idea. It is clearly expressed by Hardenberg, "Die Lehrlinge zu Sais," *Novalis Schriften*, I, 15, and "Heinrich von Ofterdingen," *ibid.*, I, 104. Cf. also Maria von Olfer, "Die Überreste vorweltlicher Riesenthiere in Beziehung zu Ostasiatischen Sagen und Chinesischen Schriften," *Physikalische Abhandlungen der Berliner Akademie* (1839), pp. 51ff.

Poetry in connection with magnetism brings up the subject of *Der Dichter als Seher*. This must be reserved for a separate book.

simply that a distance, in time or space, has been reduced to nothing. In other words, the distance has been covered at an infinite speed, which presupposes an infinite force. It must be a psychic force, and the experience of it may be called intuition, enthusiasm or simply "an increased imagination." This last phrase, as also the principle of the foregoing deduction, is taken from Eschenmayer's *Psychology* of 1817.[80]

A more explicit association of the universal sense organ with somnambulism and dream life is presented by Eschenmayer's collaborator Kieser. In 1822 he wrote:[81]

If one who sleeps deeply and who thus dreams deeply could upon awakening remember something about his dream life, or if it [the dream life] could be made to speak,[82] then, since visionary somnambulism is only the higher potency of sleep, all the phenomena of television through space and time would appear here before us, for they are the products of the activity of the universal sense of night.

This conception, together with its most fruitful implications, seems to be lucidly summarized in a passage by Johann Jakob Wagner, a thinker who does not usually excel in clear statements. In *Religion, Science, Art, and the State* (1819), he speaks of the universal sense of the ancients, who embraced with its help space and time, annihilating the manifestations of both in something which we poor creatures of a rationalized age should have to call miracles. Of this sense, Wagner continues,[83]

nothing is left at present except the pathological phenomena of animal magnetism on the one hand and the poetic genius which dies out with

---

[80] Cf. C. A. Eschenmayer, *Psychologie*, pp. 256 and 275: "§277. Sezen wir die Seele als unendliche Kraft, so müssen auch, da die Kraft der Geschwindigkeit proportional ist, Erscheinungen möglich sein, welche von einer unendlichen Geschwindigkeit zeugen. Und es fragt sich dann nur noch, ob das, was als möglich erkannt ist, auch unter bedingten Umständen zur Wirklichkeit gelangen könne, und diß bejahe ich für das Phänomen des thierischen Magnetismus . . . §286 . . . Wir nehmen an . . . daß eine gesteigerte Phantasie das Endliche dem Unendlichen, das Wirkliche der Idee gleichsezen, und durch eine unendliche Geschwindigkeit Entfernung und Zukunft zur Gegenwart machen könne."

[81] Dietrich Georg Kieser, "System des Tellurismus oder tierischen Magnetismus" (1822), in Chr. Bernoulli and H. Kern, *Romantische Naturphilosophie*, p. 106.

[82] To cause dream life to speak! That, indeed, covers all the problems of modern psychoanalysis.

[83] Johann Jakob Wagner, *Religion, Wissenschaft, Kunst und Staat in ihren gegenseitigen Verhältnissen betrachtet* (Erlangen, 1819), pp. 240f.

Goethe on the other. Both, however, are only isolated branches of the whole which I [Wagner] mean by the universal sense of the Greeks in its combination with the power to work miracles. It was by no means an illness, which somnambulism is, but, on the contrary, the highest form of health. It was not one-sided and frivolous, which the genius of poetry is, but, on the contrary, highly subjective and therefore religious. This universal sense . . . was as instinctive and universal [as the phenomena of magnetism and the talent of poetry]. Yet, it differed from both in that it penetrated the whole of man and for the whole of his life. Those other phenomena, poetry and magnetism, are limited to passing states and to certain single aspects of man.

The miracles of which Wagner speaks are neither less nor more than what Hardenberg meant by the miracles of his magic idealism. "Magic," said Hardenberg,[84] "is the art of using the world of phenomena at will." What it achieves is a *"creatio rationalis"*.[85] Natural truth, he admits, may be different from magic truth, but human conviction can force the former to coincide with the latter.[86] Magic is a universal force. "Through it man becomes as powerful as the stars."[87] It seems possible, however, to discern in Hardenberg's magic idealism a highly personal note. This is a peculiar solipsism which solves the problem of the parallel between the world of actualities and that of thoughts or ideas almost before it has found time to become formulated. The sensually perceptible world of phenomena had often been said to consist of the thoughts of God. Hardenberg imparts metaphysical validity to this poetic metaphor through his peculiar philosophy of mathematics. "Genuine mathematics is the proper element of the magician."[88] Hardenberg calls mathematics a tool which manipulates the psychic energies of reason.[89] The energies actuate the movements of our organs, which is a supercausal or magic use of the world of matter.[90] The miracle that we are able to move a hand or a foot is dissolved in the idea that these organs are merely embodiments of the will which dominates them. Yet also "the

[84] *Novalis Schriften*, II, 336.
[85] *Novalis Schriften*, III, 46.
[86] *Novalis Schriften*, II, 345.
[87] *Novalis Schriften*, III, 54.
[88] *Novalis Schriften*, III, 295.
[89] *Novalis Schriften*, III, 71.
[90] *Novalis Schriften*, III, 263.

whole world is only a sensually perceptible imaginative force which has assumed the shape of a mechanism."[91] There is, consequently, no reason whatsoever why the range of our own will, of our thought, our imagination should be limited to the microcosm of our own body. We are clearly much more than we are, simply through the phenomenon which we call love. "Our thought [like God's thoughts, of which they are microcosmic repetitions] are potent factors in the universe."[92] What the mind thinks, it produces. "The organs of thought are the generative or sexual organs of nature."[93] Some thoughts give their originator the wondrous thrill of successful parenthood. They are what Hardenberg calls "dangerous thoughts,"[94] which approach the magic line and "turn *ipso facto* true." With God nothing is impossible. This means: with thought nothing is impossible. Thus Hardenberg concludes: "I can what I will. With man nothing is impossible."[95] There is surely no more perfect and complete summary of Hardenberg's magic idealism than the simple suggestion: "Scholasticism transformed all things into abstracts. It is too bad that it did not try to reverse this process."[96]

Successful thinking, Hardenberg declares, is a difficult, a dangerous art It requires care and practice. Furthermore, the human mind is but one of nature's many organs of regeneration, and naturally not all of its products will prove fit to survive. Only the most mature, the most elevated thought is magic. Below it there is a tremendous scale of less fertile or entirely barren thinking. After all, what we call thought is only one, although a peculiarly human, manifestation of a universal principle which has also its animal, vegetable, and mineral forms. There is only the word "life" which might be applied to this general principle. "Life is the veritable *menstruum universale*. And every organ [every material form] is but an excrement or product of life."[97] That establishes finally the synthesis of Hardenberg's two statements that

[91] *Novalis Schriften*, III, 71f.
[92] *Novalis Schriften*, III, 337.
[93] *Novalis Schriften*, III, 272.
[94] *Novalis Schriften*, III, 325.
[95] *Novalis Schriften*, III, 334.
[96] *Novalis Schriften*, III, 169.
[97] *Novalis Schriften*, III, 98.

"thinking is galvanization"[98] and that "everything or nothing must be galvanism."[99]

In Hardenberg we reach thus the same biocentrism which is commonly identified with the name of Goethe. It ought to be considered as the most basic concern of the entire age. Did not a Blake, in telepathic affinity, reach the same position? "The body," he said,[100] "is only a portion of the soul discerned by the senses!"

[98] *Novalis Schriften,* III, 82.
[99] *Novalis Schriften,* III, 304.
[100] William Blake, *Marriage of Heaven and Hell.*

X

VITAL FORCE

MESMER'S CONCEPTION of a material *fluidum universale* was dissolved in Hardenberg's simple statement: "The veritable *menstruum universale* is life."[1] Yet, what is life? The idea that life should be represented by a special material agent proved strangely obstinate. By the middle of the Nineteenth Century it was still, or again, going strongly. The *Researches on Magnetism* by Baron von Reichenbach were designed, as Braid described them in 1846,[2] "to bring to our notice 'a new imponderable,' through which we should realize a clear and satisfactory solution of many problems in the mental and physical constitution of man which had puzzled and perplexed alike the savage and the sage from the earliest age." Reichenbach's brochure, according to Braid, created a vast interest "evinced by the extent to which it was quoted, referred to, and reviewed "[3] However, it seems to have been rather through his notable work as an engineer and industrialist that this Austrian nobleman deserved the attention of the public. Indeed, in many respects he might be called the Swedenborg of the Nineteenth Century,[4] but about his "new" imponderable nothing was new

[1] Cf. p. 181, n. 97.

[2] James Braid, *The Power of the Mind over the Body* (London, 1846), p. 3.

[3] Cf., e.g., the passage, equally characteristic of its author and of Reichenbach, in which Carl Vogt, *Köhlerglaube und Wissenschaft* (Gießen, 1855), pp. 125f., refers to "die Vorrede jenes dickleibigen Werkes, das ein gewisser Freiherr von Reichenbach, Besitzer mehrerer Schlösser und Rittergüter, in die Welt hinaus gesandt hat, um die Ungläubigen zum Od zu bekehren. Der findet es denn nun vollends unsittlich, daß man an sein Od nicht glauben will, und zieht in dieser Schrift ebenso zornig gegen mich zu Felde wie in derjenigen zum ersten Bande gegen Liebig, Dubois-Reymond und Andere." Reichenbach's publications on "odylism" have not been examined for purposes of the present study.

[4] Cf. Max Neuburger, *Die Wiener medizinische Schule im Vormärz* (Vienna, 1921), p. 203n: "Karl Freiherr von Reichenbach, der 1821 auf den Eisenwerken zu Blansko (Mähren) großartige industrielle Schöpfungen ins Leben gerufen und in der Nähe von Blansko eine Runkelrübenzuckerfabrik ins Leben gerufen hatte, war der Entdecker des Paraffin. Er legte eine wertvolle Meteoritensammlung, Herbarien u.s.w. an. Später auf Schloß Reisenberg bei Wien lebend, erregte er großes Aufsehen und lebhaften Widerspruch durch seine 'odischen' Studien, die insbesondere in den

apparently except the name of *Od* or *Odyl* which he invented for it. This was, by definition,[5] a force "held to pervade all nature, manifesting itself in certain persons of sensitive temperament, and exhibited especially by magnets, crystals, heat, light, and chemical action." It explained the phenomena of mesmerism and animal magnetism and was responsible for the highest as well as for the lowest manifestations of life, for the growth of a human organism as well as for that of a crystal. The affinity of Reichenbach's "odylism" with the earliest eighteenth-century version of material mesmerism is obvious. However, the question arises how far either of these doctrines may be identified with the vitalistic theories which characterize the intervening period of Romanticism.

The idea of a peculiar agent of vitality was branded by the thinker Lotze[6] as "a hollow, nebulous emphasis of imagination." This representative verdict is frequently quoted[7] and generally and vaguely applied to all the various kinds of romantic vitalism, regardless of whether their vital force was meant as a peculiar substance or merely as a philosophical construct.[8] It is customary to credit the science of chemistry with having demonstrated the absurdity of all hypotheses of special vital forces, as though a successful synthesis of organic substances out of inorganic com-

---

Schriften 'Odisch-magnetische Briefe,' 'Der sensitive Mensch und sein Verhalten zum Od,' 'Aphorismen über Sensitivität und Od' niedergelegt sind."

[5] *OED*, s.v. "Od."

[6] In Rudolf Wagner's *Handwörterbuch der Physiologie,* I (1842), s.v. "Lebenskraft."

[7] Cf. e.g., J. M. Verweyen, *Naturphilosophie,* p. 108.

[8] It is important to note that the word "Lebenskraft" carries the double meaning of vitality and animating force. The natural confusion of the two is not regrettable, for it emphasizes the fact that "vital force," "élan vital," etc., are merely constructs for the less scientific "vitality." It seems, for example, quite unimportant to know whether Yeats in "The Song of the Old Mother" spoke of vitality or of vital force:

> I rise in the dawn, and I kneel and blow
> Till the seed of the fire flicker and glow;
> And then I must scrub . . .
> And the young lie long . . .
> While I must work because I am old,
> And the seed of the fire gets feeble and cold.

Cf. William Butler Yeats, *The Collected Poems* (New York: Macmillan, 1935), p. 67.

ponents could prove anything but the homogeneity of all chemistry, which, also in its organic branch, is not concerned with the riddle of life. The strongest condemnation of material vitalism does not come at all from a representative of chemistry or even the exact sciences in general. It is, characteristically, Carus, the fullest, though last and latest, embodiment of the spirit of the romantic sciences, who called the idea of a special, detachable vital force "one of the worst aberrations of the human mind."[9] Elsewhere[10] he explained that "this aberration was due to the odd fact that people conceived, as it were, of two kinds of nature . . . The one was animate and embraced men, animals, and plants, while the other, the inanimate, included the earth and the firmament, whose phenomena were something basically heterogeneous." Such a dichotomy is certainly anything but romantic. Indeed, a major contribution of romantic thought was precisely that it recast all sorts of dualistic conceptions in terms of a biocentric universalism. Obviously, this tendency must have had its effect also on the romantic reconstruction of eighteenth-century vitalism. The peculiar nature of these effects is the subject of the following exposition.

The socio-psychic field in which the struggle around the concept of a vital force was waged in the later Eighteenth Century has been described by Neuburger[11] in the following terms:

The question of all questions, what is life?, is as old as thinking mankind. It is as unsolved today as of yore. It is silenced at times by pseudo-solutions, half truths, or apathetic resignation, yet it is constantly presented anew. This question becomes particularly acute when great discoveries have widened man's knowledge of nature, and when the whole of his conception of nature is in a state of fermentation. Such an epoch began in the last decades of the Eighteenth Century. Never before had the conflict between vitalism and mechanism been waged with similar passion, never before were the contrasts of these two views equally striking. Vitalism had grown out of the science which was most fundamentally interested in the issue, i.e., out of medicine. It had appeared about the middle of the century[12] as a reaction against a crude sort of iatrophysics

[9] C. G. Carus, *Organon der Erkenntnis,* p. 164.
[10] C. G. Carus, *Briefe über das Erdleben,* p. 13.
[11] M. Neuburger, *Johann Christian Reil,* pp. 18f.
[12] This refers most probably to Théophile de Bordeu of Paris, who is frequently mentioned as the "founder" of the doctrine of the vital force through a publication of 1752.

and iatrochemistry. It had been prepared for by Stahl's animism and Hoffmann's partly dynamic system and found support in Haller's demonstration of irritability and sensibility as basic biological phenomena.

The result was a period of chaotic conflict around a host of new concepts such as "nervous fluid," "principle of life," and "vital force." Certain German physicians, Neuburger continues, "went finally so far as to postulate a vital force which was not dependent on the ordinary laws of nature but acted in accordance with its own specific purposes. They reorganized the whole of physiology and pathology in the sense of this transcendental potency." An entirely new light was thrown on the question when the discovery of galvanism revealed a previously unknown class of natural phenomena. There were some

who believed the mystery of life to be solved. They accepted special chemical substances as the source of the process of animation or identified simply all of life's phenomena with those of electricity.[13] Others, however, considered what their age had discovered as the ultimate for all times. They embraced, in view of the inadequacy of all mechanistic explanations, a mystic sort of vitalism, swearing by a vital force which alone was deemed capable of preserving the body from destruction through chemico-physical energies.

This summary of Neuburger's analysis emphasizes the fact that the discovery of galvanism marked a critical moment in the entire development. A full appreciation of the importance of Galvani's twitching frog's legs can best be attained in connection with a discussion of the Brunonian doctrine which identified animation with irritability. The Scotsman Dr. John Brown published his *Elementa Medicinae* in 1780. They taught that "all diseases arise either from deficiency or excess of excitement, and must be treated with stimulants or sedatives."[14] However, the importance

---

[13] Cf. p. 162, n. 20.

[14] Cf. *OED*, s.v. "Brunonian." Brown's ideas may be stated more fully. Excitement as a manifestation of life is caused in human beings by two kinds of stimulants. Emotions, sensations, ratiocination, etc., are internal; air, heat, food, blood, poisons, etc., are external. Health corresponds to a certain mean of excitement. Above and below this level the manifestations of illness appear which are grouped accordingly as sthenic and asthenic. Later the term "hypersthenic" is introduced to replace sthenic which corresponds henceforth to the state of health. Medical treatment consists in the neutralization or administration of irritants. "The less an individual is accustomed to irritants, the less will be needed for the production of a mean of excitement,"

of this simple principle is very hard to appraise, for it merges
not only with the older ideas of Francis Glisson, a physician of
the Seventeenth Century, and of Brown's teacher Cullen,[15] but also
with those of the Swiss German Albrecht von Haller. This great
physiologist had reduced in principle all the problems connected
with the complicated machinery of an animated organism to two
basic problems: that of the irritability of muscles and that of the
sensibility of nerves. The significance of these ideas is perhaps
best illustrated by a reference to Herder's essay *On Cognition
and Sensation of the Human Soul*. Among all of Herder's works
this essay comes closest to being a systematic survey of his entire
philosophy. It precedes Brown's publication by two years, yet
hinges entirely on the conception of a stimulated sensitive fiber
as the elemental manifestation of the mystery of life.[16] The Brunonian vogue which reached its climax in Germany in the last
decade of the Eighteenth Century[17] must consequently be inter-

[15] Francis Glisson, *Tractatus de natura substantiae energetica* (London, 1672),
observed that the contraction of a muscle does not change its volume. His discussion of irritability of muscles became the basis for Cullen's and Brown's work.

William Cullen, 1710-1790, professor in Edinburgh, developed in 1740 his entire
medical doctrine on a neuropathological basis. He survived his student John Brown
by two years.

[16] This can be recognized from a mere synopsis of the work. Johann Gottfried
Herder, *Vom Erkennen und Empfinden der menschlichen Seele* (Riga, 1778, third
version), "Bemerkungen und Träume."

Erster Versuch. Vom Erkennen und Empfinden in ihrem menschlichen Ursprunge
und den Gesetzen ihrer Würkung.
   1. Vom Reiz.
   2. Sinne.
   3. Erkennen und Wollen.
Zweiter Versuch. Einfluß beider Kräfte ineinander und auf Charakter und
Genie des Menschen.
   1. Unser Denken hängt ab vom Empfinden.
   2. Was würkt unser Denken aufs Empfinden?
   3. Was würkt das menschliche Erkennen und Empfinden auf die mancherlei
      Genies, Charaktere, etc.?
Cf. J. G. Herder, *Sämmtliche Werke*, VIII.

[17] Brunonianism reached Germany in the early eighties, according to Ricarda
Huch, *Ausbreitung und Verfall der Romantik,* p. 264, through the German-
Russian physician Weikard. Brown's book was translated by Röschlaub (1768-
1835). A list of early German Brunoniana includes:

Christoph Girtanner, *Ausführliche Darstellung des Brown'schen Systems,* Göttingen, 1797.

Karl von Eckartshausen, *Ideen über das negative Prinzip des Todes, zur Bestäti-
gung des Brownischen Systems,* Frankfort-on-Main, 1798.

Id., Ideen über das affirmative Prinzip des Lebens, Munich, 1798.

preted as a complex phenomenon, symbolically represented rather than exclusively conditioned by the conceptions of the individual personage John Brown.

The most important representatives of Brown's doctrine, in the sense just qualified, were Johann Peter Frank and Johann Andreas Röschlaub.[18] "The famous centers of this art," as Schubert put it,[19] were Bamberg and Würzburg. The important rôle which Schelling played in German Brunonianism and in turn the importance of Brown's ideas for Schelling's philosophy have been developed by Ricarda Huch.[20] It was, on the whole, a short-lived movement, but that is precisely the reason for its importance in the present discussion. By the turn of the century a marked movement away from Brown is already to be noticed. In July 1802, Görres wrote to his cousin H. von Lassaulx, who studied

---

Alexander von Humboldt, *Versuche über die Stimmung der Erregbarkeit durch chemische Stoffe* (1798), vol. II of *Über die gereizte Muskel- und Nervenfaser*, 1797f.

Johann Andreas Röschlaub, *Untersuchungen über Pathogenie oder Einleitung in die medizinische Theorie*, 3 vols., 1798ff.

Joseph Görres, "Principien einer neuen Begründung der Gesetze des Lebens durch Dualism und Polarität," *Allgemeine Medizinische Annalen*, April to August, 1802.

Friedrich Gottlob Wetzel, *Briefe über Browns System der Heilkunde* . . . Leipzig, 1806.

Cf. also Robert Stein's introduction to Joseph von Görres, *Gesammelte Schriften*, II, 1 (Cologne, 1932), and Franz Peuten, *Johann Gottfried Rademacher*, especially pp. 2ff.

[18] Johann Peter Frank, 1745-1821, published in 1792 a *System der medizinischen Polizei*. Cf. also p. 226, n. 29.

On Johann Andreas Röschlaub, cf. n. 17 above.

[19] Cf. F. R. Merkel, *Der Naturphilosoph G. H. Schubert*, p. 23. Schubert's name suggests an additional source of German "Brunonianism," viz., the works of Erasmus Darwin. Schubert was engaged in a translation of Darwin's *Botanical Garden*. The work was never completed, but Schubert's active interest cannot be solely explained by the financial difficulties which drove him into the manufacture of translations. Erasmus Darwin was first of all the author of the *Zoonomia* (1794-1796), which is concerned with ideas related to those put forth by Brown. The primary purpose of this work was to determine the basic factors in the formation of diseases. Cf. R. B. Crum, *Scientific Thought,* pp. 123f.: "After a detailed study of the various fibrous motions, Darwin concluded that there were four kinds—Irritative, Sensitive, Voluntary, Associative—and furthermore that this same classification extended down the scale to the lower animal forms and also into the vegetable domain. In order to understand these movements it was necessary to study what stimulated them and how they functioned, and thus he concluded that in the higher forms of animal life, ideas were a contributing cause, while in the lower forms, instincts played a similar rôle. The term 'disease' then, implied a disturbance of one or more of these classes of fibrous activities, and the physician's place was to apply remedies which would restore their normal functioning."

[20] Ricarda Huch, *Ausbreitung und Verfall der Romantik*, pp. 264ff.

medicine at the University of Würzburg:[21] "I may be mistaken, but it seems that the opponents of Brunonianism are preparing a reaction of which its protagonists have no idea."[22] One year later an *Anti-Röschlaub* was published. Yet, more important still, Röschlaub himself, hardly in reaction to this attack, began to reconsider the bases of his science and arrived at conclusions which make it possible to see in him a precursor of modern bacteriology.[23] A highly revealing case is that of Röschlaub's friend and colleague Johann Benjamin Erhard, whose memoirs were published by Varnhagen von Ense in 1830. The editor appended a brief biography of the deceased author and explained in it why Erhard, as Röschlaub before him, had discontinued to practice medicine on the basis of Brown's system. His belief in it had been undermined by continued experience. Yet, Varnhagen continues,[24]

[21] J. v. *Görres, Gesammelte Schriften,* II, 1, p. XVI.

[22] Here a *sottise* of August von Kotzebue must be mentioned, which it seems best, however, to handle in a mere note. It is "Das Neue Jahrhundert, eine Posse in Einem Akt" (1801), *Neue Schauspiele,* vol. 5. Cf. J. v. Görres, *Gesammelte Schriften,* II, 1, p. 347. The *Medizinisch-Chirurgische Zeitung,* I (1801), 253, reported correctly that Kotzebue again made a fool of himself and concludes: "Uns wundert, daß Kotzebue die Sottise beging über Dinge zu sprechen, die er nicht verstand." *Uns* wundert es nicht, but Kotzebue might at least have tried to hide the fact. Dr. Reiz and Dr. Potenz are two ridiculous Brownists, who cannot settle the question whether Schmalbauch's death was sthenic or asthenic. When they opine that an autopsy might solve the problem, the patient gets up, for he merely pretended to be dead. The supposed fun of the farce consists in chasing to death the meager pun suggested by the double meaning of *Reiz.* Minchen concludes: "Meine Seelenreitze sind nicht so wirksam als der Metallreitz auf Scheintodte." Schmalbauch says: "Die Kerls sind beyde verrückt. Reitze?—wo hab ich denn die Reitze?— ja, vor 30, 40 Jahren."

[23] Cf. Ricarda Huch, *Ausbreitung und Verfall der Romantik,* pp. 285ff. It was on the basis of Röschlaub's later teachings that Ringseis developed his conception of disease as a parasitic secondary organism. He belongs thus to the sphere of Ferdinand John of Meiningen, 1804-59, the follower of Karl Wilhelm Stark, 1787-1845, whose school, the *naturhistorische Schule,* conceived of disease as a positive entity. This doctrine was developed by Stark in his book *Allgemeine Pathologie oder allgemeine Naturlehre der Krankheit,* 1838. For further details, cf. P. Diepgen, *Deutsche Medizin vor hundert Jahren;* also the introductory chapters of F. Peuten, *Johann Gottfried Rademacher.* The later discoveries of bacteriology may, indeed, be thought of as verifications of these speculations. Traces of Brunonianism are nowhere noticeable in this entire development.

[24] Karl Varnhagen von Ense (editor), *Denkwürdigkeiten des Philosophen und Arztes Johann Benjamin Erhard* (Stuttgart, 1830), editor's appendix. Erhard had died in 1827 at the age of sixty-one. His book was reviewed by Arnim in *Blätter für literarische Unterhaltung,* II (1830), No. 197 (July 16), pp. 785f. On Erhard and mesmerism, cf. p. 163, n. 22.

he did not admit that it had been an error on his part to adhere to its principles. He rather held that the humor of man's organism and the character of his diseases are variable, so that it is possible to suppose that a medical doctrine, which we at present have to condemn, was quite appropriate in its time.

This would mean, as Kieser[25] suggested, that Brown was the physician of the diseases which owed their peculiarities to the cultural crises among whose manifestations in various media the French Revolution was only a peculiarly obvious one. Windisch-mann[26] concluded in a similar fashion and likewise after due appreciation of Brown's merits, that he was a Newton of medicine. This meant at the time that he was the founder of a mechanistic system. "The rhythm," Windischmann felt, "is something which Brown could not understand." The meaning of this accusation becomes clearer through a remark of Adam Müller's in his *Doctrine of Opposites*.[27] "Brown's therapy," he wrote, "would doubtless have exerted an incomparably greater and more lasting influence on the development of medicine, if its famous author had replaced his concept of asthenia by a clear and fully thought out antisthenia as the opposite of sthenia." What Müller had in mind can perhaps be expressed in simpler terms. The fact that Brown used a terminological pair like "sthenic—asthenic," later even the series "hypersthenic—sthenic—asthenic,"[28] indicates that he could not think in terms of polarity. The normal state, which Brown designated later on as the sthenic condition, was not, according to Müller, conceived as the result of a tension of opposites.[29] Brown's system, this reasoning implies, was consequently unable to grasp the essentials of living organization. It was two-dimensional, arrhythmic, unorganic, or in brief, it was mechanistic. Several years earlier, Hardenberg arrived at the same conclusion and expressed it in a way which typifies the entire trend. In 1798 he seems to have read the Brunonian treatise by Eckartshausen.[30]

---

[25] Cf. p. 159, n. 3.

[26] Cf. Ricarda Huch, *Ausbreitung und Verfall der Romantik*, p. 268.

[27] A. Müller, *Lehre vom Gegensatz*, p. 234n.

[28] Cf. p. 186, n. 14.

[29] Cf. p. 142, n. 34, which might be applied to Brown as well as to Robinet.

[30] Cf. p. 187, n. 17. Karl von Eckartshausen's *Ideen über das negative Prinzip* is an item in the "Verzeichnis der Bücher, so sich auf der Stube des Salinenassessors von Hardenberg befinden," *Novalis Schriften*, IV.

At that time already, he notes critically:[31] "The best in Brown's system is its amazing poise." Shortly thereafter he observes in anticipation of Windischmann and others:[32] "Brown and his adherents belong to the mechanistic school of physiologists, just as the humoral physiologists belong to the chemists." He finds[33] that "he discovers more and more reasons against Brown" and summarizes them in the formula: "Life, after all, can be explained only through life!"

Brown himself, to be sure, can hardly be accused of having intended his system as an "explanation" of life. It seems, however, that that was precisely what his German followers expected from it or at least what they tried to develop out of its principles. Yet, instead of a solution, nothing had been gained but the simplified conception that the phenomena of animation could be studied in the behavior of nervous and muscular fibers,[34] and that, after all, had been known before and without Brown. It is thus quite plausible that the Brunonian vogue had to recede when a series of experiments became known which seemed to allow conjectures on the final cause of the behavior of nervous and muscular tissues. Through them it was apparently possible, not only to observe the special agent, the "vital force" which caused the contraction of muscles, but also to recognize in it a variation of a more general principle whose polar manifestations could be traced through all the various realms of nature.

This is, greatly simplified to be sure, the importance of Galvani's experiments with twitching frog's legs of 1789, one year after the death of Dr. John Brown and less than a decade after the publication of the *Elementa Medicinae*. The details of the event are familiar. Its most important aspect is the fact that Galvani suc-

---

[31] *Novalis Schriften,* II, 335.

[32] *Novalis Schriften,* III, 20.

[33] *Novalis Schriften,* III, 213.

[34] We disregard certain details. O. Walzel, *Romantik,* p. 40, distinguishes three schools of thought developing from the basis of Haller's ideas. "Die eine sah in der Irritabilität eine Folge der Sensibilität, die andere, von dem schottischen Arzt Brown geleitet, erblickte in der Irritabilität das oberste Prinzip, die dritte suchte beide Gegensätze in einem höheren Prinzip zu verschmelzen. Die erste führte alle Lebenserscheinungen auf den Einfluß der Nerven zurück, die zweite wollte in der Muskelerregung die Quelle finden, die dritte vertrat die vitalistische Theorie, indem sie so Reizbarkeit wie Erregbarkeit zum Ausdruck einer allgemeinen Lebenskraft erhob."

ceeded in making dead organic matter move without the application of metallic conductors. This was the basis of his conception
of the muscle as a sort of Leyden jar or battery. The nerve represented the inner, the muscle the outer tinfoil coating; as for the
glass of the phial, it could be seen in the extremities of the nerve.[35]
The cause of the artificial movements of dead organic matter was
consequently a sort of electricity,[36] which was named animal
electricity or galvanism.[37] Was it not plausible to assume that
the living movements of vegetable and animal organisms were
due to the same or at least a basically related agent?[38] To be sure,
the exact nature of this highest principle of organic life remained
to be investigated, but that it was there seemed assured. Furthermore, whatever it was, the observation that its functions included
the determination of the behavior of organic matter, meant at the
same time that it had the power to force inorganic substances to

[35] Cf. Aloysi Galvani, *Abhandlung über die Kräfte der tierischen Elektrizität* . . .
Deutsch von Dr. J. Mayer (Prague, 1793), especially the chapter "Mutmaßungen
und Folgerungen." The book is more readily available in an edition by A. J. von
Oettingen (Leipzig, 1894), No. 52 in "Ostwalds Klassiker der exakten Wissenschaften."
For the Italian text, cf. Galvani, *Opere,* Bologna, 1841.

[36] We disregard for the moment certain other explanations. On Girtanner, cf.
p. 195, n. 45; on the entire situation more generally, Edmund Hoppe, *Geschichte
der Elektrizität* (Leipzig: Johann Ambrosius Barth, 1884), p. 119: "So meinten
andere, die Nerven seien von einer besonderen elektrischen Materie durchflossen,
welche bald aus Äther und Phlogiston, bald aus Sauerstoff, Lichtstoff und Wärmestoff und dergleichen bestehen sollte."

[37] The term "galvanism" was introduced by Galvani's opponent Volta in 1796.
It was meant to stand for electricity generated by chemical action, i.e., exactly what
it stands for today. However, it came to be used for the animal electricity of
Galvani's (anti-Voltaic) theory, a meaning which it carries today only secondarily
and in an historical context. It is of interest to note that the twitching of frog's
legs had been observed thirty-three years before Galvani by his countryman
Marco Antonio Caldani. In 1756, however, there was apparently no need for a
theory of animal electricity.

[38] This conclusion was facilitated by the fact that electric charges could be
demonstrated in certain living organisms. Theodoric the Great was said to have
emitted sparks when he walked. To be sure, he was no longer a living organism,
but similar phenomena could actually be observed in certain species of fish. In
1751 Michel Adanson of Paris studied the movements of the now so-called electric
catfish. He recognized their electric nature and explained them by visualizing the
animal as a sort of Leyden phial. The experiments of L. S. van s'Gravesande on
gymnotus, now commonly known as the electric eel, led to similar conclusions in
1755. In 1772 Walsh followed with his proof that the crampfish, *raja torpedo,*
now also called electric ray, is charged with electricity. The whole subject of ich-
thyoelectricity was finally given a systematic re-examination by John Hunter in
1775.

submit to the laws of animate organization. This view, we anticipate, could not be final. It represents a peculiar form of that dualism which Carus[39] called "one of the worst aberrations of the
human mind." This, however, does not impair its historic importance, which is sufficiently indicated by the fact that it was
upheld by a man like Alexander von Humboldt in his younger
years.

In his *Aphorisms on the Chemical Physiology of Plants* of 1793,
Humboldt defined the vital force as that "inner" power which
dissolves the bonds of chemical affinity and prevents the free
combination of the elements in organic bodies.[40] In this statement
we have the key to Humboldt's myth "The Genius of Rhodes,"
which Schiller published in the *Horen* of 1795.[41] It tells of a
mysterious painting which was cherished by the people of Syra-
cuse, none of whom, however, was able to explain the significance

[39] C. G. Carus, *Organon der Erkenntnis*, p. 164.

[40] Alexander von Humboldt, *Aphorismen aus der Lehre der chemischen Pflanzen-
physiologie*, 1793. Cf. Löwenberg in Karl Bruhns, *Alexander von Humboldt* (Leipzig, 1872), I, 206.

[41] Alexander von Humboldt, "Die Lebenskraft oder der Rhodische Genius," *Die
Horen*, I, 5 (1795), pp. 90-96.

Humboldt was the only representative of the exact sciences whom Schiller invited to contribute to his new periodical. The letter of acceptance of August 6,
1794 contains a fascinating list of topics which the young scientist believed to be
of interest for the lay public. Having outlined the deplorable state of the now
purely classificatory sciences, Humboldt continued: "Aber Sie fühlen mit mir,
daß etwas Höheres zu suchen, daß es wiederzufinden ist . . . Die allgemeine Harmonie in der Form, das Problem, ob es eine ursprüngliche Pflanzenform gibt, die
sich in tausenderlei Abstufungen darstellt, die Vertheilung dieser Formen über den
Erdboden; die verschiedenen Eindrücke der Fröhlichkeit und der Melancholie,
welche die Pflanzenwelt im sinnlichen Menschen hervorbringt; der Contrast zwischen
der toten unbewegten Felsmasse, selbst der unorganisch scheinenden Baumstämme
und der belebten Pflanzendecke, die gleichsam das Gerippe mit milderndem
Fleische sanft bekleidet; Geschichte und Geographie der Pflanzen oder historische
Darstellung der allgemeinen Ausbreitung der Kräuter über den Erdboden, ein
unbearbeiteter Teil der allgemeinen Weltgeschichte; Aufsuchung der ältesten Vegetation in ihren Grabmälern (Versteinerungen, Steinkohlen, Torf, u.s.w.); all-
mähliche Bewohnbarkeit des Erdbodens; Wanderungen und Züge der Pflanzen, der
geselligen und isolierten; Karten darüber, welche Pflanzen gewissen Völkern gefolgt
sind; allgemeine Geschichte des Ackerbaus; Vergleichung der cultivierten Pflanzen
mit den Haustieren, Ursprung beider; Ausartungen: welche Pflanzen fester, welche
loser an das Gesetz gleichmäßiger Form gebunden sind; Verwilderung gezähmter
Pflanzen (so amerikanische, persische Pflanzen, wild von Tajo bis Obej); allgemeine Verwirrungen in der Pflanzengeographie durch Colonisationen—das scheinen
mir Objecte, die des Nachdenkens wert und fast ganz unberührt sind." Cf. Löwenberg in K. Bruhns, *Alexander von Humboldt*, I, 204.

of its unusual theme or the origin of its current name, "The Genius of Rhodes." It showed a crowd of young men and women who stretched out their arms toward each other in desperate longing, but between them there stood a genius with a burning torch and a butterfly on his shoulder. He seemed to represent that which prevented the young people from indulging their natural desires. Finally a pendant to this picture was found in Rhodes. Here the young people had united in ecstatic embraces. The genius no longer stood separating them but lay crushed under the impact of their falling bodies. The butterfly was not there, and the torch was extinguished. A philosopher who examined both these paintings found the correct explanation. The young people represent the elements in an organism. Their urge to submit to the laws of their chemical affinities is restrained by the vital force which is represented by the chaperoning genius with torch and butterfly. As soon as he, or it, loses control over them, they unite in what we call putrefaction.[42] The most striking aspect of this fable is doubtless that the vital force is understood as a tyrant over brute matter, which is constantly ready to revolt. "Life is, above all, a tendency to act on brute matter." "Life means consciousness thrown into matter." Such is actually the meaning of Humboldt's "Genius of Rhodes," but the two phrases just quoted do not come from him but from Bergson's *Creative Evolution*.[43]

This idea of a hostile dualism of life and matter is a philosophical *impasse*. The question how Humboldt may have escaped from it reminds us naturally of a passage in Herder's "Gott,"[44] where one of the participants in the conversation asks "how these forces and these organs have come together" to form what we call a living organism. The answer given by Theophron-Herder is strikingly simpler than that in Humboldt's fable: "Through their respective natures!" This does not evade the issue, for there follows the explanation:

In the human body, e.g., nothing is without life. From the end of your

---

[42] Cf. also F. Strich, *Mythologie*, I, 407ff.

[43] Henri Bergson, *l'Évolution créatrice* (1907), pp. 105 and 197. Related ideas of modern thinkers, including Sir Oliver Lodge, are discussed by R. Eucken, *Geistige Strömungen*, p. 138.

[44] J. G. Herder, *Sämmtliche Werke*, XVI, 545f.

hair to the tip of your nails everything is penetrated by one maintaining and nourishing power. As soon as that withdraws from the smallest or largest part of the body, this is separated from the rest. It is then no longer within the sphere of the living forces of mankind. It cannot, however, escape at any time from the realm of the forces of nature. The withered hair or the broken nail enters now into another region of the world's continuity, and there it acts and suffers again, just as it was doing before in accordance with its former nature.

This last sentence sounds modest and yet is tremendously rich in meaning. Matter in organisms depends on the laws of life. They are mysterious and as such can be known, but not understood. Matter not bound in an organism depends also on laws. These are also mysterious and can also merely be known, but not understood. The laws of life may be taken to refer to the construct "vital force" only if the other laws are taken to refer to a similar construct, "natural force." These two are not opposed to each other. They represent merely two different forms of one and the same thing.

There is, then, a possibility of bridging the gap between the hostile forces of life and matter as represented in Humboldt's "Genius of Rhodes." An allusion to such a synthesis is found in Christoph Girtanner's essay On the Kantian Principle. This was published in 1796, one year after Humboldt's fable and one year before his book On the Muscular and Nervous Fibre, in which he repudiated his former position completely. Yet, it is not only a matter of chronology which enabled Girtanner to mediate between Humboldt's earlier and later views. This versatile Brownist[45] was, in a way, a follower of Galvani. Nevertheless, he belonged to those who rejected the electric principle of galvanism and conceived of the "genius of organization" as located in the newly discovered oxygen, the air of life.[46] His "vital force" was thus associated with a substance known to belong to the general realm of matter, which it could not, consequently, be assumed to govern

[45] Cf. p. 187, n. 17. In 1794 Girtanner worked on the differences between milks from various mammals. In 1796 he published his book On the Kantian Principle, in 1797 his survey of Brown's system, and from 1791 to 1797 twelve volumes of antirevolutionary Historische Nachrichten und politische Betrachtungen. He died in 1800 at the age of forty.

[46] Cf. p. 192, n. 36, also the speculative importance of the aër vitalis in F. W. Schelling, Weltseele, passim.

with a tyrannous sway. In his correspondence with Girtanner[47] Humboldt expressed a hesitant agreement with these ideas as early as 1793. Three years later Girtanner presented on their basis a definition of the vital force which avoided the dualism of "The Genius of Rhodes." "Vital force," he said,[48] "is that force by virtue of which the physical and chemical laws are subordinated to the laws of organization." To be sure, the term "subordination" in this context remains ambiguous. Yet, in addition to the idea that the lower laws are oppressed by the laws of organization, it permits also the interpretation that the laws of chemistry and physics are *integrated* in the higher laws of life. This latter view was finally formulated by Humboldt in his book on muscles and nerves of 1797. "Thought and research in the fields of physiology and chemistry," he wrote,[49] "have shaken my former belief in so-called vital forces." In organisms we have to do with configurations of effects

of a number of well-known substances and their material forces. The difficulty we encounter in trying to trace the phenomena of living organisms to physical and chemical laws in a satisfactory fashion, depends on the whole, almost as it does in the prediction of meteorological processes in the atmosphere, on the multiplicity of simultaneously active forces and of conditions of their action.

This means that the chemistry, physics, mechanics, optics, etc. of the organism are ordinary chemistry, physics, mechanics, etc. It does not mean, however, that the entirety we call an organic individual is simply dependent on the laws of those various scientific disciplines. "A secret law," as Humboldt put it elsewhere,[50] "governs all the parts of the organism, which exists only as long

[47] Humboldt to Girtanner, letter of February 12, 1793: "Ihrem Aufsatz: 'Sur le principe de l'irritabilité,' für den gute Köpfe wie Sömmering, Scherer, Planck, Herz gern fechten, verdanke ich die Veranlassung, mich ernstlich mit dem antiphlogistischen System, oder vielmehr mit den antiphlogistischen Wahrheiten bekannt zu machen . . . [Ich] bin von dem Oxygen als Princip der Lebenskraft (trotz des noch rätselhaften, gewiß nicht magnetischen oder elektrischen galvanischen Fluidums) ebenso überzeugt, als Sie es waren, da Sie mir in Green Park zuerst davon erzählten." Cf. Löwenberg in K. Bruhns, *Alexander von Humboldt*, I, 152.

[48] Chr. Girtanner, *Über das Kantische Prinzip*, p. 17.

[49] Alexander von Humboldt, *Über die gereizte Muskel- und Nervenfaser*, 1797. Cf. Löwenberg in K. Bruhns, *Alexander von Humboldt*, I, 209.

[50] *Briefwechsel und Gespräche Alexander von Humboldts mit einem jungen Freunde* (1861), p. 35.

as all its elements are mutually means and purpose of the whole."
The important point is thus simply that the laws of the organism
are not hostile to, but rather higher variations of, the laws of
what we normally call dead matter. These latter laws, to be sure,
are factors in the laws of organic existence, but organic existence
is not to be considered simply as their product. A very modern
formulation of this thought was given by Aloys Wenzl: "Inorganic
phenomena are specializations (*Sonderfälle*)" of the organic.[51]
This sounds revolutionary even now, more than a century after
those earlier discussions.

Organic laws, we may then summarize, are higher forms of other
laws of nature; and similarly, organic forces are higher variations
of other forces. Upon this basis the concept of a vital force must
be defined as the philosophical construct which points out that a
given object is alive. This conclusion is not quite so meager as it
sounds. It means that the idea of a vital force is essentially identical with that of a "formative urge" as an integral characteristic
of every animate organization. The *nisus formativus,* as Blumenbach called the concept of a formative urge when he introduced
it as a technical neologism in his monograph of 1781,[52] is first of
all a scientific construct which describes the fact that all organisms
tend toward a form of maturity which is characteristic of their
entire species. It is a simple term for an involved phenomenal con-
stellation. It is, consequently, neither capable of explaining nor of
being explained. It merely refers. The facts which it tries to cover
are an observed reality. They turn problematic only when it is attempted to develop them causally from chemico-physical factors,
which, indeed, are known to be active in their total configuration.
The importance of a progressive clarification of the rôle played by
these factors cannot be doubted,[53] but the idea that the whole con-

[51] Aloys Wenzl, "Das Leib-Seeleproblem," *Forschungen und Fortschritte,* XII
(1936), 393f.

[52] Johann Friedrich Blumenbach, *Über den Bildungstrieb und das Zeugungs-
geschäft,* Göttingen, 1781.

[53] This observation might be developed further on the basis of Goethe's *Versuch
die Metamorphose der Pflanzen zu erklären,* Gotha, 1790. This essay is definitely and
exclusively concerned with the achievements of a botanical "Bildungstrieb." In
Goethe's own terms, §113, it is, however, concerned with the manifestations of a
vegetable "Lebenskraft." It is generally known that Goethe did not try to explain this "Bildungstrieb-Lebenskraft" in terms of a chemico-physical nexus of

figuration as represented by the construct "formative urge" (*Bildungstrieb*) could be elaborated from them, is obviously absurd. It certainly did not occur to Blumenbach, to Goethe, to Hülsen, or to any of the other thinkers whom a comprehensive history of the *nisus formativus* would have to discuss.[54]

---

cause and effect. Yet, greater attention should be paid to the extent to which Goethe emphasized the contributing importance of such chemical and physical factors. Cf. especially §§24 to 28, 30 and 38 to 39.

[54] A few miscellaneous allusions to the fertility of the concept are offered as a contribution to its history. The semantic value of the term "Bildungstrieb" underwent a curious yet characteristic alteration at the hands of Schiller. It occurs repeatedly in "Über Anmut und Würde" (1793), and in the "Briefe über die ästhetische Erziehung" (1795), *Werke*, edited by Ludwig Bellermann, second edition (Leipzig: Bibliographisches Institut, n.d.), VII, 121 and 378, signifying a transitive urge to create rather than an intransitive urge to grow. Steffens used it in a way fit to destroy the last remains of confidence which the reader may have had in the stylistic capabilities of this writer. Cf. W. Koch, *Briefe deutscher Romantiker*, Steffens to Schelling, letter of July 26, 1799: "Von dem Granite aus ist ein versteinerter Bildungstrieb unaufhörlich wirksam, der gegen das eigentliche Lebendige immer ankämpft." Steffens meant, most probably, "ein versteinernder Bildungstrieb," which would be the power of death described in a phraseology reserved for the description of life. This is the ill-famed dialectic use of the magic rod of analogy. Friedrich Creuzer referred to the formative urge as an illustration of his conception of mythology. In a passage written in 1822, reprinted in Ernst Howald's collection of texts, *Der Kampf um Creuzers Symbolik* (Tübingen: J. B. C. Mohr, 1926), p. 36, mythology is defined as the product of an attitude toward nature "which represents the something we call with Blumenbach *Bildungstrieb* as an active individual." Here Creuzer may have thought of August Ludwig Hülsen's essay "Über den Bildungstrieb," in Fichte-Niethammer's *Philosophisches Journal*, IX (1800), 99ff., where such a mythological personification had been attempted. For Hülsen nature was "die sichtbare lebenverbreitende Gottheit unseres Innern, in der wir Freude atmen und sind, und die ewig, als die unsrige, nichts andres hervorbringen kann als was der Bildung freier Wesen vollkommen entspreche." Friedrich Schlegel spoke of "Wilhelm Meisters unendlichem Bildungstrieb," *Jugendschriften*, II, 174, suggesting thus a biological interpretation of the term "Bildungsroman" as also the conclusion that it is really an anachronism if representatives of this genre are said to have occurred before Goethe's *Meister* and Moritz' *Anton Reiser*. Indeed, Schlegel's remark does not only imply a full characterization of Wilhelm Meister but also of Wilhelm Meister's author ("Autor heißt Urheber," *Kritische Fragmente*, 68). It points to the "Mittelpunkt und Base seiner Existenz." In an autobiographical fragment of 1797, *Goethes Autobiographische Schriften* (Leipzig: Insel-Verlag, n.d.), III, 680, Goethe wrote: "Immer tätiger, nach innen und außen fortwirkender poetischer Bildungstrieb macht den Mittelpunkt und die Base seiner Existenz. Hat man den gefaßt, so lösen sich alle übrigen anscheinenden Widersprüche. Da dieser Trieb rastlos ist, so muß er, um sich nicht stofflos selbst zu verzehren, sich nach außen wenden." It is fascinating to visualize a complete Goethe-biography developing in ever expanding circles around the central concept *Bildungstrieb*. Finally, if Goethe's life must be understood on this basis, then a similar statement may also be made with reference to his age. R. Berthelot,

The assertion of a philosophical equivalence of "formative urge" and "vital force" will doubtless be challenged by a reference to the material nature currently assigned to the latter. Here it will be remembered that the development of Alexander von Humboldt's personal conception of vitalism presented itself in our discussion as a process of continued dematerialization. Thus the question arises as to whether this idea of Humboldt's was exceptional or rather characteristic of a general contemporary trend. The following considerations may replace the answer, which can hardly be given in unequivocal terms.

A typical representative of the conception of a material vital force was the physician and mesmerist Christoph Wilhelm Hufeland. In his *Art of Prolonging Life*[55] he defined "the vital power as the most subtle, the most penetrating, and the most invisible agent of nature with which we are as yet acquainted. In those respects," Hufeland continued, "it exceeds light, electricity, and magnetism, with which, however, it seems to have the closest affinity." To be sure, this is the sort of materialization of forces which Baader[56] had ridiculed as early as 1792, when he suggested that the tendency of his time to invent a special matter for every individual quality of matter would finally necessitate the assumption of a matter-making matter. Yet, the most striking aspect of Hufeland's statement is not that it materializes the vital force but rather that it conceives of this quality of organic matter as a finer variation of the manifestation of other natural forces. All of these are not only materialized but considered as peculiar variations of one basic materialization. If everything is materialized, then it becomes possible to speak of the matter of forces, for instance of the matter of electricity, and yet to remain in basic accord with those who prefer to conceive of these forces as "qual-

Science et philosophie chez Goethe, p. 42, suggests that the problems of the *nisus formativus* were "analogues à ceux que Herder s'était posés pour la poésie, pour le langage, en poussant à ses conséquences extrêmes la méthode même de l'école historique du XVIIIe siècle dont il devait pourtant rejeter en partie les conclusions; ce qui avait tourné Herder, à la suite de l'Anglais Percy et avant les romantiques, vers l'étude des chants populaires, des littératures primitives."

[55] Christoph Wilhelm Hufeland, *Art of Prolonging Life,* edited (translated) by Erasmus Wilson (Boston, 1854), p. 26.

[56] Cf. p. 68, n. 38.

ities of matter" rather than as "material qualities."[57] From this point of view the question as to whether the vital force is to be conceived as a material agent or simply as a configurational quality of material complexes, loses much of its significance. It turns out to be a question of secondary importance, and its decision may well be left to the discretion of each individual thinker.

This may explain why most Romanticists treated the question of the materialization of forces with extreme nonchalance. Referring more in particular to the related problem of the agent of an *actio in distans,* Friedrich Hufeland, Christoph Wilhelm's brother, refused to discuss the detail of its possible materiality because "that would take him too far afield."[58] Ennemoser, who personally saw no need for the supposition of such an agent, stated even indifferently that "he would not object"[59] if others saw fit to believe in one. The romantic attitude seems to be that the mysterious cause of what we call dynamic effects will not be clarified in the least by a final decision regarding its material or immaterial nature. It is perhaps precisely this indifference which characterizes romantic thought in contrast to that of the preceding and following periods.

Here it may be important to note that modern science is aiming again at a quantitative interpretation of the phenomena of electricity and other related forces. Modern biology speaks again of a "substance of growth" (*Wuchsstoff*).[60] Together with hormones and other agencies discovered by modern gland research, these things must be interpreted from the viewpoint of the history of thought as quite akin to the older notions of heat matter, substance of electricity, to phlogiston and psychic matter,[61] to the eighteenth-

[57] Furthermore it may be suggested that Hufeland was a practitioner and in matters of thought, at best a popular philosopher not given to speculative niceties. His "materialism" is perhaps merely a cruder variation of Herder's synthetic "sensual supernaturalism." Cf. p. 68, n. 40.

[58] F. Hufeland, "Über Sympathie," p. 51.

[59] Joseph Ennemoser, "Beiträge zur Seelenkunde der Thiere," *Zeitschrift für psychische Ärzte,* III (1820f.), 85f.

[60] Cf., e.g., Hans Söding, "Wirkt der Wuchsstoff unspezifisch?", *Forschungen und Fortschritte,* XI (1935), 439f.

[61] Cf., e.g., G. H. Schubert, "Geschichte der Seele," p. 124, where an interpretation is given of Sir Humphry Davy's account of the appearance of a female guardian angel as published in *Consolations in Travel, or the last days of a Philosopher,* London, 1830.

century nervous liquid or Mesmer's universal fluid. If this is correct, then it may be stated that the materializing tendencies recede actually during the romantic era. They survive Romanticism, but they are not characteristic of it. A final illustration may help to substantiate this point.

The last decade of the Eighteenth Century saw a considerable number of essays and books published on various aspects of the vital force.[62] The best known among them is Reil's introductory essay in his physiological *Archiv* founded in 1795.[63] In the preface to the first volume of his new publication Reil presented an outline of the principles on the basis of which the enterprise was to be conducted. In it he gave at the same time in one sentence a summary of the essence of the following essay *On the Vital Force:*[64]

We must cease to consider the animal body as a mysterious and supersensual being and begin to class it, if we disregard the psychic phenomena,[65] as merely one physical object in the sequence of natural bodies which submits like iron or wood to the general laws of nature, but which, again like iron or wood, is characterized by its specific peculiarities.[66]

"The cause of all the phenomena observed in animal organisms," Reil further explains in the essay proper, "I shall seek in animal matter, either in the original difference of its elements or in their specific mixture and form." The concept of force Reil feels to be

[62] Some of them are listed by M. Neuburger, *Johann Christian Reil*, p. 51:
Ackermann, Jacob Fidelis, *Versuch einer physikalischen Darstellung der Lebenskräfte organischer Körper*, 2 vols., Frankfort-on-Main, 1797-1800; Brandis, Joachim Dietrich, *Versuch über die Lebenskraft*, Hannover, 1795; Hufeland, Christoph Wilhelm, *Ideen über Pathogenie und Einfluß der Lebenskraft auf Entstehung und Form der Krankheit*, Jena, 1795; Reil, Johann Christian, "Von der Lebenskraft"; etc. Cf. n. 63 below.

[63] Johann Christian Reil, 1758-1813, founded the *Archiv für die Physiologie* in 1795. He remained its editor until he died during the Wars of Liberation. For data on the periodical's later history, cf. "Bibliography." Volume I (Halle, 1795) opens with a program of eight points. The first is particularly significant: "Chemische Untersuchungen der Bestandteile und Mischungen organischer Körper. Wenn die Erscheinungen tierischer Körper, wie es höchst wahrscheinlich ist, Wirkungen ihrer Materie, und ihre besonderen Erscheinungen Resultate einer eigentümlichen und besonders gemischten Materie sind, so muß die Chemie, die uns mit der Materie und ihrer Mischung bekannt macht, vorzüglich den Weg zur rationellen Naturlehre der tierischen Körper bahnen."

[64] Johann Christian Reil, "Von der Lebenskraft," *Archiv für die Physiologie*, I (1795), 8-162. For later editions, cf. "Bibliography."

[65] Reil's word is *"Vorstellungen."*

[66] In the dedicatory preface addressed to Gren and Jacob.

dangerously lacking in conciseness, and he would prefer to replace it entirely by that of quality of matter. Organic matter can be called living matter (*Lebensstoff*), and its qualities, if one does not dare to get along without the idea of force, may be summarized in the construct of vital force. This is not anything added to matter from without, but simply a function of the specific organization of this specific kind of matter. In this respect vital force is quite analogous to gravity, cohesion and the like, which it is also no longer customary to interpret as independent potencies added from without to the matter characterized by them. A very clear parallel situation is to be found in crystals. The cause which precipitates salts in symmetric shapes is basically as far beyond the range of our understanding as the cause which has organic bodies grow in irregular but purposeful configurations. In both these cases, as in many other simpler as well as more complicated ones, we cannot, consequently, proceed beyond the conception of qualities of matter; and our further work will have to consist exclusively of attempts to determine more exactly in how far these qualities are those of the simpler elements or of the peculiar mixture and form in which they appear. That the qualities of a more involved configuration should be hostile to those of a simpler one is obviously absurd.

Reil states explicitly that the vital force, at least in the sense in which he uses the term, cannot possibly be interpreted as counteracting the laws of chemical affinities. How could a higher metamorphic manifestation of a given protophenomenon counteract an "earlier" one? Reil, to be sure, does not use the concept of metamorphosis in this connection; but it is almost impossible to eliminate it from the discussion if one observes how the various qualities of natural existences, organic or otherwise, are finally interlinked in a veritable hierarchy of nature. This begins with the crystallization of minerals, reaches the vegetative power of plants, the animal power of the next realm, and is crowned in the power of rational consciousness in mankind.[67] From the point of

[67] The foregoing summary deviates nowhere from the outline offered by M. Neuburger, *Johann Christian Reil*, pp. 22ff. Cf. also W. Olshausen, *Friedrich von Hardenberg*, pp. 30ff., whose analysis concludes rather unexpectedly that Reil's

view of the history of medicine Diepgen[68] summarizes that Reil thought of the vital force "not as something standing above matter but as something conditioned by material organization. He thus approached modern conceptions."

From the more general viewpoint of the history of thought it must be added that Reil's simple universal structure represents the frame into which it is possible to build the totality of the romantic view of the world. This world is one and is structured organically. Organic structure is that in which every organ is a metamorphic repetition of the whole or of any other organ. Metamorphosis is rhythmic transformation in the point or moment of rest in a polar tension. Polarity is the reality-producing tension between unrealities as poles. Vital force is the directing and energizing power that permeates all.

---

vital force was "ein Analogon zu Descartes' *esprits animaux* . . . zum Wärmestoff, zum Lichtstoff, zum Imponderabile der Elektrizität."

[68] P. Diepgen, *Deutsche Medizin vor hundert Jahren*, p. 37.

XI

MAN THE MEASURE OF ALL THINGS

THE ROMANTIC world of thought is a living chaos which prepares for a new systematic order.[1] It presents a multiplicity of aspects and includes a host of contradictory notions. Yet all its divergencies, its extravagances and absurdities seem somehow to be organized into a meaningful cosmos by one basic principle: the tendency to understand everything on the basis of the human soul.[2] Man is the child of the powers of light and earth[3] in whose

[1] L. Tieck. Cf. p. 5, n. 8.
[2] J. G. Herder. Cf. p. 109, n. 61.
[3] F. Hölderlin, "Der Mensch," II, 1ff.:

> Da auf der Inseln schönster, wo immerhin
> Den Hain in zarter Ruhe die Luft umfloß,
> Lag unter Trauben einst, nach lauer
> Nacht, in der dämmernden Morgenstunde
> Geboren, Mutter Erde! dein schönstes Kind;—
> Und auf zum Vater Helios sieht bekannt
> Der Knab.

In anticipation of a later discussion of poetic imagery (cf. chapter XII, "Physiognomics") we may emphasize the "realism" of Hölderlin's metaphors by contrasting them with a passage in which exactly the same material is presented in the form of mere figures of speech. Cf. Charlotte Albertine Ernestine von Stein-Kochberg, *Dido, Ein Trauerspiel in fünf Aufzügen* (1794), edited by H. Düntzer (Frankfort-on-Main, 1867), act IV, end of second scene, the hermit speaking:

> Erde, du meine Mutter! und
> du mein Vater, der Lufthauch!
> und du Feuer, mein Freund! du
> mein Verwandter, der Strom!
> und mein Bruder, der Himmel!—ich
> sag' euch allen mit Ehrfurcht,
> freundlichen Dank! Mit euch hab' ich
> hienieden gelebt,
> und gehe jetzt zur andern Welt,
> euch gerne verlassend.
> Lebt wohl, Brüder und Freund, Vater und
> Mutter, lebt wohl.

The Franciscan beauty of this passage vanishes as soon as it is asked why it is precisely the air that functions as father, etc. When death is alluded to, not as a return to nature but rather as a departure from her, this "poetry" is recognized as manufactured prose.

tension the world is pending.[4] God created man in His image,[5] so that the meaning of all of Creation should be pressed into his heart.[6] The world is but a slow realization of God,[7] yet man is God fully manifested.[8] The world is striving to be a macroanthropos,[9] a human being in infinite deployment.[10] It cannot explain the existence of man, but man's soul implies an explanation of the world of things.[11] We can know about the world because we are its equal;[12] we are the higher organ[13] through which the universe perceives; the mirror[14] in which the cosmos beholds its beauty; the flower[15] in which the world seeks fruition; or the temple in which God rules[16] and awaits His perfection. The laws of the world are the laws of the human soul,[17] and man alone is thus equipped to measure Creation.[18] The romantic chaos is ruled and ordered by the simple wisdom that man is the measure of all things.

[4] F. W. Schelling, e.g., *Weltseele*, p. 17: "Im Licht, so wie es von der Sonne ausströmt, scheint nur Eine Kraft zu herrschen, aber ohne Zweifel tritt es in der Nähe der Erde mit entgegengesetzten Materien zusammen, und bildet so . . . mit ihnen zugleich die *ersten Principien des allgemeinen Dualismus der Natur.*" Italics Schelling's.

[5] Johann Caspar Lavater, *Physiognomische Fragmente*, 4 vols. (Leipzig and Winterthur, 1775-1778), motto on the title page of vol. I: "Gott schuf den Menschen sich zum Bilde."

[6] J. G. Herder. Cf. p. 110, n. 67.

[7] L. Oken, "Naturphilosophie," p. 22; *Novalis Schriften*, III, 124: "Weltgeist . . . Weltseele . . . Die Welt ist noch nicht fertig."

[8] L. Oken; Cf. p. 94, n. 5.

[9] Hardenberg. Cf. p. 104, n. 43 and p. 116, n. 91.

[10] Cf. below; also K. Joël, *Der Ursprung der Naturphilosophie*, p. 34: "Oken faßt das ganze Tierreich als den in seine Bestandteile auseinandergelegten Menschen."

[11] F. v. Baader, *Werke*, XI, 72: ". . . daß der Mensch, was um ihn ist, durch sich und nicht sich durch das, was um ihn ist, erklären soll." Cf. also p. 114, n. 87.

[12] J. W. Ritter. Cf. p. 117, n. 96.

[13] *Novalis Schriften*, II, 350: "Der Mensch [ist] der höhere Sinn des Planeten."

[14] Karoline von Günderode. Cf. p. 112, n. 74.

[15] *Novalis Schriften*, II, 377: "Über die Natur . . . als einen Baum, woran wir die Blütenknospen sind."

[16] F. Hölderlin, "Hymne an die Menschheit," X, 8: "Zum Herrscher ist der Gott in uns geweiht"; XI, 8: "Und zur Vollendung geht die Menschheit ein."

[17] G. H. Schubert. Cf. p. 119, n. 102.

[18] L. Oken. Cf. C. G. Carus, *Lebenserinnerungen und Denkwürdigkeiten*, I, 72: "Ausgehend von dem Gesamtbegriff des einen und ganzen Organismus des Menschen, tat er—Oken—zuerst den orphischen Ausspruch: 'Der Mensch ist das Maß und der Messer der Schöpfung,' und gleichsam mit einem Schlage war so die ganze ungeheure und unermeßliche Mannigfaltigkeit der Welt gegenübergestellt dem *einen* menschlichen Organismus und seiner besonderen Geschichte."

This, to be sure, is old wine in new bottles. Yet, the Romanticists knew that the discovery of truth is always a recovery.[19] Whether new or renewed, there was bliss and relief in the knowledge, as Carus put it,[20] "that the movement of astral bodies, the revolution of planets and comets and moons, was as much a manifestation of a peculiar form of life as the metamorphosis of plants and the circulation of blood corpuscles in the humors of animals." What the experience of this conception of a "new" cosmic order, of the unity of all life, could mean to the sensitive was formulated by the same thinker in the following passage:[21]

No longer was it necessary—something which had always filled me with horror—that I should have to consider nature, and more especially the realm of animals, as an infinitely and aimlessly varied mass, for I had found the key to all these differences. I no longer had to limit myself to loving the body of Creation, for I had found its soul and was enthusiastic about it.

These passages from the memoirs of Carus refer to his experiences as a student in the first decade of the Nineteenth Century. They occur in a context which acknowledges his obligation to the inspired teaching of men like Schelling[22] and Oken. Carus, who was born in 1789, belonged thus to the last generation of Romanticists, to the heirs in whom Romanticism was to reach its fulfillment. This is the generation for whom the horrible thought that nature is "an infinitely and aimlessly varied mass" had lost its tragic power. It had been disproved in an heroic "intellectual war," waged in order that "sweet Science should reign."[23] In retrospect the course and scope of this romantic war can be surveyed in something like a sudden vision if, let us say, the Kant-

---

[19] A. Müller. Cf. p. 112, n. 78.

[20] Cf. Hans Kern, *Die Philosophie des Carl Gustav Carus* (Berlin, 1926), p. 27. This passage from Carus' memoirs occurs in a context which explains why he selected the theme *Specimen Biologiae generalis* for his first lecture as a *Privatdozent* in 1811.

[21] Cf. Sophie Gräfin von Arnim, *Carl Gustav Carus* (Dresden, 1930), p. 16.

[22] Cf. also the rôle which Schelling played in the development of Henrich Steffens. In *Was ich erlebte* (Breslau, 1840-1844), III, 338f., this thinker relates how Natural Philosophy saved him from shipwreck in an epistemological crisis. It is characteristic that Carus, who was sixteen years younger, does not seem to have experienced anything of the sort.

[23] William Blake. Cf. p. 22, n. 24.

experience of Kleist and Carus' early Schelling-cult are grasped together in a single thought. In 1801 Kleist wrote to his sister: "I am disgusted with everything we call knowledge."[24] Four years later Carus wrote about Schelling that "like a Christian God he could redeem from error all those who bore in their souls the spark of divine truth."[25] In these two statements despair and faith appear as different expressions of the same romantic quest for knowledge. The one led to "death," the other perhaps to "transfiguration."

The romantic quest for knowledge can be summarily defined as an endeavor to achieve, first, the comprehension of a universal order of metaphysical, not merely of pragmatic validity; second, in this order of things the determination of a place for man compatible with the faith in a human superiority of more than relative importance; third, together with this a substantiation of the belief in man's brotherhood and even identity with all of life and thus with all existence. This may be taken as the comprehensive program of all romantic thought. Ideas contributory to its elaboration have been expressed by most romantics in many vague or unconvincing ways. They did not, however, attain the fullest clarity of systematic formulation until after the middle of the Nineteenth Century. It was, characteristically, Carus, the representative of the last romantic generation, who functioned at the same time as the executor of the romantic heritage in a basically antiromantic age. In his works we find the clearest outline of the romantic conception of the order of things, the key to all the differences in nature.

[24] Heinrich von Kleist to his sister, letter of March 23, 1801: "Mich ekelt vor allem, was Wissen heißt."

[25] Carus to Schelling, letter of July 7, 1805, published from the MS by G. Stefansky, *Das hellenisch-deutsche Weltbild*, p. 126. The passage quoted occurs in a context of more general interest. Schelling's "granitoid" nature is beautifully characterized when Carus implores him not to crush his disciples as a *Jupiter tonans*, but to be for them what he was destined to be, a redeemer from error like a Christian God. Cf. also C. G. Carus, *Lebenserinnerungen und Denkwürdigkeiten*, I, 68ff., where he speaks of the "Prinzip einer höheren Einheit im Licht der damals zuerst sich geltend machenden Naturphilosophie" as having caused the concentration of his interests as a young student on various branches of the natural sciences. In the years 1804ff. Carus attended university lectures on chemistry, physics, botany, philosophy, zoölogy, geology, medicine, anatomy, mineralogy, psychology, mathematics, etc.

Carus, it must be emphasized again, offered no original contribution of basic importance. He was merely "the great harvester" of the romantic crop,[26] but this in so complete a sense that his achievements remain, nevertheless, admirable. As far as the present problem is concerned, he represents, as it were, the final link in a long series of earlier solutions. He was, to reinterpret an expression of Hardenberg,[27] "the ideal representative of the sum total of this entire series." His views may be traced "retrotensively"[28]—within the limits of this investigation—to Oken, Steffens, Schelling, Reil, to Herder, Robinet, and finally to Wieland.

In 1839 Oken lectured in Bologna *On the Philosophical Classification of the Three Realms of Nature*.[29] This lecture, as published in the following year, represents the most compact survey of Oken's ideas on the order of things. The entire conception looks as though it had been built on Friedrich Schlegel's definition of a classification "as a definition which contains a system of definitions."[30] The mammals, to give one illustration, are called the "sense family." They are subdivided according to the predominance of one or the other sense organ. All the sense families appear synthesized into one in the form of the next higher class, which is characterized by all the sense organs alike. This is the class of man. Below the mammals Oken arranges the nerve family, the bone family, the muscle family. All of these are summarized in the mammals or sense families, each one of which is equipped with a system of nerves, of bones, of muscles. The system of the several systems which are characteristic of a given family is thus deployed on the next level below in a corresponding num-

[26] This expression was coined by Eduard Erdmann, *Grundriß der Geschichte der Philosophie* (1869-70), II, 580 and 598. It was applied to Hegel, but it fits Carus even better.

[27] Cf. also p. 148, n. 52.

[28] This highly useful term has been introduced by A. O. Lovejoy, *The Great Chain of Being*, pp. 276f. Cf. also *id.*, "The Meanings of 'Emergence' and its Modes," *Journal of Philosophical Studies*, II (1927), pp. 167-181, especially p. 176. The "retrotensive method" depends, according to Lovejoy's definition, on "the rule that whatever is empirically found in or associated with the more complex and highly evolved natural entities must inferentially be read back into the simpler and earlier ones." Cf. also p. 214, n. 49.

[29] L. Oken, *Idee sulla classificazione filosofica dei tre regni della natura*, Milan, 1840.

[30] F. Schlegel, "Athenäums-Fragmente," 113.

ber of separate families, each one of which is characterized by one of those systems. In other words, the systems which are characteristic of a number of families on the same level are summarized into one system which is characteristic of a family on the next higher level. In this fashion Oken works his way through all the realms of nature, shaping them in perfect symmetry into a pyramid or cone of beings.

In 1801 Steffens published his *Contributions to an Inner Natural History of the Earth*.[31] This work is considered by Strich as an epitome of all of Steffens' ideas. It endeavors to reveal God's thought in nature and conceives of the order of things as a hierarchy of progressive individualization which reaches its climax in the free personality of man. For these thoughts Steffens was indebted to Schelling.[32] Schelling depended on Herder,[33] and Herder had been preceded by Robinet with his idea that nature made all her beings in gradual preparation for her human masterpiece,[34] and by Wieland with his conception of an uninterrupted palingenetic ascent.[35]

As far as the problem under discussion is concerned with an orderly conception of the "varied mass" of the animal realm, we find its systematic solution in Carus' outline of *Comparative Psychology* as published in 1866. The basic idea of this work is that the successive stages in the development of a human individual from conception to death are deployed in the animal realm, but only in the same sense in which all the stages in the development of a flower are represented in deployed form in other organs, leaves, buds, etc. of a vegetable individual. The successive stages of animal life can be illustrated by reference to a definite animal family and also by reference to a stage in the development of

---

[31] Henrich Steffens, *Beiträge zur inneren Naturgeschichte der Erde*, Freyburg, 1801. Cf. F. Strich, *Mythologie*, II, 146: "Das Werk, das Steffens in der Mythologie vorgebildet fand, ist seine innere Naturgeschichte der Erde. In ihm liegt das Grundthema seines ganzen Lebens: das Denken Gottes in der Natur zu enthüllen . . . Der Sinn der Erdbildung ist die von Stufe zu Stufe steigende Individualisation, die mit der freien Persönlichkeit ihren Gipfel erreicht."

[32] Cf. p. 76, n. 9.

[33] In this respect Herder's *Gott* and books IV and V of the *Ideen* are particularly important.

[34] Cf. p. 146, n. 45.

[35] Cf. p. 40, n. 29.

human individuals. On the lowest level Carus[36] speaks of a mere center of life which is ordered to an *animal vegetativa* or *animula*. In man this corresponds to the unconscious germ of a soul and in the animal realm to proto-organisms and the lowest organisms without specialized nerves. On the second level life is centralized in a first multiplicity of cells with the beginnings of organization and of a nervous system, ordered to an *anima reproductiva*, which corresponds in man to the unconscious soul of the embryo and in animals to the soul-like center of life in the higher oözoa (protozoa). The third level is ordered to an *anima sensitiva* and is characterized by a center of sensation and reaction, with a more independent organization of the whole, as also of the nervous system. This appears in man in the form of the unconscious soul of the newborn with its dawning consciousness; in animals in the unconscious soul of lower molluscs. The concept *psyche* begins to be applicable on this level, but here as also on the two following levels Carus tries to express the idea that we have to do with a psyche limited, on the whole, to indistinct sensations by describing it as a psyche "without wings." The fourth level, ordered to an *anima activa*, exhibits signs of a living soul; it reacts internally to dim sensations, especially to hunger and the sexual impulse, and externally to all sorts of physical stimuli. It is capable of specific reactions which are due to a nervous system with an imperfectly developed brain. In man this corresponds to the unconscious soul of the suckling and in animals to the dimly world-conscious soul of the higher molluscs, insects, and lower brain-equipped animals. The soul life of the fifth level is ordered to an *anima reflectiva* and characterized internally by more distinct sensations, as also by the ability to retain these sensations, externally by the reaction to stimuli and the ability to remember them. All of this can lead to specific activities, since the nervous system is generally concentrated in a brain. In man we have now the world-consciousness of the small child with the dawn of ego-consciousness; in animals the world-consciousness of the higher vertebrates. The sixth and last level leads to a thinking and ego-conscious soul, which manifests (*darleben, darbilden*)

---

[36] C. G. Carus, *Vergleichende Psychologie,* pp. 8ff.

itself in a still higher type of brain, with an initial disposition to god-consciousness. This level is ordered to the *anima cogitativa*, has its only representation in the *anima humano-divina*, and justifies the idea of a "winged psyche," characterized[37] by ego-conscious cognition, refined sensation, and freedom of will. The beauty of this soul has reached a level which is sharply delimited against the rest of the animal kingdom by an impassable barrier.[38] This is the climax of the entire system, which is here sharply delimited against all other biological systems of the later Nineteenth Century by an impassable barrier indeed.

Carus' views typify the peculiar romantic anthropocentrism, which is perhaps most fully described by the term *panenanthropism*. In it the world is not viewed from the narrow center of man's bodily sphere; on the contrary, man is forced to expand in it until the admission of his limitation to a subjective knowledge of himself coincides with the proud conviction of his being equipped to know the entire universe. Man conceives of all things as contemporary metamorphoses of the one protophenomenon, viz., existence, of which he himself is the all-repeating sum and synthesis. Yet, the highest essence of existence cannot manifest itself merely in another physical form, i.e., merely in the human body. It must manifest itself also in the awareness of what the structure of the whole is like. Thus it is seen that the very fact that man *can know* of his being the measure and crown of Creation must be at the same time the proof of the truth, human and natural (for the two coincide), of this knowledge of his. This is the impassable barrier which separates man from the animal realm, of which he remains nevertheless the fullest representation. It is also the impassable barrier which separates Carus from all forms of descendentalism.

Friedrich Schlegel remarked once:[39] "Man is a creative survey (*Rückblick*) which nature makes of her own self." Hardenberg,

---

[37] C. G. Carus, *Vergleichende Psychologie*, p. 18.

[38] It cannot be our task to write a critique of Carus' system from the point of view of the exact sciences concerned. Nevertheless, it seems safe to assert that the subjective bases from which Carus operated lay nearer to those of present-day tendencies than did the generally accepted theories of the later decades of the Nineteenth Century.

[39] F. Schlegel, "Ideen," 28.

for whom everything was "emanation and revelation of man,"[40] elevated the same idea to the level of sublime poetry in the simple phrase: "Nature wanted to participate in the enjoyment of her own great artistic beauty (*Künstlichkeit*), and therefore she assumed the shape of man."[41] These aphorisms are mottoes for which Carus wrote the book. They are, as Schlegel would have put it,[42] "the square and the root" of Carus' philosophy and illustrate again the peculiar rôle which this thinker played as the survivor and heir of Romanticism. Of this he was fully aware. His close affinity with the romantic mind is, furthermore, amply illustrated by the remarkable conciseness of his verdicts on romantic authors and works.[43] Nevertheless, on the whole it is Goethe whom he considered as having laid the foundations and begun the construction which he wished to further or to complete. It is quite natural then that he summarized one of his major works in a concluding quotation from Goethe. At the end of his *Physis,* which, together with the parallel *Psyche,* forms the substructure of his work on *Comparative Psychology,* Carus lifts the panenanthropism of his final generalizations into the sphere of poetic solemnity: "What is the good of all this display of suns and planets, moons, and stars, and milky ways, of comets, and nebulae, of worlds a-growing and of worlds complete, unless in the end a happy human enjoys his life in their midst?" This thought, al-

[40] *Novalis Schriften,* IV, 227. Letter of February 5, 1798, to Karoline Just.

[41] *Novalis Schriften,* I, 115. The traders in *Ofterdingen* are discussing the plausibility of the different arts. They find all of them represented in nature except poetry. They explain the parallel between music, painting, etc. and the corresponding aspects of nature by the passage quoted.

[42] F. Schlegel, "Kritische Fragmente," 8: "Eine gute Vorrede muß zugleich die Wurzel und das Quadrat ihres Buchs sein."

[43] Some of these have been compiled by Erwin Wäsche, *Carl Gustav Carus und die romantische Weltanschauung* (Cologne, 1933), p. 10. The best cover their subject in one brief sentence. Cf. e.g., *Lebenserinnerungen und Denkwürdigkeiten,* I, 317, on Hardenberg and his *Ofterdingen:* "Das ist ein Gemüt, welches in Welt und Menschheit sich abspiegelt." *Ibid.,* II, 303, referring to Bettina, Carus speaks of a "gewisse Überreife und Ostentation mit karikierter Natürlichkeit." *Ibid.,* II, 218: "Hoffmann scheint mir auch einer von denen, welche der Wirbelwind der Zeit schwindlig gemacht hat, und die sich, obwohl mit eminenten Anlagen, doch nicht fest auf den Füßen erhalten konnten." *Ibid.,* III, 109: "Es ist eigen, daß man bei Tieck [by whom Carus admitted to have been 'im allgemeinen stark angeregt'] immer einen gewissen festen Grund, einen Grund, wo in dem Dichter selbst ein wahres, seliges Vergnügen wohnt, vermissen muß."

ready referred to,[44] is then restated in the humbler prose of a scientific treatise:[45]

From all this we learn to understand that we can find a perfect justification of the world's strangeness and refinement and wisdom in the fact that the possibility emerges from them to grant our soul its noblest possession, its consciousness, its vision of self and universe.

Now, we have read all this before in Hardenberg or Baader, in Oken or Schubert. We have read it certainly in Ritter:[46]

The earth exists for the sake of man. The earth is but man's organ,[47] his physical body. The earth is man. A description of the earth in terms of chemistry, of physics, etc. becomes a description of man. The history of the earth is the history of man. The physiological pattern of the individual is the physiological pattern of the earth. The entire world must be found again in man as a world *en miniature*. His anatomy and that of the body of the earth and that of the universe as man are one.

Yet, there is a strange difference. Having read the passage from Ritter for the first time, one passes on and remembers perhaps one or another of his bold metaphors. If one returns to Ritter after having spent some time with Carus, one finds no metaphors at all. The passage is still beautiful, but it no longer owes its beauty to a free imagination but rather to a realistic longing which has neither words nor facts enough to make its aim quite clear. This clarity can be found in Carus, who teaches that the notion of man as a microcosm[48] and many other typically romantic metaphors are not at all intended as mere figures but rather as metaphors in a literal sense, as mutual vicariates of polar identities between which there exists an actual and verifiable sympathetic consensus as between the consensing organs of a living body.

[44] C. G. Carus, *Physis*, p. 475. Cf. p. 135, n. 34.

[45] C. G. Carus, *Physis*, pp. 476ff.

[46] Johann Wilhelm Ritter, *Fragmente aus dem Nachlaß eines jungen Physikers* (Heidelberg, 1816), No. 420 (Kluckhohn's counting).

[47] In anticipation of the contention that Ritter's "metaphors," as those of other Romanticists, were meant to be taken literally, it seems necessary to conclude that the phrase "the earth is man's organ" was to suggest a possible substitution of the round terrestrial globe for the human head with its similar form. This is, indeed, but a cruder repetition of what Ritter actually said. Cf. his letter to Schelling, of May 24, 1808, excerpted from MS by G. Stefansky, *Das hellenisch-deutsche Weltbild*, p. 130: "Ich . . . will . . . andeuten, daß die große Erde sich des Organismus annimmt, ihm Kopf und Gehirn wird, wo die 'kleine' ihm zerbricht."

[48] C. G. Carus, *Psyche*, p. 25.

Carus is, indeed, the most reliable guide through the maze of romantic naturalism. He is a fulfillment of the romantic prophecy in the sense in which Goethe spoke of organic growths as the fulfillment of prophecies which are later on recognized as having been no mere predictions but rather complete outlines of the entire solution.[49] Yet, the assertion that Carus was the "ideal representative" of Romanticism requires a qualification which, it is true, cannot be presented in factual terms susceptible of substantiation by quotations and dates. In reading one of the major works of Carus the student of German Romanticism is impressed by two observations. On the one hand, he feels perfectly at home here. He continues, it seems, to stay with Schelling, with Hardenberg, with Schlegel, or with Oken. On the other hand, there is something which it is hard to define directly but which forces the reader, again and again, to think of Goethe. There is in Carus the same classical *mâze,* the same faith in eternal standards and values[50] which is responsible for the common misnomer of Goethe as the "Olympian." To call it the expression of perfect mental equilibrium or simply the restfulness of one who has risen above the turmoil[51] to the quiet heights of Lynceus' tower, would be entirely wrong; it seems, nevertheless, to be at least the positing of Olympian restfulness as an ideal which is more than an idea, since its actuality is attested by a trust in the fate-given necessity of that which is and will be.

With reference to Carus it is thus possible to speak of a classical romanticism. This may simply mean that his thought impresses us nowhere as the product of speculative demands. His philosophy is not a structure rising above the world of realities in the hope that this latter might agree to support it since it would otherwise have to be forced into obedience and submission to duty. It is, rather, designed as the series of blue prints which the Creator did not deem worthy of preservation and which man, in his

---

[49] This idea of Goethe's is identical with that for which Professor Lovejoy introduced the term "retrotension." Cf. p. 208, n. 28.

[50] This phrase is suggested by Thomas Mann's bimonthly *Maß und Wert.*

[51] This phrase is suggested by Romain Rolland's war book *au-dessus de la Mêlée,* Paris, 1915. Goethe appears in it as an "Olympian" in the worst sense of the word.

natural curiosity, decided to retrace after the finished construction.

Of Schelling, Carus remarked once in his later years that nature had been for him a sort of wall covering in the living quarters of his mind.[52] In Carus' rooms, to use his own simile, there was no wall covering, for with him the identity of ideality and reality was no achievement of speculative ratiocination nor a jealously guarded fulfillment of previously frustrated wishes but the result of an unusual harmony between outer and inner, basic and educational experience. Carus knows nothing of the duality of physics and metaphysics. The schema[53] in which he proposes to organize the totality of human mental endeavors has its first principle in the polarity of form and substance. Both of these may then be viewed, first, in their aspects of ideality and secondly, in their aspects of reality. This dichotomy, as Carus insists, is, however, again a matter of merely methodological importance. His two works *Psyche* and *Physis* do not differ in their subject matter. It is not even correct to say that they complement each other as covering two different aspects or sides of one and the same nature. They differ merely in method and terminology. The phenomenal world is the manifestation of the ideal in the medium which Carus calls ether. The phenomenal world means reality, and therefore it is absurd to investigate the reality of idea or ether. Neither the

[52] Quoted by Bernoulli in Chr. Bernoulli and H. Kern, *Romantische Naturphilosophie*, p. XIII. Cf. also E. Cassirer's verdict, *Idee und Gestalt*, p. 70: "Schellings Begriff der Natur erweist sich bei schärferer Analyse als ein Zwitterding, als eine unhaltbare spekulative Mitte und Vermittelung zwischen der Goetheschen Intuition und den Forderungen einer rein theoretisch-begrifflichen Begründung und Ableitung."

[53] C. G. Carus, *Organon der Erkenntnis*, p. 320: ". . . ein folgerichtiges und übersichtliches System . . . von dem hier nur noch angedeutet werden darf, daß, wenn die formale Wahrheit und Wissenschaft sich notwendig gliedert in die Lehre von den abstrakten Verhältnissen der Realität nach Zahl und Form (Mathesis als Inbegriff der Arithmetik und Geometrie) und in die Lehre von den abstrakten Verhältnissen der Idealität (Logik), alles substantiale Wissen ebenfalls nach Realität und Idealität zerfallen wird in die Lehre von der Wesenheit des Realen (Physik im weitesten Sinne als Umfassen des Wissens von aller Natur, und zwar theils nach der Analyse in Chemie und Physik, theils naeh der Synthesis als Kosmologie, Geologie, Biologie und Geschichte aller uns bekannten Lebensformen, oder Naturgeschichte im weitesten Umfange) und endlich in die Lehre von der Wesenheit des Idealen und zwar theils wieder analytisch (Philosophie als Inbegriff des Wissens vom Geiste) oder synthetisch (als Anwendung der Philosophie auf Kunst und sämmtliche Lebensformen und Geschichte der Menschheit)."

one nor the other can be real. They belong together, and together they are neither the one nor the other but rather a something which we should have to call activated ether or realized idea if it were not for the fact that we can designate it by the more common synonymous terms *existence* and *life*.

The philosophy of Carus, in whom we recognize the classical executor of Romanticism, may thus be construed as a metaphysically valid system of philosophical physiognomics. The same, indeed, might again be said about all of romantic thought, but this in a sense which poses a series of new problems, and these it seems best to discuss in a new approach.

XII

PHYSIOGNOMICS

"BY THE ACT of parliament 17 George II. c. 5 (1743) all persons pretending to have skill in physiognomy were deemed rogues and vagabonds, and were liable to be publicly whipped, or sent to the house of correction until next session."[1] The sense in which it is possible to consider Carus and many other romantic thinkers as philosophical physiognomists is thus in need of careful qualification. To be sure, romantic physiognomics did not have to defend itself against the accusation that it was a superstitious system of divination. This immunity was one of the things it owed to the age of Enlightenment, which had sought to annihilate "physiognomy"[2] in that sense by branding it as roguery and vagabondage. An equally serious misconception, however, and one against which the romantic physiognomists had actually to defend their science, was a sort of rational causalism, doubtless inherited from the preceding century and hard to annihilate because it could not simply be branded as roguish vagabondism. This misconception has survived into the recent past and seems to have been definitely displaced only by the modern science of characterology. It is thus important to note that romantic physiognomics may have furnished the basis on which modern characterology has achieved its most signal success in that it overcame the old erroneous belief in the possibility of determining a parallelism between an immaterial reality called character, personality, soul, mind, etc., and the body as its medium of expression. "There is no parallel between characteristic and symptom," as Kaßner[3] puts it. "The basic idea of *rational* or *constructive* physiognomics is, to be sure, a parallelism of spirit and body, but *differential* or *rhythmic* physiognomics rejects it."

[1] *Encyclopaedia Britannica* (14th edition), unsigned article "Physiognomy."

[2] Cf. *OED*, s.v. "Physiognomy," I. 2. "The foretelling of destiny from the features and lines of the face . . ." The date of the most recent occurrence of the word in this sense is given as 1651.

[3] Rudolf Kaßner, *Die Grundlagen der Physiognomik* (Leipzig, 1922), p. 19.

The nonrational or noncausal conception of physiognomics can be described very simply yet fully as reflecting a modern re-evaluation of the concept of symbols. It is no longer adequate to define a symbol as "something that stands for, represents, or denotes something else, not by exact resemblance but by vague suggestion, or by some accidental or conventional relation."[4] A symbol must be more than such a useful device for vivid or aesthetic description. With Klages' method of "literal interpretation"[5] one succeeds here excellently. Through it the symbol becomes again that in which form and substance or, in Carus' terminology, idea and ether are "thrown together." This simple conception is nevertheless extremely rich in implications. It represents the basis of modern characterology as developed especially in the school of Ludwig Klages; it defines the whole of Carus' symbolically physiognomical philosophy; and lastly, a point of particular interest for our purposes, it penetrates deep into romantic symbology, that is, into romantic natural philosophy and thought in general. This has been correctly described by a disciple of Klages as "cosmic symbolism";[6] and Klages himself observed[7] that

romantic philosophy is entirely dominated, if not by the concept symbol, at least by the thing itself. The world is an infinite language of signs which are to be deciphered by speculative penetration. Observation does not so much concern the phenomena themselves as rather the physiognomy of things. One looks into their faces and asks what pulsation of life, what urge of formation and what evolution of the soul seem to be speaking there.

This is a very subtle observation. To make it need not be easy, but it is certainly easy to substantiate it by a host of data. There is, for instance, the fact that all of Eichendorff's poetry depends on the feeling that the world of things is asleep and that the magic of lyrical perception may cause it to reveal its meaning in song.

> Schläft ein Lied in allen Dingen,
> Die da träumen fort und fort,

[4] *OED*, s.v. "Symbol."
[5] "Wörtlichnehmen." Cf. Ludwig Klages, *Prinzipien der Charakterologie* (Leipzig: Johann Ambrosius Barth, 1921³), p. 31.
[6] Cf. Chr. Bernouilli and H. Kern, *Romantische Naturphilosophie*, p. XIX.
[7] L. Klages, *Prinzipien der Charakterologie*, p. 13.

Und die Welt hebt an zu singen,
Triffst du nur das Zauberwort.[8]

This, as Nadler[9] contends plausibly, is an idea which connects
Eichendorff with Hardenberg and thus with the essence of early
German Romanticism.

A peculiar interest attaches, however, to the genesis of this
romantic attitude, which can be developed out of its eighteenth-
century past in various ways. It seems necessary, as Strich[10] suggests, to see more than a coincidence in the fact that both Storm-
and-Stress and Romanticism were equally interested in the problems of physiognomics and of the origin of language. A combination of these two things seems, indeed, to be capable of explaining the peculiar expressionism which characterizes the Storm-
and-Stress as well as the romantic movement. A detailed study of
the romantic philosophies of language forces Eva Fiesel[11] to conclude that "the most decisive statement which can be made about
the romantic idea of language is that it is the idea of an inner
language. The word has for it a merely indicatory significance."
This conception of language in the conventional sense is, however,
really but one aspect of the more general notion that everything
is sign and symbol, that the whole world has "merely indicatory or
physiognomic significance." The whole world should be interpreted as a gigantic system of hieroglyphics, as the *language* of
God or the *book* of nature.

This notion seems to have developed during the latter part of
the Eighteenth Century. Hamann, Kant, Schiller, Hemsterhuis,
and others had it.[12] From Herder, Wackenroder, Hardenberg,
Schubert, Ritter, etc.[13] it moved forward. To Baader it came from
St. Martin,[14] establishing thus a connection with Böhme. Yet,

[8] J. v. Eichendorff, "Sängerleben," 48.
[9] Josef Nadler, *Eichendorffs Lyrik, ihre Technik und ihre Geschichte* (Prague, 1908), p. 231.
[10] F. Strich, *Klassik und Romantik*, p. 181.
[11] E. Fiesel, *Die Sprachphilosophie der deutschen Romantik*, p. 2.
[12] Cf. P. Kluckhohn, *Novalis Schriften*, I, 7.
[13] Cf. E. Wäsche, *Carus*, pp. 70ff.
[14] Cf. F. v. Baader, "Über den Einfluß der Zeichen der Gedanken auf deren
Erzeugung," *Werke*, II, 125-36. This essay follows Louis Claude de St. Martin,
*Essai relatif à la question proposée par l'institut: déterminer l'influence des signes
sur la formation des idées*, 1799.

whatever its actual transitions may have been, the important thing is to watch it grow from the earlier form, in which it speaks of a meaning hidden behind the phenomena of nature, to its maturity, when meaning and phenomenon become identical. Baader has reached this point with the suggestion[15] that nature is a language which we must again learn how to pronounce. This is important: not how to interpret or to translate but merely how to pronounce. Hardenberg, in a passage which shows also his deep understanding of the phenomenon "language" in the narrower sense, expresses the same idea when he tries to conceive of bodies and shapes as substantives, of forces as verbs. The science of nature would then represent the art of deciphering.[16] A more exact account of the form in which these thoughts were assimilated by Hardenberg leads again deep into the heart of his magic idealism. There is, for example, in the very first paragraph of the *Lehrlinge zu Sais*[17] a long list of phenomena which might be interpreted as sounds and symbols of nature's mute language. The meandering course of any one individual's earthly life would, indeed, be a strange letter in nature's alphabet. Yet, there are even stranger ones. There follows a passage which seems to refer to Chladni's recent sound figures (1787) and to Lichtenberg's somewhat older electric dust figures (1777); and these, too, are hieroglyphics in nature's complicated orthography. A little farther on[18] the reader of Hardenberg is led to a similar point by a new and quite unexpected approach. One of the apprentices talks about the art of thinking. If we concentrate on it, he suggests, we shall achieve strange and unforseeable associations. A special pleasure, however, consists in letting this play of thought associations proceed freely while the sense organs fulfill simultaneously and with equal freedom their duty of bringing in new impressions. If this is done with the skill of an expert, a most remarkable result will ensue. There will be a progressive clarification of thought, and parallel with it, a progressive clarification of the sense impressions. Yet, the two will seem to be functionally interdependent. The

[15] F. v. Baader, *Werke*, II, 129n. The passage is not found in St. Martin.
[16] *Novalis Schriften*, III, 170.
[17] *Novalis Schriften*, I, 11.
[18] *Novalis Schriften*, I, 30f.

free play of thought will be accompanied by a clearer understanding of the phenomenal world, and the unguided registration
of sense perceptions will be related to an increased fertility of
ratiocination. It is because of this parallelism that it is so important that we should learn more about the mechanism and the
laws of intellection, for it follows that if one understands but a
few of these laws, one will have deciphered some of nature's
symbols.

The power over the production of thoughts would then enable the
observer to produce thoughts of nature without a preceding and real
impression. He would be able to produce compositions of nature, and the
final goal [i.e., magic or divine creativeness in man] would be attained.

The simplest and therefore the most convincing later formulation of the idea that nature is a language and that man should
learn to speak it, occurs in the *Ofterdingen:*[19]

Language, said Heinrich, is really a small world in symbols and sounds.
As man masters it, so he would also like to master the greater world in
order to be able to express himself freely in it. It is this delight in
revealing within the world what is outside it, in the ability actually to do
what the original urge of our existence tells us to do, which marks the
origin of poetry.

When we "speak poetry," we pacify our creative urge by a surrogate. What we are really longing for is the ability to "speak
nature." That is the highest goal which any symbolic world view
can conceive. Basically, however, this is merely one peculiar
aspect of the general longing for redemption from the curse of individuation. If man understands nature, if he can speak her
language, and if by doing so he can even create her as God did
at the beginning of time, then he can no longer feel isolated and
excluded from the infinity of life around him. In a less poetic and
less exaggerated form this merely means that the psychic deter-
minant of the conception of a universal symbolism is the quest for
metaphysically valid truth, the quest for a form of knowledge
which transcends the limits of the individual.

This, it seems, is the deeper reason why times of growing individualism are always struggling for a scientifically satisfactory

[19] *Novalis Schriften,* I, 191.

conception of physiognomics. It is certainly no mere coincidence that Lessing, in this respect a contemporary of Lavater, was the first modern of whom a death mask was made for the express purpose of perpetuating in a spirit of reverence the physiognomy of the deceased,[20] that is, in a spirit of deeper understanding for the expressive value of individual form.

On the basis of these considerations it becomes obvious that Lavater's fragments of a physiognomic philosophy could not have been regarded as an adequate solution. Young Schiller wrote as early as 1780:[21] "A physiognomics of organisms is perhaps not impossible, but it will probably not appear in the near future, even though Lavater continues to rave through another ten quartos." The reason, however, why Lavater could not produce it lay in the fact that he, as Schiller put it, continued to conceive of "an intimate correspondence between our two natures" as the basis of all physiognomic investigations. This principle, with which Schiller, by the way, was in whole-hearted agreement, caused Lavater, as it were, to look for the meaning of physiognomic traits behind them instead of in them. Instead of a symbolistic conception of physiognomics, he developed a physiognomic system of allegories. Only nine years intervene but a whole world of theoretical readjustment lies between Lavater's fourth folio and Herder's brief, yet extremely significant observation of 1787[22] that "it would be possible to base on Spinoza's principles a science of physiognomics which could bring order into our physiognomical dreams and lead them back to a definite truth." At least some of the implications of this suggestion are alluded to in the preceding sentence, in which Herder points out that, "Spinoza considers the notion *body* as the essential form of the human soul, deriving therefrom conclusions as to the nature, changes, perfec-

---

[20] Cf. Georg Kolbe, "Zur Geschichte der Totenmaske," *Das ewige Antlitz,* edited by Ernst Benkard, Berlin: Frankfurter Verlags-Anstalt, 1926. The death mask in its modern form goes back to the early *cuatrocento.* At this time, however, a growing realistic trend saw in it merely a convenient help for the making of busts, portraits, and mainly effigies in wax or wood, which were used in the burial ceremonies in accordance with a much older tradition.

[21] Schiller, "Versuch über den Zusammenhang der tierischen Natur des Menschen mit seiner geistigen," §22.

[22] J. G. Herder, "Gott," *Sämmtliche Werke,* XVI, 549.

tion, and imperfections of that notion." Herder is here, as so often in other respects, the source of the text to which the Romanticists supplied but the sermon. Nevertheless, it is safe to assert that Herder could not have succeeded fully where Lavater failed, although, of course, he might have offered a few hints as to the right direction. For an actually scientific outline of at least the principles of physiognomics in the romantic, i.e., the symbolistic sense of the term, a wealth of biological data was needed which simply was not available at the time.

Nevertheless, one at least of the early Romanticists, August Wilhelm Schlegel, forecasts the direction in which the new science must proceed. In his Berlin *Lectures on Literature and Art,* after rejecting the rhapsodical "spook visions" of Lavater and the "crass materialism" of Gall, he calls attention to the existence of a science of physiognomics in works of art, particularly in the ancient sculptured figures of the gods. "This much is certain," he concludes, "that in a scientific treatment of physiognomics it is the general and not the particular which must be used as the basis of investigation, for the particular, when considered as primary, will always remain insoluble and irrational."[23]

It is customary to see in Carus' *Cosmo-Biological Letters* of 1841,[24] especially No. 7, and still more in his book *The Symbolism of the Human Figure*[25] of 1853, the earliest successful scientific

---

[23] A. W. Schlegel, *Vorlesungen über schöne Literatur und Kunst,* I, 78f.: "Man hat über die Physiognomik als Wissenschaft häufig gespottet, und bey der Art wie man es anfing, sie wissenschaftlich zu bearbeiten, sey es nun die rhapsodische Geisterseherei eines Lavater, oder der crasse Materialismus eines Gall, war dieß freilich leicht genug. Allein die Physiognomik ist nichtsdestoweniger vorhanden, nicht im Gebiete der Wissenschaft, sondern in der bildenden Kunst. Die großen Bildner und Mahler sind die Physiognomiker *par excellence,* und man kann sagen, daß in der Antike ein streng wissenschaftliches rationales System der Physiognomik aufgestellt ist, wovon die verschiedenen Götterideale als Kategorieen zu betrachten sind. Wieweit sich dieß nun aus der Anschauung in Begriffe würde übertragen und bis zum Individuellen herunterführen lassen, will ich hier nicht untersuchen. So viel ist gewiß, daß man bey einer wissenschaftlichen Behandlung der Physiognomik nicht vom Einzelnen sondern vom Allgemeinen ausgehen müßte, da das Individuelle, als das erste betrachtet immer unauflöslich und irrational bleibt." Cf. also J. Minor's introduction, pp. XLVf. for extracts of physiognomic interest from Schlegel's "Vorlesungen über Theorie und Geschichte der bildenden Künste," 1827.

[24] C. G. Carus, *Briefe über das Erdleben.*

[25] Carl Gustav Carus, *Symbolik der menschlichen Gestalt,* Leipzig, 1853. Ricarda Huch, *Ausbreitung und Verfall der Romantik,* p. 66, calls this book "ein meisterhaftes und das erste wissenschaftliche Werk über den Gegenstand."

presentation of a nondualistic, or as Kaßner calls it, a differential and rhythmic system of physiognomics. This is probably correct, if one thinks of more than an outline of the basic principles. In the present connection, however, only these basic principles are needed. In them the distinctive traits of symbolistic physiognomics may be expected to appear in clearer relief than in a fully developed theory. We therefore proceed with a somewhat detailed analysis of Aemilius Huschke's summary and systematic outline of romantic physiognomics as found in his *Mimic and Physiognomic Studies* of 1821. This book, which preceded Carus' corresponding publications by two and three decades respectively, is almost entirely unknown. Yet it is, as the following paragraphs will seek to show, a representative expression of the romantic mentality, and fully deserves to be rescued from the oblivion into which it seems to have fallen, for quite accidental reasons.[26]

In a preface Huschke presents a polemic clarification of his position with regard to that of his predecessors.

What Lavater," he says for instance, "and others contributed with great acumen and through many observations to the science of physiognomics, is excellent as far as it is empirical. What he [Lavater] failed to give, however, are the deeper reasons why this or that emotion or disposition

[26] It was written in Latin. As a result of it Huschke obtained the *venia legendi* at Jena. The first edition of 1821 remained, it seems, also the only one until a German translation was published in 1931. Both are quite rare. The present discussion of Huschke's ideas is based exclusively on the modern version, Aemilius Huschke, *Mimische und Physiognomische Studien,* translated from the Latin by Dr. med. Will Rink, "Der Körper als Ausdruck, Schriftenreihe zur Gestaltenkunde," edited by Theodor Lessing and Will Rink, vol. 2, Dresden: Madaus, 1931. For the use of his private copy of this book I wish to express my appreciation to Mr. Herbert Lindemann, Bremen.

Huschke's position is indirectly but fully identified by K. F. J. Sudhoff, *100 Jahre deutscher Naturforscherversammlungen,* p. 33, in an account of the Gotha meeting of 1851. Oken had died quite recently. "Seinem Freunde Huschke, dem Jenenser Physiologen, hatte man das Gedenkwort übertragen, als dem am tiefsten in Okens Denken Eingedrungenen. Er legte den Nachdruck auf Okens genetische Methode, die erst Leben, Zusammenhang und Fruchtbarkeit in die biologische Wissenschaft gebracht habe, zugleich in der Morphologie eine deutsche Wissenschaft als deutsches Eigentum schuf und der deutschen Sprache erst wahre Vollgeltung in der Naturwissenschaft verschaffte."

The position of Huschke's *Studien* is further identified by a note of the translator, W. Rink, introduction, p. 3: "Huschke fußt auf der Identität der Bildungsgesetze von Wirbel- und Kopfknochen, wie sie Goethe vermutete, Oken nachweisen konnte und Gegenbaur später weiter ausbaute in seiner Lehre von den Metameren." On Oken and Goethe, cf. p. 226, n. 29.

of character is expressed by a definite and always identical motion and
also through a definite and external form and shape (p. 13).

It should, however, be obvious that a *science* of physiognomics
must see its major problem in the formulation of the laws which
regulate such correlations. Yet, these laws cannot be based on
empirical statistics about physiognomical phenomena alone. In
addition to static observation we need a clearer understanding of
the formative process and of the peculiar characteristics of the
individual elements through which the various physiognomical
phenomena are produced. "The significance of individual traits
[as active elements in the formation of a total physiognomical
configuration] can be found only by comparison with the more
primitive movements of which they are repetitions on a higher
plane." That is, the physiognomic significance of any one trait,
be it a permanent structural quality of the skeleton or a passing
muscular activity, can be understood only on the basis of its
correspondence or co-ordination with the entire group of other
traits with which it forms a configuration and without which it
simply does not occur. In other words, mimic and physiognomic
phenomena are always configurational. The "selection" of the
individual elements which may enter into a given physiognomic
configuration follows definite laws. These must be known before it
is possible to discuss an individual trait as representative of the
group of traits with which it is organically and necessarily connected.

Up to the beginning of the present century," Huschke continues, "we
saw in the multiplicity of bones and muscles of the head only a crude
and ill-shaped mass. Lavater and others, to be sure, saw in them the
mirror of the soul and the royal road to it, but the imperfect physiology
of the time could not clear up the general darkness (p. 14).

At this point it is necessary to interrupt the discussion of
Huschke's ideas to investigate his suggestion that a more recent
development in physiology (referring to the first two decades of
the Nineteenth Century) had brought order into the "crude and
ill-shaped mass of bones and muscles" which make up the animal
organism. The ordering principle which Huschke has in mind
must be more than a principle of classification or description, for

the organically necessary co-ordination of physiognomic traits is to depend on it. It must be concerned with the grouping of organs and their parts according to their genetic affinity and is, in brief, the idea of the *organic consensus*.

Without implying an actual causal dependence in one way or the other, it seems best to define the concept of *consensus* as a special form of the idea of homologies. Homology as a biological concept means identity of type of structure. "If the vertebrates have an intermaxillary bone, man must have one too. Thus Goethe found it." Before the advent of descendentalism, organic homologies had meaning only under the principle of metamorphosis. Each animal had to be considered as a more or less varying repetition of the protoanimal. Oken stated this most dogmatically:[27] "The animal realm is only the dissected highest animal— man." The fact that this highest animal appeared in outline in all the others was not understood as meaning that it was the product of the others, but rather that all of them belonged together as variant metamorphoses of an identical protophenomenon. "The independent animals are but parts of that great animal which is the animal realm. The whole of this animal realm is but one animal, that is, the representation (*Darstellung*) of animality with all of its organs, of which each one is a whole."[28] Now, the basic principle of all organic thinking is that that which is true of the whole must also be true of each part, which in turn is also a whole.[29] If there are homologies in the "animal" which we call the animal realm, then there must also be homologies in each

---

[27] L. Oken, "Naturphilosophie." §216.

[28] L. Oken, "Naturphilosophie," §§214f.

[29] This is also the basis of Goethe's and Oken's vertebrae theory. On the importance of this theory for Huschke, cf. p. 224, n. 26, §3. Giovanni Malfatti, "Studien über Anarchie und Hierarchie des Wissens" (1845), in Chr. Bernoulli and H. Kern, *Romantische Naturphilosophie,* p. 230, asserts that Peter Frank was the first to consider "the vertebrae as repetitions of the brain [i.e., of the skull] on a smaller scale." This might suggest that it would be best to settle the priority controversy of Oken and Goethe, not in favor of Frank but of the *Zeitgeist*. Something like an "organic" contemporaneity of Oken's and Goethe's discoveries is also the solution offered by Rudolf Virchow, *Goethe als Naturforscher* (Berlin, 1861), p. 117. Virchow concludes first in favor of Goethe, but then he points out that "we know of no single fact which would prove that Oken got the idea from Goethe, while it is undoubtedly true that Oken was the first to develop it publicly and in a scientific form."

animal which is merely a member of the animal realm. Homologies within the individual relate apparently distant organs through genetic identity. This is called *"consensus."* It may be defined as ontogenetic homology.[30]

A few illustrations follow. They come from Huschke's teacher and friend Oken, who also seems to have been the first systematic investigator of the present problem. Brain and skin, for example, are genetically identical. The skin is consequently a peripheric brain and the brain a central skin.[31] Similar identities connect stomach and saliva glands, breast and uterus, iris and nose, saliva gland and testes, nose and diaphragm, and so forth. The deeper implications of these thoughts are compactly summarized in Oken's essay *On the Universe as a Continuation of the Sensory Organs* of 1808:

Consensing organs," Oken states,[32] "are necessarily independent phenomena, as, e.g., brain and skin. It would not be hard for a system of physiology to prove this, and it is admitted by anyone who sees in all individual organs but the graded (*stuffenverschieden*) repetition of the basic organs. He, however, for whom the organism is a conglomerate of alien components will never be able to see two organs as chalice and petals of one flower, and sympathy is a lost actuality for him. If one is not able to see in the stomach the brain, in the kidneys the lungs, in the nose the thorax, in the ear the entire trunk, in the sex organs the entire body, in the female sex organs the male organs, he will not feel what sympathy is. How much do you think you can explain by nerve connections? Nothing! Nothing at all!

The idea of consensing organs thus being clarified and, especially through the last quotation from Oken, being connected with a series of other romantic notions, we might return to Huschke's doctrine of physiognomics. It seems more profitable, however, to do so only on the basis of a further digression concerning a certain aspect of the problem of poetic imagery. This may seem to lead far afield, but it will enrich the ensuing dis-

---

[30] It seems, indeed, that Oken's *"consensus"* is identical with Owen's "serial homologies." Cf. Sir Richard Owen, *On the Archetypes and Homologies of the Vertebrate Skeleton,* London, 1848.

[31] Lorenz Oken, *Über das Universum als Fortsetzung des Sinnessystems* (Jena, 1808), pp. 5ff.

[32] L. Oken, *Über das Universum als Fortsetzung des Sinnessystems,* p. 7.

cussion considerably. George Eliot says in *The Mill on the Floss*
(II, 1) of the Reverend Mr. Stirling that "it was his favorite
metaphor that the classics and geometry constituted that culture of the mind which prepared it for the reception of any subse-
quent crop." This agricultural simile suggests to the novelist other
possibilities. "It is astonishing," she says, "what a different result
one gets by changing the metaphor. Once call the brain an intellectual stomach, and one's ingenious conception of the classics
and geometry as ploughs and harrows seems to settle nothing."[33]
It is a very remarkable fact that the vernacular is quite familiar
with the idea that the brain digests or assimilates intellectual food,
while phrases about the fertility or barrenness of the mind seem
to be purely literary. This suggests that the double illustration
from George Eliot represents possibly a deep and general contrast between metaphors in the literal sense of the word (i.e.,
metaphor) and pseudo-images. The latter are either historically
derived from realistic descriptions (to side with someone, etc.), or
they signify an actual (symbolic) identification intended and expressed by the unconscious wisdom of the living language.

These suggestions are made because it might be shown that
romantic imagery[34] tends unconsciously to be of the identity type.
When Hardenberg says, for instance, that the brain resembles
the testes,[35] he is doubtless in the midst of his magic idealism
and conceives of thinking as a procreative act. However, when
he asserts that the lung is our root,[36] he seems to be convinced
of the scientific verifiability of his equation. Boerhaave's statement[37] that an animal is a plant with roots in the form of a
stomach, had possibly no other meaning than that plants get their
food through roots, while animals absorb, not through the mouth

[33] Quoted from Henry Willis Wells, *Poetic Imagery* (New York, 1924), p. 12.
[34] This assertion is based on material from Hölderlin and Hardenberg.
[35] *Novalis Schriften*, III, 171.
[36] *Novalis Schriften*, III, 81.
[37] Hermann Boerhaave, *Elementa chemiae* (1732), I, 64: "Alimenta plantarum
radicibus externis, animalium internis, hauriuntur." Quoted by Kant, "Träume eines
Geistersehers," *Schriften*, II, 330. Kant's comment is strangely uninterested: "Vielleicht könnte ein anderer ebenso ungetadelt mit diesen Begriffen spielen und sagen:
Die Pflanze ist ein Thier, das seinen Magen in der Wurzel (äußerlich) hat." Such
"plays" with concepts and words were to become the serious concern of Kant's direct
successors. Cf. also p. 231, n. 41.

but through the stomach and intestinal walls. In the light of the conception of the entire animal realm as one animal, Boerhaave's thought assumes a much deeper significance. Hardenberg was conscious of such a deeper meaning, for the sentence just quoted is preceded by the remark: "We are children of the ether, while plants are children of the soil." This, in turn, is but a more poetic reiteration of the prosaic statement: "As we fertilize the soil of vegetation, so the plants fertilize the atmospheric soil," which is simply a fact. The excrements of plants are what we inhale. Now, and this leads back to Huschke, there are in Hardenberg a great many references to physical correspondences, sympathies, identities which depend, it is true, on nothing but accidental resemblance of structure but which prove clearly the poet's awareness of something which assumed later on an absolute clarity in the scientific concept of organic *consensus*.

In this fashion Hardenberg, parallels, e.g., the eye and the mouth.[38] The lashes become the lips. The pupil is the tongue, a consequence which must have delighted the poet who was so fond of the language of the eyes. The iris is the throat. Finally even the adjacencies must correspond. The nose is the forehead of the mouth, and the forehead is the nose of the eyes, while the cheekbones are the chin of the eyes and *vice versa*. None of these last correspondences is valid from the point of view of genetic anatomy. That is, we suggest, why they are also poetically quite useless. The poetic appeal of the identification of tongue and eye is an exception. It depends exclusively on an idiomatic coincidence. We are wont to call all expression, thus also that of the eyes, a language, but we could not possibly say "I glance my tongue" for "I address quickly" as a "metaphoric" development from "I glance my eyes."[38a]

Hardenberg's examples are at least negatively valuable. If it were a physiognomic fact that the lids (Hardenberg's lashes are a *pars pro toto*) close when the lips do, we should be struck by the poetic truth of their identification. Our next endeavor would then

[38] *Novalis Schriften,* III, 109.

[38a] This latter phrase, now rare, occurs in Jane Austin, *Pride and Prejudice,* chapter XVIII, and in Nathaniel Hawthorne, *The House of the Seven Gables,* also chapter XVIII.

have to be to prove their identity from the point of view of genetic anatomy. Then only could one feel that the physiognomic "coincidence" had been reduced to an inner significance. If, on the other hand, and this is Huschke again, the major purpose is to lay the foundations of a scientific system of physiognomics, the procedure must be reversed. It is only in genetic anatomy that the basic, that is, the most general laws of physiognomics can be visualized. The first and more important part of Huschke's book is, consequently, anatomical.

We may now proceed with an analysis of this section of the work. The statement, "life is polar tension" may be extra-empirical. Its organic consequence, "the law of polarity is evident in all phenomena of life (§1)," is empirically verifiable. The pertinent data support the principle in which they have their extra-empirical roots, and this principle, in renewed contact with the world of realities, becomes an axiom of all biotic science. "In observing the simplest form of muscular polarity in the digestive organs and blood vessels, one finds linear and circular fibers (sphincters) (§2)." They work in a mutual antagonism, which is particularly clear in the muscular mechanism of the anus, etc. This antagonism Huschke proceeds to show in the origin (genetic descent) and growth of individual muscles (§§3f.). It is recognized as the fundamental principle of ontogenesis. The total development of a given individual is dominated by the tendency to progress from preparatory contractions through various stages of increasingly pronounced expansion.[39]

This principle has also phylogenetic validity. No attempt is made to justify the parallelization of onto- and phylogenesis. The basic law of biogenetics is apparently not felt to be in need of further substantiation. It is accepted as a matter of course. This may be illustrated by a phrase which Huschke uses in the discussion of a certain membrane in the organ of sight. "This membrane," he says (§5), "appears in the embryo of man and the

---

[39] The alternation of expansion and contraction as the principle dominating the ontogenetic development had been applied to plants by Goethe in his essay on the metamorphosis of plants. The vertebrae theory (cf. p. 224, n. 26, and p. 226, n. 29) was a zoölogical adaptation of the thoughts of this essay.

mammals only at the exact moment when the rest of the organism is also passing from the state of birds to the level of mammals." The phylogenetic interpretation of Huschke's basic principle organizes the hierarchy of species according to the degree of relative predominance of expansion over contraction. "We can say that the degree of stretching (extension) of the limbs of a given animal is an indication of the relative height of its development (§6)." Man with his upright gait shows the highest degree of expansion.[40]

On the other hand, there are many animals of a lower order whose head and oral extremity are turned toward the earth but whose anus and genitals look upward (cephalopodes, many testaceae, some medusae, etc.). Their attitude must probably be considered as the lowest possible. It is diametrically opposed to the maximum of extension in the attitude of man and leads backward, perhaps, to the attitude of plants. The root might correspond to the mouth of animals if one thinks of it as lowered into water and soil.[41] Leaves and blossoms could be compared to the branchiae and genitals with their nearness to the anus. This would then lead to the statement that the height of organic development in man reaches an attitude directly opposed to that of plants and lower animals (§6).

The remaining paragraphs of Huschke's anatomical section are devoted to a further exemplification of these basic ideas by reference to factors of special mimic and physiognomic importance. They are the breathing apparatus (§7) and the head as the crowning and all-inclusive repetition of the entire body (§8). The jaw and its muscular mechanism on the one hand (§9), and skull and face in their interrelation on the other (§10), complete the survey.

The second half of Huschke's book is the physiological section. In it the anatomically derived principles are applied (1) to mimics and (2) to physiognomics. The aim is to reduce the empirical findings of earlier students of characterological problems to general physiological laws. "The observations of a Lavater," Huschke remarks in an aside (§11), "cannot be used as a founda-

---

[40] " 'Anthropos' means 'one who looks up.' " Translator's note in the German edition.

[41] This is what Kant called playing with concepts. Cf. p. 228, n. 37.

tion, because this author indulges too often in general enthusiasm and because he presents isolated sketches rather than regular dependences." The first mimically significant consequence of part I is that "any sort of harmony between two muscles of head or trunk in the manifestation of an emotional state depends on the homogeneity (*Artgleichheit*) of these muscles (§12)." As for the identity of structure in the emotional field and in that of muscular dynamics,[42] we may describe it as a "harmony between soul and muscular system." This expression, however, remains totally devoid of meaning unless we specify that soul and muscles are united in "an identity of direction and of type of movement." At this point Huschke reminds us (§14) of the polar basis of all organic existence:

There are two polar kinds of movement, one turned outward, the expansive kind, and another turned inward toward the individual, the contractile kind. Expansion of the soul, i.e., its direction outward, will consequently activate the extensors, while contraction of the soul, i.e., its turning inward, must correspond to an activity of the flexors. Expansive affects are thus ordered to an activity of the extensors and of their modifications (or consensing partners), while contracting affects belong to the flexors. The muscular system works in agreement with the emotional state. Bodily movements which occur under emotional stress are merely muscular remanifestations of affects.

All of this, which concerns only a qualitative interdependence of emotion and muscular activity, should be made more specific in the form of exact quantitative analyses. These will have to be undertaken by future physiognomists (§15). Various illustrations of the identity of muscular and emotional movement are given under the headings of "fear and hope" (§§16f.), "stupor, fright, curiosity" (§18), "timidity and reverence" (§19), "anger" (§20), "joy" (§21), and finally "sadness" (§22). Fear "may correctly be called the bending movement of the body." It occurs in a great many affects, especially those with pronounced displeasure. "It paralyzes the reasoning power and the free will as correspondingly also the entire muscular system. It presents to the penetrating outside world a broken and shaken organism." Hope, on the other hand, is called by Huschke a "widening of the soul, and the

[42] These terms are not Huschke's.

stretching factors in the muscular system must therefore correspond to it."

These very simple considerations lead now to an extremely important conclusion, which might and should have caused a basic reorientation of all characterological research. "It is possible," Huschke finds (§21), "that two different affects coincide with regard to their form of movement in one or the other respect, and this simply because they observe the same direction." Illustrations of such identities follow. The teeth are exposed in extreme anger as well as in fits of laughter or in sexual excitement. The eyes have the same rigid expression in a snake which is ready to attack as in a man when his fright or his hope has reached a very high pitch. All of this means that the language of physiognomics is highly synthetic. An itemized dictionary of it cannot exist since each one of its expressions, representing in and by itself only a direction, can formulate a definite meaning only together with all the other components of the entire configuration. Furthermore, the individual expression is not in the configuration what it is in an isolated state, for each such expression is at the same time a function of all the others. There is no specificity of physiognomic traits.

In this connection it is interesting to note that Lavater too had been vaguely aware of the insufficiency of his method of an itemized parallelization of physical and psychical traits. The reason why he failed to advance beyond the limits of a mechanical dictionary method was fundamentally that this rational method constituted, despite his qualifications of it, his physiognomic ideal. His dissatisfaction with some of its implications had not resulted from an understanding of its unorganic nature but rather from a Christian abhorrence of its apparent determinism. Again and again Lavater felt the urge to console parents and educators of physiognomic monstrosities, assuring them that it was possible to reorganize these monstrosities into models of beauty in soul and body without violating the basic law according to which all the individual elements of the physiognomic whole could vary but could not be eradicated.[43] Nevertheless, Lavater stuck to his

---

[43] J. C. Lavater, *Physiognomische Fragmente*, II, 149f.: "Dieselbe Kraft kann wie

ideal of specificity of physiognomic traits.[44] The wildest product of this tendency of his is probably the royal curve which he thought it possible to find in the profile of the queen in a beehive.[45] His suggestion that the poor queen would have to be shaven, together with the statement that the dryness of the bedbug reveals clearly how utterly incapable this beast is of love and of being loved,[46] seems to have contributed more to bringing his whole work into disrepute than any of its basic weaknesses.

These, however, were not overlooked by contemporary critics. It is interesting to find an explicit reference to Lavater's misconception of a physiognomic parallelism in the rather distasteful conglomeration of relevant and irrelevant attacks of Musäus' *Physiognomic Journeys* of 1778 to 1779. Says Sempronius in one of the rare moments of sanity granted him by Musäus:[47]

The first axiom which I have found on my travels, was that this whole business of the specificity of meaning of individual traits of the face is empty straw. All the individual parts of a face are to be taken like individual sounds. Only the harmony of several makes a chord of which it can be said whether it is minor or major.

One and the same sound, this means, can occur in a multiplicity of chords, major as well as minor. Or in Huschke's more direct terms, one physiognomically relevant movement or trait can occur as the expression of a multiplicity of affects.

Lavater's and Huschke's positions and also the importance of the transition from the one to the other can be more fully ap-

---

derselbe Reichthum zum Nutzen oder Schaden der menschlichen Gesellschaft angewandt werden. Mit demselben Reichthum kann einer ein Heiliger, oder ein Teufel werden." Cf. also *ibid.*, II, 146, 196, and *passim*.

[44] It must be admitted that these brief remarks cannot do justice to Lavater. The problems which he poses are much more involved than seems to be generally recognized. As early as 1772 he spoke in his essay *Von der Physiognomik* about the *Zusammenschicklichkeit* of the elements in an organic whole. If this meant *Gestalt*, and it can hardly have meant anything else, it is difficult to understand why Lavater failed to advance beyond this promising start toward a configurational or organic conception of physiognomics.

[45] J. C. Lavater, *Physiognomische Fragmente*, IV, 4. There follows a passage which refers to the curve of the profile of ordinary bees. This is a curve, "aus der sich vielleicht eine Grundlinie zur allgemeinen Physiognomik abstrahieren ließe."

[46] J. C. Lavater, *Physiognomische Fragmente*, III, 82.

[47] Johann Karl August Musäus, *Physiognomische Reisen*, 2 vols. (Altenburg, 1778-1779), part IV, pp. 40f.

preciated in the light of a few brief allusions to later stages in
the development of our problem. The idea that physiognomic
traits are specific is a variation of the idea of the localization of
psychic centers. The basic weakness of Lavater's approach to
physiognomics is thus identical with the basic weakness of the
ideas of his and Brown's and Mesmer's mental contemporary Gall.
It is no longer customary to ridicule Gall's phrenology as a sad
proof of the fact that the Germans after about eighteen hundred
"buried their genius"[48] and that German Romanticism excelled in
taking seriously all sorts of absurd quackery. We understand
clearly that Gall was neither characteristic of, nor a product of,
German Romanticism. Carus' critique of Gall's methods in one
sentence shows very clearly what the romantic approach to
phrenology would have been. Gall, says Carus,[49]

made the enormous mistake of stating that some special activity (*Aufre-
gung*) in the brain and the corresponding elevation of the skull were
actually the seat, or—as he put it—the organ of such and such a mental
tendency. This idea was no better founded than if the physiognomist
were to conclude, because a nose of such and such a shape occurs
generally with witty individuals, that it must be the organ of wit.

The exact sciences began promptly to ridicule Gall's ideas as a
typically romantic extravagance. They continued, nevertheless, to
proceed along the same lines without, to be sure, repeating the
mistake of seeing in them a "romantic" pattern, yet also without
recognizing them as a sort of posthumous product of the Eighteenth Century.[50]

The earliest scientific data in support of the doctrine of psychic
localization are generally credited to Jean Bouillaud, who observed

[48] Frank Woodyer Stokoe, *German Influence in the English Romantic Period
1788-1818* (Cambridge, Engl., 1926), p. 14, William Taylor to Robert Southey, letter
of April, 1800: "Dr. Reere is here, fresh from Germany . . . The Germans have
buried all their genius . . . Good sense has not thriven; physical and metaphysical
quacks have usurped the thrones of reputation. Dr. Gall and Fichte are more talked
of than Soemmering and Martens."

[49] C. G. Carus, *Physis*, p. 207.

[50] The first investigations of the breathing center had actually been undertaken
by Anne Charles Lorry in 1760. Professor Gustav Retzius stated at the "International
Congress of Anatomists" in Heidelberg in 1903 that Swedenborg was the discoverer
of the principle of localization of faculties in the brain. This fact had been brought
to his attention by Max Neuburger. Cf. George Trobridge, *Swedenborg, Life and
Teaching* (New York, 1936), p. 275. First edition, London, 1907.

in 1825 that speech disturbances due to strokes were always paralleled by definite changes in a definite spot near the island of Reil. Marie Jean Pierre Flourens, whose studies in this field go back to 1823, demonstrated through extirpation of the labyrinth in doves the importance of this organ for motor co-ordination, and in 1828 he recognized the cerebellum as the corresponding center. The famous discovery which this scientist made in 1836 of the *medulla oblongata* as the vital knot (*noeud vital*) remained for a long time the irrefutable proof of the validity of the doctrine of localization.[51] The details of the later development of this doctrine from theory to generally accepted fact are of no consequence for the present discussion. For more than a century the sciences concerned assembled abundant material in its support. Yet all these admirable and productive discoveries were finally recognized as necessary preparations for the modern refutation of the ideas which they seemed to have established as definite truths. The transplantation of "specific" brain centers, as carried out in more recent times, has added to our knowledge of specificity that of an extreme adaptability of brain and spinal cord which, as Giersberg formulates it,[52] "we consider no longer as a rigid mechanism but as a representation of the totality of the organism whose changing needs it has to serve." Whatever the peculiar phenomena underlying this last formulation may be, the dynamics of thought which is characteristic of their interpretation must be recognized as akin to the organology of a Huschke and his romantic contemporaries. Similar observations can be made with respect to a great many branches of modern science. *Gestalt* psychology, field theory, functional and configurational approaches tend all in the same direction. The basic principle of modern physiognomics, as quoted above[53] in Kaßner's formulation, that there can be no parallel between character trait and physiological characteristic, is also but one of the symptoms which seem to signify that we are about to reach the position which "the romantic intermezzo" had already attained.

[51] A. Ch. Lorry (cf. note 50 above) and Julien J. C. Legallois, 1812, had paved the way for Flourens' discovery.

[52] Hermann Giersberg, "Gehirnverpflanzungen bei Amphibien," *Forschungen und Fortschritte*, XII (1936), 326f.

[53] Cf. p. 217, n. 3.

Such seems to be the deeper significance of Huschke's short reference to the fact that identical traits can represent opposite emotions. It was through a comparison with Lavater that the remarkable maturity of Huschke's thought became apparent. Exactly the same procedure should be followed with regard to Huschke's ideas concerning the other crucial problem of physiognomics, i.e., the relation between its two major subdivisions, between mimics and physiognomics in the narrower sense. The plan of Lavater's work did not provide for a methodical differentiation between these two branches of his science, but the problem as such could not escape his attention. "Traits which are often repeated," he wrote in a typical passage,[54] "positions which are often assumed, frequent transformations of features, produce finally a permanent impression on the soft parts of the face and in early childhood even on the bones." Huschke passes from mimics into physiognomics (§23) by stating that "the form of the body follows the same laws as its movements. A variable process has now become stable." As for the causes of this stabilization, it is interesting to note that Huschke does not reject Lavater's suggestion; he merely finds it incomplete. "The fixated forms," Huschke says, "have their cause not exclusively in permanently repeated movements, as most writers on the subject maintain, but they are also a crystallization and formation of inner life." This sounds rather vague, but it suggests at least that the basic problems of genetic physiognomics coincide with those of embryology. It leaves the mysteries of characterology where they belong, viz., in the problem of an inherited predetermination of the final goal of organic growth. Thus Huschke feels obliged to admit (§27) that "nothing more definite can possibly be said until the relation between psychic state and bodily functions has been investigated in a number of lower organisms." This is a task of comparative psychology in the sense in which it was to be treated by Carus.

On the basis of his general laws Huschke proceeds, nevertheless, to present a somewhat more detailed analysis of the significance of different skull forms (§24), of the curve of the

---

[54] J. C. Lavater, *Physiognomische Fragmente*, I, 62.

vertebral column (§25), of noses (§§26f.), eyes (§28), and of jaws and lips (§29). The common factor in all these discussions is again a clear rejection of the principle of individual specificities. Positively, there is again a general preoccupation with the dynamism (tendency, direction) of traits and physiognomic configurations.

An eye," Huschke says for instance, "which is deeply hidden in the orb and characterized by a narrow opening of the lids, can just as well be filled with fear and perfidy as animated by reverence and modesty, for these four affects coincide in the premise of an identical direction.

Such are the conditions," Huschke concludes (§30), "according to which the general antagonism of movements, recurring everywhere in new modulations, corresponds in a consistently equal and homologous fashion to the brain and its functions. The only possible further development of mimics and physiognomics as a science rests on this law as a foundation. The mere observer may continue to look for harmonies between definite organs and emotional powers, but it will be the task of the physiologist to investigate the character of this special interrelation on the basis of the degree of affinity and of the repetition of the functions of the body in the brain. The cause for such special correspondences will not become evident until comparative physiology has been studied more fully.

Huschke's conception of the science of physiognomics is a dynamic conception. It speaks of tendencies and movements and never of static representation. It is a genetic conception, inasmuch as it interprets the physiological origin of characteristic tendencies and movements as variations of others in co-ordination (*consensus*) with which they are bound to occur. Huschke does not aim at a parallelistic interpretation of physiognomic traits; he tries to determine their symbolic significance. Their meaning is not what they hide, but what they are. This, in fine, is the reason why Aemilius Huschke's *Mimic and Physiognomic Studies* are a significant expression of the symbolistic world view of the romantic era.

Now it may be suggested that romantic symbolism, taken in this sense, coincides with that romantic mythicism which strove for a rebirth of art and science, of thought and life in the spirit of a cosmic religion to be expressed in a new mythology,[55] the

---

[55] This phraseology is adapted from Ernst Michel, *Der Weg zum Mythos. Zur Wiedergeburt der Kunst aus dem Geiste der Religion,* Jena, 1919.

myth of modern times. Indeed, there is no better definition of what
we mean by mythology, new or old, than to call it a system of
universal physiognomics. Myths achieve a tangible conception
of the intangible essence of living nature,[56] just as physiognomics
endeavors to visualize life in its physical representation. The following passage from Ennemoser (1820)[57] occurs in a chapter
entitled "Physiognomic Observations," but it will be agreed that
it could serve as well as the basis for a philosophical treatise on
mythology.

There is nothing in all of nature," Ennemoser wrote one year prior
to the publication of Huschke's *Studies,* "which does not reveal an
active, spiritual or inner life through and in its physical external
existence. Every natural being expresses by virtue of its personality
(individuality) the permanent qualities of an unique spirituality. There
is, consequently, [Ennemoser does not say a mythology but] a physiognomics of all of nature. There is, e.g., a physiognomics of the mineral
realm, for here, too, we have succeeded in finding certain laws for
definite relations in crystals, and we know about certain specific forces
which manifest themselves in characteristic shapes and colors. There
is a physiognomics of plants. Here it is an old doctrine that all those
plants which agree in form and kind (*Geschlecht*) must also agree in
their virtues (plantae quae genere conveniunt, etiam virtute conveniunt,
says Linné in his *Philosophia Botanica,* and Bapt. Porta in his *Physiognomics,* tali formae, tales vires conveniunt). Finally there is a
physiognomics of animals. Into this we can penetrate more deeply
because of its proximity to that of human nature. In animals we understand the harmony of the internal and external more readily than in the
quiet stationary plant, and a still greater darkness will doubtless continue to cover the physiognomic harmony in minerals.

[56] Cf., e.g., Oswald Spengler, *Der Untergang des Abendlandes,* II (Munich, 1930[54]),
354: "Wir wissen heute gar nicht mehr, was ein Mythus ist, nämlich nicht ein
ästhetisch bequemes Sichvorstellen, sondern ein Stück leibhaftigster Wirklichkeit . . ."
[57] J. Ennemoser, "Beiträge zur Seelenkunde der Tiere," pp. 56f.

XIII

COSMIC POETRY: THE QUEST
FOR A MODERN MYTHOS

"WHY IS IT," HERDER ASKED in 1801,[1] "that none of the modern philosophic systems has been given a poetic presentation on which time could place the seal of perfection and of unsurpassable beauty, as it did in the case of Lucretius?" The reason why there is no modern epic of Lucretian merits cannot be sought in the inefficiency of our poets. It must rather be found in the imperfection of our philosophies, for if a philosophic system is complete and thus capable of satisfying the most secret needs of man's rational urge to know, its presentation becomes automatically poetic. "A strong and pure expression (*Aussprache*) of truth is by its very nature poetry. A philosophic system is a poem if it is consistent in itself, complete and pure." These reflections suggested themselves to Herder in the course of a critical review of Cardinal Polignac's *Anti-Lucretius* of 1747. "All the wealth of modern discoveries," Herder concluded, "the entire philosophy of Descartes, of Kepler, of Newton and others with which the Cardinal's poem is equipped" do not change the fact that it is "on the whole merely a beautiful harangue in Latin verse." *Mutatis mutandis,* Herder could have applied this verdict as well to all the other Lucretian attempts of his age.

The first work of this category which comes to mind in this connection is, naturally, Wieland's poem *On the Nature of Things.*[2] This is a poetic representation of a universal system. The philosophy which it depicts is cosmic in scope, and the poem itself is characterized by its ambition to be accepted as a *Christian Lucretius.* Yet, if one looks at it as a whole, one must conclude that it is after all "merely a beautiful harangue in smooth alexandrines." This proves according to Herder's reasoning that the philosophy of Wieland's poem was not consistent in itself and

---

[1] J. G. Herder, "Früchte aus den sogenannten goldenen Zeiten," chapter IV, *Sämmtliche Werke,* XXIII, 243f.
[2] Cf. chapter III, "The New Lucretius."

not complete and pure. The universal order which it reflects was "merely made,"[3] not "known" in a deeper sense. Consequently it was not possible "to delight in knowing about this order and to live safely within it."[4] It is true, Wieland's personal failure we did not find hard to explain. He was very young when he wrote his poem; his knowledge of the sciences was incomplete; and he tried to veil the weak spots in his work by a certain insincere pathos.

Yet, all this does not answer Herder's question why modern philosophy, i.e., modern science, did not inspire any other poet to create the perfect epic which might deserve to be called a "modern Lucretius." Today we know, what Herder as a contemporary could not know, that there was in the later Eighteenth Century a noteworthy trend of didactic poetry which saw its goal, as it were, in the production of a poetic complement to Le Sage's scientific *Newtonian Lucretius*. It exhausted itself, however, in the creation of mere fragments, which at the time did not reach the attention of the general public. On the whole we may thus speak of a failure of Lucretian didacticism in the Eighteenth Century. This, it seems, is as characteristic as the fact that the trend manifested itself particularly in French letters.[5] Both these assertions can be elucidated by a brief discussion of André Chénier's magnificent torso *Hermès,* which is to be considered as the most important *De rerum natura*[6] of the age preceding the French Revolution. Upon this background the Lucretian problem, as understood in contemporary German letters, will then appear in sharply contrasting relief.

The plan of Chénier's poem[7] provided for three major sections. The first two are represented by notes and scattered metrical lines. In addition to these only a somewhat longer fragment, apparently pertaining to part I, is extant. The first section was to treat the

[3] Cf. p. 52, n. 56.
[4] Cf. p. 52, n. 55.
[5] Cf. C. A. Fusil, *la Poésie scientifique.*
[6] C. A. Fusil, *la Poésie scientifique,* devotes a special chapter to "Les de Natura Rerum." On Écouchard-Lebrun, cf. p. 64, n. 34.
[7] André Chénier, *Poésies,* edited by L. Becq de Fouquières (Paris, 1862), pp. 334-68. The fragments of "Hermès" are connected by extracts from Sainte-Beuve, *Portraits littéraires,* "Documents sur André Chénier."

origin of the earth, the formation of animals and of man. The
second would have discussed man from a physiological point of
view and by way of his psychic constitution, also in his sociological
dependencies. Section III would have traced the growth of society in its political implications with the emphasis on the consequent establishment of morality and science. A final climax was
to be reached in a presentation of a universal system based on the
most modern scientific theories. The general tenor of the poem
and of its first part in particular is fully indicated by a brief note
which the poet jotted down to remind himself of "the necessity to
represent the earth magnificently under the metaphoric emblem
of a great animal which lives, moves, and which is subject to
changes, revolutions, fevers, derangements in the circulation of
its blood, etc."[8] Of this "metaphoric emblem" a French critic has
said[9] that it was of "Alexandrian taste," which means that it was
an artful ornament, somewhat too intricate, exaggerated, and out
of keeping with the character of the whole. This accusation is
grave, indeed. "In the style of a genuine poet," said August
Wilhelm Schlegel,[10] "nothing is adornment, everything is a necessary hieroglyphic." Now, Chénier's "Alexandrian" panpsychism is
not limited to one isolated metaphor. There is, e.g., a passage which
occurs in a sort of invocation of the Muses and which seems to
state the purpose of the entire work:[11]

[8] A. Chénier, *Poésies*, pp. 354f.
[9] C. A. Fusil, *la Poésie scientifique*, p. 79.
[10] "Athenäums-Fragmente," 173. Ascribed to August Wilhelm by Minor. Cf. F.
Schlegel, *Jugendschriften*.
[11] A. Chénier, "Hermès," lines 33ff.:

     Souvent mon vol, armé des ailes de Buffon,
     Franchit avec Lucrèce, au flambeau de Newton,
     La ceinture d'azur, sur le globe étendue.
     Je vois l'être et la vie et leur source inconnue,
     Dans les fleuves d'éther tous les mondes roulants
     . . . les comètes . . .
40. Je voyage avec eux dans leurs cercles immenses.
     Comme eux, astre, soudain je m'entoure de feux;
     Dans l'éternel concert je me place avec eux:
     En moi leurs doubles lois agissent et respirent;
     Je sens tendre vers eux mon globe qu'ils attirent;
     Sur moi qui les attire ils pèsent à leur tour.
     Les éléments divers, leur haine, leur amour,
     Les causes, l'infini s'ouvre à mon œil avide.
     Bientôt redescendu sur notre fange humide,
     J'y rapporte des vers de nature enflammés.

Together with Lucretius, equipped with the wings of Buffon and following the torch of Newton, my flight crosses the azure girdle extending
over this globe. I see existence and I see life in their unknown source,
where all the worlds are revolving in streams of ether. I travel with
the comets in their immense circles. Like them a star, I suddenly sur-
round myself with fire and take with them my place in the eternal
concert. Their double laws act and breathe in me. They weigh heavily
upon me, and I, in turn, attract them. And the various elements with
their hatred and love, the causes of things and the infinite are open to
my eager eye. And when I return to our humid marsh, I bring back with
me verse which nature set on fire.

The essence of these brilliant lines is simple. The poet himself
is represented magnificently under the metaphoric emblem of a
star, which revolves and moves and is subject to the laws of
gravity summarized in their basic principle of equality of attraction and repulsion. Yet there is again the same touch of Alex-
andrianism. Sir Isaac Newton wore a wig, which made it impossible for him to function as torch bearer. Buffon was a sedate
scientist and had no wings. As for Chénier himself, he should have
known that he did not have to girdle himself with fire in order
to be admitted into the hierarchy of things. Indeed, it is amazing
that a poet like André Chénier could become guilty of such
flagrant violations of the code of the *bon goût*. This riddle, however, is easily solved. Chénier, like Friedrich Schlegel, was a disciple of the Greeks. He felt, again like Friedrich Schlegel, that the
Greeks cannot teach us to be Greeks, that we fail to understand
their lesson unless we learn through it how to be moderns. From
a German point of view we may describe Chénier's classicism
as identical with that of Lessing and Herder:[12]

Without following the steps of the Greeks, we should imitate their
example. We should move away from them and do as they would do
if they were living among us . . . so that Calliope, as a disciple of Urania,
may play her golden lyre in a nobler strain and make a Newton speak
the language of the gods.[13]

[12] This is not meant to imply any sort of dependence.
[13] A. Chénier, "l'Invention," *Poésies,* pp. 325-343, lines 288ff.:
    . . . sans suivre leurs pas imiter leur exemple,
    Faire, en s'éloignant d'eux avec un soin jaloux,
    Ce qu'eux-mêmes ils feraient s'ils vivaient parmi nous!
    Que la nature seule, en ses vastes miracles,
    Soit leur fable et leurs dieux, et ses lois leurs oracles . . .

Unlike Friedrich Schlegel, Chénier could undertake to carry out this program as a creative poet. This meant that he considered it his task to force the theories of modern science to be poetic. Something like a program of this kind is forecast in a note which Sainte-Beuve believed to refer to part II of "Hermès":[14]

In the chaos of the poets each germ and each element is alone and obeys but its own weight; but when everything has been arranged, each one is still a whole by itself, yet at the same time also just a part of the great whole. Each world revolves about itself and about the center. All the worlds have their individual laws, yet all these diverse laws tend toward one common law and form of the universe.

This is not yet poetry. It is the raw material which Chénier wished to transform into poetry. It is merely Newtonian science visualized in its totalitarian consequences by an imaginative mind. Yet precisely as a system of science it would necessarily, according to Herder, appear as poetry if "it were consistent in itself, complete and pure."[15] Now, in Herder's sense, Newton's science was never meant to be consistent and complete. It refused to theorize on the ultimate bases of things;[16] metaphysical and religious questions had no place in it; briefly, it was not a science of life but of laws. To "complete" it, to develop it into a philosophic system which, in Herder's terms, had only to be stated in a "pure and strong expression" to appear as poetry, it was thus necessary to give life to Newton's laws. This is what Chénier tried to achieve by representing the earth "magnificently under the metaphoric emblem of a great animal."[17]

Here it is necessary to pause briefly in order to confront Chénier's "animation" of Newtonian science with a trend of totally different forces, which aim, nevertheless, at exactly the same goal. These forces represent a certain panpsychism which

---

296. Et qu'enfin Calliope, élève d'Uranie,
　　　Montant sa lyre d'or sur un plus noble ton,
　　　En langage des dieux fasse parler Newton.
Similar principles dominate the entire poem. Cf. especially, lines 14ff., 107ff., 141ff. and also the famous line 184: "Sur des pensers nouveaux faisons des vers antiques."

[14] A. Chénier, *Poésies*, p. 365.
[15] Cf. p. 240, n. 1.
[16] Cf. p. 34, n. 8.
[17] A. Chénier, *Poésies*, pp. 354f.

had its beginning with Newton himself, continuing, it is true, a related trend which had descended from the heights of the Renaissance to Newton as its lowest point. Draper[18] alludes to this latter development in a striking summary. "The genii of Kepler," he says, "gave way to the vortices of Descartes, and these in their turn to the central force of Newton." It is, however, the post-Newtonian development which claims particular attention in the present connection. Newton's discovery of an antagonism of centripetal and centrifugal forces which determine together the behavior of the phenomenal world invited naturally a metaphoric interpretation. According to Ferdinand Bulle[19] in his work on Hemsterhuis (1911) Newton himself suggested the figurative transfer into the moral realm of his triadic conception of action, reaction, and resulting phenomenal movement. The interpretation of love and hate as analogous to attraction and repulsion began as a metaphor, but it ended as an actual identification.[20] Herder could thus state[21] that Empedocles, who had conceived of love and hate as the moving principles in the world of things, had anticipated as in a dream the entire Newtonian system.

Early German Romanticism, as typically represented by Franz von Baader, went still farther. It accused Newton of having misinterpreted a thought of Böhme's by identifying attraction with passive gravity.[22] The force of attraction, Baader held, is an active

[18] J. W. Draper, *Conflict between Religion and Science*, p. 95.

[19] F. Bulle, *Franziskus Hemsterhuis*, p. 29. On Bulle's treatment of the present problem, cf. P. Kluckhohn, *Die Auffassung der Liebe*, p. 230n: "Die Bedeutung von Newtons Entdeckung des Antagonismus zwischen Zentripetal- und Zentrifugalkraft für die Weiterbildung von Shaftesburys Pantheismus in Hemsterhuis und dessen Fortwirkung in Herder und anderen ist hier gut dargelegt, aber auf das Problem der Geschlechterliebe geht Bulle gar nicht ein."

[20] The transition may be found to be illustrated by young Schiller's "Phantasie an Laura" (1781), "Die Freundschaft" (1781), and "Theosophie des Julius."

[21] J. G. Herder, *Vom Erkennen und Empfinden* (1778), p. 4, *Sämmtliche Werke*, VIII.

[22] Cf. J. Nohl, "Franz von Baader," p. 631: "Newtons Gravitationstheorie vergleicht Baader mit Kants Versuch das moralische Prinzip auf eine Verstandesformel zu bringen; er wirft ihm vor, die Zentrumsleerheit der Materie nicht erkannt und infolgedessen Schwere und Attraktion = Durchwohnung und Inwohnung, das heißt die zentrifugale Ohnmacht mit dem wahrhaft zentripetalen Triebe verwechselt zu haben. In Wirklichkeit sei die Attraktion im Äußeren dasselbe, was die Begierde, das Verlangen im Innern, die Attraktion sei aktiv, die Schwere passiv. Böhme sei der erste, der den Begriff des Wesens (= Materie) als mit dem Schweren zusammen-

principle. It is in the outer world what longing, desire, craving, love are in the inner world. In this view it is no longer an anthropomorphic metaphor when celestial movements are described in psychic terms. On the contrary, the psychic phenomena are prior to all material events, and the world of things must be explained on the basis of the human soul, not *vice versa*.[23] As early as 1786 Baader formulated these thoughts in a veritable program of the romantic philosophy of love. In it he saw "the general bond which binds and weaves together all the beings in the universe." Then he exclaimed:[24]

Call it general gravity, attraction, cohesion, affinity, corrosibility, etc. These are words which one may use but which do not explain anything. Yet how could they? It is quite enough to know that there is a general striving of all parts of matter toward their reunion and that it is manifest below and above our moon. Attraction, attachment is thus an undeniable fact, a phenomenon which admits perhaps of no further explanation, but which, as such, does not need any. Without affinity there is no whole, no world. It is not conceivable. Our globe would be a deserted and eternally dead chaos. It would be a pulp without figure and form and a real monstrosity.

In the romantic view love is the all-pervading central force which moulds the cosmos into a living whole. "It rules over the stars as over the elements and the earth. It produces the flowers, the plants, and the trees; it is due to love that the rivers flow and that the wind is blowing . . ."[25] It gives everything, it takes

---

fallend erfaßt hätte; Newton habe übrigens nach Law den Begriff der Attraktion aus den Böhmeschen drei ersten Gestalten der ewigen Natur entlehnt, ihn aber fälschlich doch nur materiell gefaßt."

[23] Cf. p. 205, n. 11 and p. 114, n. 87.

[24] F. v. Baader, "Vom Wärmestoff" (1786), *Werke*, III, 39: "Liebe ist das allgemeine Band, das alle Wesen im Universum an- und ineinander bindet und verwebt . . ." On this passage and the relation of its thought to Kant, Hemsterhuis, Herder, young Schiller, and Eckartshausen, cf. also P. Kluckhohn, *Weltanschauung der Frühromantik*, p. 58.

[25] This romantic passage is not modern. It is taken from Longus, *Daphnis et Chloé* (Paris, 1878), p. 51. This edition by A. Pons was not selected for any pertinent reasons. Poetry of similar beauty and identical thought is found in Lucretius, *De rerum natura*, invocation of Venus as muse, especially I, 1-5 and 21-23. Cf. also Friedrich Wilhelm Schelling, "Das himmlische Bild" (after 1807), *Sämmtliche Werke*, first series, X (Stuttgart: Cotta, 1861), 448, stanza 5, lines 5ff.:

> Die ewige Liebe kann nur der verkünden,
> Dem sie aus sich die Dichtungskraft gewährt,
> Denn sie, die ewig schaffet und vernichtet,
> Hat auch die Welt von Ewigkeit gedichtet.

everything.[26] "It is the basis of the possibility of creation."[27] "It is the final goal of history, the *amen* of the universe."[28] "It is the basic law of existence in all of Creation."[29]

It is not necessary at present to pursue these ideas any farther.[30]

[26] *Novalis Schriften*, IV, Hardenberg to Karoline Just, letter of March 28, 1797.

[27] *Novalis Schriften*, III, 74.

[28] *Novalis Schriften*, III, 68.

[29] In 1793 Karl von Eckartshausen delivered an address "Über das erste Wesensgesetz in der Schöpfung: die Liebe" before the Bavarian Academy of Science.

[30] Cf. P. Kluckhohn, *Die Auffassung der Liebe*. Reference must be made, however, to the fact that this problem of a universal interrelation of things furnishes the only reliable basis for a possible discrimination between classicism and romanticism. The classicist conceives of the universal bond of affinity or love as manifesting an absolutely basic principle of polarity. E. Barthels, *Goethes Wissenschaftslehre*, p. 70, states strikingly that the idea of polarity asserts "the paradoxical truth that the number two is as homogeneous as the number one and that the difference between these two concepts is fundamentally not numerical but qualitative." It seems that the Romanticists could not have understood this idea. Hardenberg wishes to dissolve what he calls an "antinomy" or "binomy" in a final "infinitomy." Cf. p. 173, n. 61. He says, *Novalis Schriften*, III, 292, that the sentimental is polar while the naïve is not. Whatever this means, it certainly indicates that Hardenberg conceived of polar tension as due to a tragic break which should be mended. He actually offers this definition, III, 189: "Polarity is the result of dissolution. . . . In it quantity and quality separate. Polarity is imperfection and in time there shall be no polarity. It can only be a means and must be transitory." Schlegel, "Ideen," 73, stated likewise that there cannot be a dualism without primacy. Cf. further I. P. V. Troxler, "Blicke in das Wesen des Menschen," p. 245. Through these ideas, it seems, we may understand the importance of Hemsterhuis as an "elective ancestor" of Romanticism. Cf. p. 245, n. 19. This thinker did not parallel the universal duality of attraction and repulsion with a psychic duality of love and egocentrism. He conceived of it rather as a cosmic correspondence to a human longing for redemption through a final reunion with the attracted or beloved partner. The *organe moral* as an instrument of cognition became then at the same time an apparatus capable of engineering the dissolution of "two" in "one." This "romantic" conception is definitely rejected by Herder. Cf. "Gott," *Sämmtliche Werke*, XVI, 55f.: The basic laws through which we can grasp the order of the world are, "1. Beharrung d. i. innerer Bestand jeglichen Wesens. 2. Vereinigung mit Gleichartigem und vom Entgegengesetzten Scheidung. 3. Verähnlichung mit sich und Abdruck seines Wesens in einem andern." Of these three laws Herder states explicitly that they are in reality but one living concept. It is certain that the bolder language of Goethe meant by polarity exactly what Herder wanted his readers to synthesize from his threefold formulation. However, the clearest expression of his views Herder reaches characteristically in a direct critique of Hemsterhuis' concept of love. Cf. *Sämmtliche Werke*, XV, 314. The passage was originally adduced by F. Bulle, *Franziskus Hemsterhuis*, p. 37. Herder says of love: "I do not look for the highest form of its charms where nature, as Hemsterhuis thinks, deceives us by a moment of earthly union; but rather in the first happy encounter, in that moment, sweet beyond all description, when the two lovers grew aware of the fact that they love each other." For the classicist love is a polar experience in which the "I" attains its fullest richness through cognition of a "you." The romanticist senses in love the possibility of dying into the partner. "Love," as Conrad Aiken put it rather brutally in his novel *Great Circle* (New York, 1933), p. 260, "is nothing on earth but a domestication of death." In Goethe's

The material adduced suffices to show that it was possible to "animate" the Newtonian laws without "representing the earth magnificently under the metaphoric emblem of a huge animal." Chénier and the German Romanticists were both aiming at a transformation of "law into life," of a scientific system into a "complete philosophy which needed but a pure and strong expression to be poetic." Yet neither Chénier nor the German Romanticists attained their goal. If they had succeeded, we should have a modern world poem of Lucretian or Dantean scope "on which time could place the seal of perfection and unsurpassable beauty."

That we have no such poem cannot be denied, but an attempt should be made to explain the fact. Friedrich Schlegel remarked once:[31] "A didactic poem has a right to exist only when the visible

---

Prometheus, Pandora relates what she saw happen to Mira and asks: "Was ist das alles was sie erschüttert/Und mich?" Prometheus explains: "Der Tod!" and calls it the sum of all joys. The fact that Herder supplies an illustration for the classicist's conception and Goethe one for that of the romanticist, may indicate that the present distinction concerns two types of mental posture, not two groups of authors.

[31] At this point our discussion could profit by a special analysis of the quest for a new mythology which is characteristic of the age of classic-romantic idealism. No such analysis will be offered, except in so far as it is implied in the treatment of other problems. This procedure seemed indicated because a detached chapter on "The New Mythology" would necessarily have looked like a mere compilation of extracts from F. Strich, *Mythologie.* As far as his book is concerned with the *new* mythology, Strich summarizes its results in the preface, p. VI: "Unsere Epoche ist eine Rückkehr zur Mythologie auf der Stufe wissenschaftlicher Erkenntnis. Der moderne Dichter hat die Aufgabe, die neue Religion der erkannten Naturgesetze in den ewig wahren Formen der auf Anschauung und Ahnung beruhenden Mythologie des Volkes darzustellen." An abridged list of the most significant passages of pertinent contents follows. Vol. I, pp. 51ff.: Herder's early rejection of Klotz' idea of a scientific mythology; I, 141: The later change in Herder's attitude. The idea of a scientific mythology, which originated in Klotz and Hamann, attains full maturity in Herder who passes it on to Schelling and Schlegel; I, 120: Herder's transitional attitude as expressed in *Vom Geist der ebräischen Poesie,* 1782; I, 141 and especially II, 54: Summary of Herder's development; I, 263: In Schiller's conception Greek mythology cannot possibly be replaced by any other; I, 276f.: Forster's defense of Schiller's "Götter Griechenlands" against Stolberg's attack and Forster's own opinion, not compatible with that of Schiller, that "the ancient rags do not fit the modern dress"; I, 291: Karl Philipp Moritz. "Die griechische Mythologie ist die dichterische Gestalt des Spinozismus"; I, 341: The romantic conception of mythology as the union of science and poetry; I, 446: Tieck's *Sternbald* and the theory of an allegorical, Dantean poem of nature; II, 91: The "mythological" *Musenalmanach* of Schlegel and Tieck for the year 1802; Chateaubriand, *l'Esprit du christianisme* (1802) and Schlegel, "Rede über die Mythologie"; II, 124f.: Schelling, *Philosophie der Kunst.* Racial and individual mythologies; II, 126: Schelling's evaluation of Goethe's *Faust* as a truly mythological poem; II, 327f.: Görres, F. Schlegel, Eschenmayer, Schelling, Hegel and the problem of *Glauben und Wissen.* Görres' conclusion:

world is animated by a mythology with its figures and fables, and when all of reality is thus raised to the level of poetry." Chénier knew this. It is precisely for this reason that he invented his myth of the earth as a living being. Yet, can a myth be invented? A myth, as Spengler, the modern romanticist, puts it,[32] is "a bit of incarnate reality." The question is not whether such a reality can be created by an individual or must be the dream of a nation.[33] The point is merely that it cannot be invented, that it must be lived.[34] Chénier forsook the mythology of the ancients because, to apply Hölderlin's criterion from "The Hypocritical poets,"[35] he "did not believe in Helios, or in the Thunderer and the God of the Ocean. The earth was dead and there was no soul in the names of the gods. Yet, a great word was needed," and thus he invented the metaphoric emblem under which the earth could appear as a living animal. Hölderlin would have called this "cold hypocrisy." At any rate, it is no mythology; it is merely an interesting allegory.[36] We hear the message, but we do

---

"Es kann dem Wissen so wenig wie dem Glauben gelingen, einseitig für sich zum wahren Gotte zu gelangen . . . Die Mythologie ist die Einheit von Glauben und Wissen"; II, 159: Öhlenschläger's new Christian mythology. *Jesus in der Natur;* II, 246: Wilhelm Grimm's rejection of the idea that a new mythology can be developed in willful endeavor; II, 347: Creuzer's interpretative conception of mythological symbolism contrasted with Goethe's direct vision of formal beauty; II, 354: Schlegel's lectures *On Ancient and Modern Literature.* "Ein Lehrgedicht aber ist nur berechtigt wenn noch eine Mythologie die sichtbare Welt mit ihren Gestalten und Fabeln bevölkert und die gesamte Wirklichkeit zur Poesie erhebt." Quoted above; II, 386: Romantic mediation between old and new mythologies; etc.

[32] Cf. p. 239, n. 56.

[33] Cf. F. Strich, *Mythologie,* especially II, 124f., 91, 246.

[34] Cf. E. Dacqué, *Urwelt, Sage und Menschheit,* p. 35.

[35] F. Hölderlin, "Die scheinheiligen Dichter." The bitter irony of line 5 appears only after repeated readings:

Ihr kalten Heuchler, sprecht von den Göttern nicht!
Ihr habt Verstand! Ihr glaubt nicht an Helios,
Noch an den Donnerer und Meergott;
    Tot ist die Erde, wer mag ihr danken?—
Getrost, ihr Götter! zieret ihr doch das Lied,
    Wennschon aus euern Namen die Seele schwand,
    Und ist ein großes Wort vonnöten,
        Mutter Natur! so gedenkt man deiner.

[36] This statement settles the problem only as far as the present discussion is concerned. For the student of Chénier, on the other hand, the assertion that the "Hermès" would have been an allegory is not the solution but the formulation of a problem. Blake's prophetic writings are allegories. Népomucène Lemercier's *Atlantiade* is also

not believe.[37] It simply is not true that the earth is a huge animal,
and Chénier knew that as well as we do.

The assertion, on the other hand, that the universe is an infinite
whole animated by the all-pervading power of love was more than
an allegorical adornment; in the romantic experience it was "a bit
of incarnate reality" and thus a genuine myth. Within it, one
should suppose, the earth or the universe might well be represented
"under the emblem of a huge animal." As a panpsychic symbol
this idea would doubtless achieve an actual embodiment, not
merely an allegorical representation of the individuality of the
earth or the universe. As a poetic simile it is, nevertheless, con-
spicuously absent from romantic literature and particularly from
the works of those authors in whom romantic panpsychism reached
its climax. Schelling, it is true, once called the world "a docile and
lazy animal which threatens neither you nor me, which submits to
its laws and lies down quietly at our feet." This passage, however,
can only strengthen the general impression that similes of this
sort fail somehow to appeal to the modern mentality, for it occurs
in a poem[38] whose archaistic naïveté of expression suggests vaguely
the atmosphere of sixteenth-century thought. Yet the most important aspect of this situation can best be clarified through an
historic approach.

There is in Shakespeare a striking instance of the peculiar
hylozoistic symbolism here under discussion. We read in act III
of *The First Part of King Henry IV:*

> Diseased nature oftentimes breaks forth
> In strange eruptions: oft the teeming earth
> Is with a kind of colic pinch'd and vex'd
> By the imprisoning of unruly wind
> Within her womb; which, for enlargement striving,

---

an allegory. Blake invented names for his figures on the basis of purely verbal
artifice: *Los,* the creative genius, is the anagram of *sol; Urizen,* the power of thought,
may mean "you reason," etc. Lemercier used similar devices. The soul of his universe
is *Psycholie,* the power of affinity is *Syngénie,* etc. The same allegorical method can
produce sublime poetry as well as utterly prosaic verse. Our statements on Chénier
are not meant to judge.

[37] "Die Botschaft hör ich wohl, allein mir fehlt der Glaube." *Faust,* "Studier-
zimmer I."

[38] Cf. p. 173, n. 61.

Shakes the old beldame earth, and topples down
Steeples, and moss-grown towers.[39]

This, to be sure, may simply be taken as an instance of the extraordinarily vigorous imagery which is so characteristic of Shakespeare's style. The robust beauty of these lines impresses us so directly that the attempt to translate their poetic realism into rational prose will not deepen the appreciation of their function in the drama as a whole. Yet even though the comment may be useless as a note to Shakespeare, it is important for the present survey that the material of this panpsychic metaphor was possibly borrowed from Giordano Bruno.[40] In that case it would not merely be a particularly striking figure of speech. Its poetic vigor would rather have to be explained as due to the fact that a creative mind visualized here a vast reality in a surveyable symbol. In other words, Shakespeare's description of the earth as a living organism would have to be considered as an illustration of the poetic fertility of Giordano Bruno's mythological realism. At any rate, whether Bruno's views were a source for Shakespeare or not, there can be no doubt that they in themselves represented the nucleus of a modern mythology of nature. In them the animation of the earth was no metaphoric emblem but rather a bit of incarnate reality. The earth had all the organs of animals and all their diseases: it suffered from colds, vertigo, fevers, vesical calculus, and so forth. In brief, it *was* an animal and did not have to be represented as one.

These ideas were naturally not without a long line of ancestors. In fact, they can doubtless be traced to Neoplatonic, Platonic, and possibly Oriental origins. Their dissemination in the Sixteenth and Seventeenth Centuries would also represent an important and interesting topic. Yet, at present it is more significant to observe their mutation in the conception of a later age. The general reaction to them is typically represented by Alexander von Humboldt's critique of Kepler's hylozoism which, on the whole, seems to

---

[39] Shakespeare, *The First Part of King Henry IV*, III, 1, 27ff.

[40] Cf. Robert Beyersdorff, *Giordano Bruno und Shakespeare* (Oldenburg, 1889), p. 5. The parallel passage in Bruno, to which Beyersdorff refers, is "de l'Infinito," *Opere*, edited by Adolf Wagner (Leipzig, 1830), II, 60.

have been identical with that of Bruno. Humboldt, who had expressed in a letter to Schelling his "deep admiration" for natural philosophy,[41] felt nevertheless that he had to brand Kepler's speculations on the terrestrial animal as "wild flights of fancy." He stated,[42] in explicit quotations, that he wished to apply this epithet to all of Kepler's thoughts "on the respiration, nutrition, and heat of the earth animal, and on the soul, memory (*memoria animae Terrae*), and creative imagination (*animae Telluris imaginatio*) of this monster." How is it possible, Humboldt wondered, that this great man came to be "so wedded to these chimeras that he warmly contested his right of priority in the views regarding the earth animal with the mystic author of the *Macrocosmos*, Robert Fludd, of Oxford!"[43] None of the typically romantic thinkers, it is true, felt justified in speaking of Kepler in similarly harsh terms. Hölderlin acclaimed him as one of the innumerable children of Suevia who had attained knowledge of light and universal life;[44] and Hardenberg called him[45] "noble Kepler, whose high-mindedness created a spiritualized and moralized (*vergeistigt, versittlicht*) universe" while our [Hardenberg's] age endeavors to kill everything and to "bend the spirit of man under the laws of mechanics." Yet, if these expressions refer to Kepler's conception of an animal nature of the planets and stars, they stress its spiritualistic tendencies and not the peculiar form in which they appeared.

At this point it may be suggested that Wieland already seems to have furnished the only plausible answer to the question why it is that we find it so hard to take the idea seriously that the globe is an animal with animal organs and instincts, and why even the

---

[41] Alexander von Humboldt to Schelling, letter of February 10, 1806. Quoted from MS by G. Stefansky, *Das hellenisch-deutsche Weltbild*, p. 65.

[42] Alexander von Humboldt, *Cosmos*, translated from the German by E. C. Otté (New York: Harper, 1860), III, 18f.

[43] Cf. Ricarda Huch, *Ausbreitung und Verfall der Romantik*, p. 48: "Wie die Romantiker so oft ihre Ideen in längstvergessener Vergangenheit wiederfanden, entdeckten sie auch diese Lehre in großartigster Einfachheit dargestellt bei Kepler, der behauptete, daß die Weltkörper tierischer Natur seien . . . " Yet, Ricarda Huch has no citations which show that the Romanticists saw in Kepler's animalization of planets more than an unusual form of animation

[44] F. Hölderlin, "Kepler," IX, 1ff.

[45] *Novalis Schriften*, II, 400.

Romanticists could not propound this idea in spite of its great poetic fertility.[46] In the second book of his poem *On the Nature of Things*,[47] it will be recalled, Wieland presented a brief critical survey of Plato's panpsychism.[48] He admitted the great poetic beauty of the idea that the world is a perfect animal which contains all the other less perfect ones. It is obviously true, he continued, that the world contains all the animals, but that does not mean that it *is* one. Plato came to this mistaken conclusion because he conceived of a finite cosmos. He animated all the individual spheres of his world. Thus there was no reason why he should not do the same in the case of the all-inclusive universal sphere. For us, however, the universal sphere is no longer a finite entity, and it would consequently be absurd to conceive of it in terms of a finite being, a living animal, a natural organism. These considerations of Wieland agree beautifully with the fact that Kepler, who animated the world in the form of a finite organism, did not conceive of it as infinite.[49] Further we understand why later panpsychistic trends, which had to cope with the problem of infinity, were obliged to conceive of a principle of animation which was not limited by finite dimensions. This, we have seen,[50] was discovered or recovered[51] in the idea of infinite love as the univer-

[46] It seems, however, that this idea is capable of spontaneous regeneration even in our enlightened age. There is a very strange little pamphlet, *Weltkörper sind Lebewesen* (Hamburg: Lüdemann, n.d.), by a certain Klüd von Niendorf, whose identity cannot be determined. Paper and binding indicate that it was published in the years after the first phase of the World War. Considerable space is given to diatribes against the narrow-minded publishers who refused to accept this work and forced the author to resort to private printing. This meant virtual starvation for him, but his message was so important that nothing could be permitted to interfere with its spread. There follows a long analysis of the name Klüd. It means *"Erdenkloß,"* and its bearer must be gifted with an unusually sensitive understanding of mother earth. The actual message is condensed to the last few pages. It states that the earth is an animal; that we kill it by tapping its blood through our oil wells; that it begins to feel the itch and is getting ready to shake us off. The idea that the earth is an animal is developed in its most extreme physical implications. Time and again the warning is interpolated that we shall suffer annihilation if we do not hasten to pacify the angry earth.

[47] Chr. M. Wieland, "Die Natur der Dinge," *Werke*, I¹, 36.

[48] Wieland referred to Plato's *Timaeus*. Cf. p. 42.

[49] Cf. p. 136, n. 3. Giordano Bruno, it is true, accepted the idea of an infinite universe.

[50] Cf. p. 246, n. 24.

[51] A. Müller. Cf. p. 112, n. 78.

sal force "which binds and weaves together all the beings in the world." Wieland called it more simply *God*. Since we conceive of the world as infinite, he reasoned, it is not possible to animate it by anything but God. He is the moving and supporting power in all existence. He is the "soul of the universe."

Love is a personal, individual, and somehow a narrow experience. God is a dogmatic and somehow an abstract concept. Yet, love could be expanded into a universal force; God could be experienced in the universal spontaneity of living Creation;[52] and both appeared thus dissolved in the higher notion of a world soul. The circle, it seems, was complete. Our philosophy, as Schelling put it,[53] had returned to its earliest beginnings. In the general principle "which combines all of nature,"[54] our philosophy could recognize "that Being which the oldest thinkers had welcomed as a universal soul." It was, to be sure, but an image, a human image as Herder[55] insisted; but this meant for him that "the innate (*innig-einwohnend*) force of God could be visualized in it." Thus it was a true symbol and more specifically, a symbol of universal scope, the summary of a complete mythology. Guided by its implication, Goethe, indeed, was able to condense an all-inclusive cosmogony into a poetic epitome of nine brief stanzas. Yet, this poem, "World Soul," of 1802 [56] was only one among many signs which indicated, to paraphrase Schelling,[57] that the mythology had finally been found in which all the ideas of the age were contained. It was not merely a "metaphoric emblem." Nor was it *"a bit* of incarnate reality."[58] It was *all* of reality and embraced the infinity of our modern world. The realistic mythology of the Greeks had disappeared. In its stead there had arisen the possibili-

---

[52] Cf. Carl August von Eschenmayer, "Spontaneität = Weltseele oder das höchste Prinzip der Naturphilosophie," *Zeitschrift für spekulative Physik*, II, 1 (1801), pp. 1-68.

[53] F. W. Schelling, *Weltseele*, p. IV: ". . . die älteste Philosophie, (zu welcher, nachdem sie ihren Kreislauf vollendet hat, die unserige allmählig zurückkehrt) . . ."

[54] Schelling. Cf. p. 149, n. 58.

[55] J. G. Herder, "Gott," *Sämmtliche Werke*, XVI, 526f.

[56] Goethe, "Weltseele."

[57] Cf. Georg Stefansky, *Das Wesen der Romantik* (Stuttgart, 1923), p. 87. Schelling to August Wilhelm Schlegel in July, 1800.

[58] Cf. p. 239, n. 56.

ty of a new idealistic and infinite mythology.[59] Yet by its very
nature as an infinite concept it could not attain realization in
finite completion. It could always become, but it could never be.
This was its fertility but also—its barrenness.

The genealogy of the mythological concept of a world soul cannot be traced. Toward the end of the Eighteenth Century it seems
to have appeared simultaneously and spontaneously in various
places, for, as Goethe has it,[60] "apples in different people's gar-
dens ripen and fall at the same time." We have seen that Wieland
felt that the idea of a world soul had nothing sacrilegious.[61] Herder
saw in it one of those images which are the only possible form of
human perception of truth.[62] It can be used to establish a series
of affinities from Plotinus to Giordano Bruno[63] and further, to
early German Romanticism, especially Hardenberg. Schelling's
use of it as the general principle of his *Hypothesis of Higher Physics,* i.e., of his essay *On the World Soul,* is inconceivable without
Herder as also without Kielmeyer's lecture of 1793 *On the Interrelation of Organic Forces.*[64] Strich[65] suggests a further dependence
of Schelling on Salomon Maimon, another recoverer of the idea
of a universal soul. Baader acknowledged in his essay *On the
Pythagorean Square in Nature* that its thought had crystallized
after a reading of Schelling's *Hypothesis,* which he considered "as
the first messenger of an approaching spring, i.e., as the first en-
joyable sign of the resurrection of physics from the death sleep
of atomism."[66] Baader's own panpsychism can be traced back to
his essay of 1792, *Ideas on Solids and Liquids.*[67] In later years,

[59] G. Stefansky, *Das Wesen der Romantik,* p. 87.
[60] Goethe: "Auch in verschiedenen Gärten fallen Früchte zu gleicher Zeit vom
Baume."
[61] Cf. p. 42, n. 33.
[62] Cf. p. 110, n. 67.
[63] Cf. J. Sarauw, *Der Einfluß Plotins auf Giordano Bruno,* pp. 52ff.: "Übereinstimmung zwischen den Lehren Brunos und Plotins . . . II. Die Weltseele. 1) Die
Weltseele beherscht das All, aber frei von Körper. 2) besteht aus höheren und
niederen Kräften. 3) Das ganze All ist beseelt. 4) Das höchste Vermögen der Weltseele ist die Vernunft. Darin die Ideen."
[64] Cf. p. 121, n. 110, and F. W. Schelling, *Weltseele,* p. 298.
[65] F. Strich, *Mythologie,* I, 385.
[66] F. v. Baader, *Werke,* III, 249.
[67] F. v. Baader, "Ideen über Festigkeit und Flüssigkeit" (1792), *Werke,* III, 181-
202. Cf. also J. Nohl, "Franz von Baader," p. 613.

especially from 1799 to 1807, it merged through his study of the
works of St. Martin with this thinker's conception of a hylozoistic world soul.[68] Hardenberg elaborated the concept of a world
psyche into the idea that a "world psychology" should be possible.[69] The study of it, he felt, had been begun by Baader, to
whom he applied the title of "psychologist of reality."[70]

The conception of a universal soul is generally romantic. It
would indeed be no easy task to find a representative author
writing in the decades around 1800 in whom panspychic thoughts
do not appear in one form or another. It seems, however, that this
trend found a particularly fertile expression in Hölderlin's ideolo-
gies. The idea of the all-pervading universal soul finds here a
poetic embodiment in the concept of ether as the quintessence of
all existence. This is not merely a terminological change. Hölderlin's ether myth must, indeed, be interpreted as a particularly
delicate form of that sensualization of the soul for which Herder
was longing.[71] Ether can be seen in the blue sky above; we breathe
it, feel it, we can almost touch it. This means that the concept
ether represents here a typically romantic synchysis of metaphysical with concrete components. The abstract principle of ether
coincides with air, atmosphere, etc., without losing any of its
metaphysical significance. It is in this sense that Empedocles'
prayer of gratitude[72] must be interpreted.

> Und wenn ich oft
> Auf stiller Bergeshöhe saß und staunend
> Der Menschen wechselnd Irrsal übersann,
> Zu tief von deinen [der Erde] Wandlungen ergriffen,
> Und nah mein eignes Welken ahndete,
> Dann atmete der Äther, so wie dir,
> Mir heilend um die liebeswunde Brust
> Und, wie Gewölk der Flamme, lösten

[68] Cf. p. 114, n. 87.
[69] *Novalis Schriften*, II, 407. Cf. also II, 340, 341, 407.
[70] *Novalis Schriften*, II, 378: "Baader ist ein realer Psychologe und spricht die
echt psychologische Sprache. Reale Psychologie ist auch vielleicht das für mich
bestimmte Feld." Cf. also J. Nohl, "Franz von Baader," p. 613. On Dilthey's misinterpretation of this passage, cf. W. Olshausen, *Hardenberg*, pp. 19f.
[71] Cf. p. 68, n. 40.
[72] Cf. F. Hölderlin, "Empedokles," *Werke*, p. 400.

Gereiniget die Sorgen mir sich auf
Im hohen Blau.

Indeed, one may feel tempted to assert that Hölderlin's ether
is related to Mesmer's *fluidum universale,* for in its most refined
form this was also the essence through which the sensitive could
learn that life had been imparted by it to all of nature.[73] Support
for this suggestion can be found in an idea of Schubert's. In his
book on *The Symbolism of Dreams* he discussed the animating
power of oxygen, that recently discovered gaseous substance in
which many saw the matter of animal electricity or even of the
vital force.[74] There must be, Schubert reasoned,[75] an animating
principle which assumes "a telluric-planetarian nature in the form
of oxygen." Then he suggests that this general vitalizer might
well be identical with, and in turn a proof for the existence of, that
principle assumed of old "which permeates the entire universe
and embraces the individual worlds as an all-pervading ether."
A further and more important point, however, is the observation
that Hölderlin's conception of a sensual-ethereal world soul demonstrates a more immediate affinity of his mentality with the
thought of the ancient Greeks than can be observed in any of the
other Romanticists. In Hölderlin's case it is correct to speak of
"a resurrection of Greek panpsychism."[76]

As Heinse's[77] summary description in *Ardinghello* of the Greek
ideology of the *quinta essentia,* ether, culminates in the simple
identification of ether and Zeus, so it was also for Hölderlin an
elemental urge to personify, to deify the sensual-ethereal soul of
the world. "The Greeks," said Gundolf,[78] "—and Hölderlin—
perceived the divine only in human form." Indeed, it is the climax

---

[73] Cf. W. Koch, *Briefe deutscher Romantiker,* p. 213. Caroline to Luise Wiedemann,
letter of January 31, 1807. Having discussed the most recent experiments with the
magic rod, Caroline concludes: "Das beste ist, daß sich ein jeder selbst von der
Echtheit dieser Kraft, von dieser Wirkung des Menschen auf sogenannte tote Materien, die also wohl auch lebendig sein müssen, überzeugen kann."
[74] Cf. p. 196, n. 47.
[75] Gotthilf Heinrich Schubert, "Die Symbolik des Traumes" (1814), in Chr.
Bernoulli and H. Kern, *Romantische Naturphilosophie,* p. 139.
[76] A. Biese, *Naturgefühl,* p. 183.
[77] W. Heinse, "Ardinghello," *Werke,* IV, 251.
[78] F. Gundolf, "Hölderlins Archipelagus," *Dichter und Helden,* p. 12.

of the development of the romantic myth of a world soul when
Hölderlin prays to *Vater Äther,* who "sows out sparks of life,"
who is "the father of all things," and who "feeds the earth and
man." "The earth opens wide her arms of fire up to the ether,"
who is the "all-preserver, all-maintainer," and who, with earth and
light, forms the "united three."[79, 80]

[79] F. Hölderlin, *Werke,* "Hymne an die Muse," III, 7f.:
> Deinem Zauber huldigen Dämonen,
> Staub und Äther ist dir untertan.

"An den Äther," 6f.:
> Nicht von irdischer Kost gedeihen einzig die Wesen,
> Aber du nährst sie all mit deinem Nektar, o Vater!

"Der Wanderer," second version, 98:
> Vater des Vaterlands! mächtiger Äther!

"Empedokles," *Werke,* pp. 335 and 397:
> Lebensfunken sät der Äther.

Ibid., p. 339:
> Ach! ich . . . lebt . . . mit . . .
> . . . dir, von dem die Seele nimmer läßt,
> O Vater Äther!

Ibid., p. 356:
> . . . Ihr Blumen
> Des Himmels! schöne Sterne, werdet ihr
> Denn auch verblühn? Und wird es Nacht alsdann
> In deiner Seele werden, Vater Äther!

Ibid., p. 385:
> Und soll er . . .
> Verweilen, wenn ihm
> Der Vater die Arme,
> Der Äther, öffnet?

"Tod des Empedokles," *Werke,* p. 400:
> Dann atmete der Äther, so wie dir,
> Mir heilend um die liebeswunde Brust.

Ibid., p. 422:
> . . . wenn . . . eingedenk
> Der alten Einigkeit die dunkle Mutter
> Zum Äther aus die Feuerarme breitet . . .
> Dann folgen wir.

The arrangement of these passages from a simple conventional substitution of the
term *Äther* for *Luft* to a final and personal deification of the original essence of all
existence, corresponds to Hölderlin's own development. The Greek character of his
final mythology appears in striking relief through comparison with parallel passages
from Sophocles, Euripides, Aristophanes, and Pindar, which have been assembled by
F. Strich, *Mythologie,* I, 356ff. In conclusion Strich defines Hölderlin's conception of
ether as "der gemeinsame Geist aller Wesen, die Seele des Menschen und der Natur,
die Weltseele."

[80] It has been stated that Hölderlin's ether may be considered as a refined form of
the magnetic fluid in the form which it assumed in the romantic conception. It must

Hölderlin's ether ideology represents a genuine myth. It contains the essence of our world. The deepest realities tend to assume in it a tangible form. Yet Hölderlin, whose soul lived in Greece, was a German and a romantic, not a Greek; and his myth which contained the infinity of his world was the goal of his longing and as such a truth which he never beheld, never touched. Nothing more can be said about Hölderlin. This is his life and the tragic beauty of his end. However, we need not speak of his life to understand the fate of his soul. This is more fully contained in his work and principally perhaps in his *Empedocles*. Here we find Hölderlin's testament and his message to the world expressed in Empedocles' exhortation: "You must have the courage to forget boldly what you inherited, what you were told and taught by your fathers, your laws, your customs, and the names of the ancient gods!" All this is necessary for the attainment of the highest goal. Yet what is this highest goal? To find truth, to seize God, to hold the infinity of life? Precisely the opposite. "The life of the world

---

also be pointed out that one may conceive of the philosophical and scientific ether hypotheses as peculiar variations of Hölderlin's ideology. On Schelling and Hölderlin, cf. F. Strich, *Mythologie*, I, 359. L. Oken formulates very simply, "Naturphilosophie," §§22f.: "Die Materie, welche die unmittelbare Position Gottes ist . . . nenne ich Urmaterie, Weltmaterie, kosmische Materie, Äther. Der Äther füllt das ganze Universum aus und ist mithin eine Sphäre, ja, die Weltsphäre selbst; die Welt ist eine rotierende Ätherkugel." In this passage ether appears as the basic essence of all things, which establishes a connection with Hölderlin. It appears as an all-pervading essence, which relates it to the conception of ether held by Huygens, Maxwell, Thomson, etc. Finally, it is identified with space, which may perhaps be said to constitute an anticipation of Einstein's abolition of ether as a special hypothetical essence. Hölderlin's ether is still more clearly identical with that which forms the basis of all of Carus' philosophy. Cf. C. G. Carus, *Briefe über das Erdleben*, p. 120: "In dieser Welt der Stoffe nun ist der Anfangspunkt aller Bildung, das reine unbestimmteste Element, jenes reine farb- und stofflose Sein, jene Ursubstanz, aus welcher alles hervorgeht und in welche sich alles zurückbildet, und welche ich am liebsten mit dem Namen des Äthers bezeichne." Existence is to be explained as an activity of this original essence. Cf. *ibid.*, p. 123: "Der Äther sieht und erleuchtet, der Äther fühlt und erwärmt sich, der Äther polarisiert sich und ist elektrisch." A less imaginative expression of these ideas of Carus is found in his volume *Natur und Idee*, pp. 25 and 28: "Der Äther läßt . . . als die wahre Indifferenz alles Stoffartigen, als Stoff an sich eine besondere Schilderung seines Daseinszustandes nicht zu, und ebenso werden seine Handlungen stets nur erst durch sein irgendwie Differenziertsein möglich . . . Die Urhandlung des Äthers ist Leben." Cf. p. 18, n. 14, and the schematic survey of Carus' philosophy in H. Kern, *Carus*. The last principle remains: *"Die Urhandlung des Äthers ist Leben."*

will seize you!"[81] And the sacred mystery of Empedocles' end is that "we who are blind and in need of miracles" may know of the possibility of a return to infinite nature.[82] In Hölderlin's myth the infinite seizes man. It is not man who grasps in it the world. This is its fertility and also—its barrenness.

Neither the myth of the *World Soul* nor that of *Father Ether* could develop into a discursive mythology. In them, at best, the infinity of the universe could be visualized but its dissolution in a finite, surveyable and presentable, mythological or poetic organism remained an impossibility. This is tersely stated in August Wilhelm Schlegel's remark:[83] "The universe can only be visualized; discursive cognition of it is impossible." Yet, the visualization of the universe in the concept of a world soul presupposes the conception of a universal order through which the infinite is bound into an organized whole. Hardenberg stated once[84] that "it is not possible to conceive of the organism without the premise of the universal soul." He might as well have stated inversely that "it is not possible to conceive of a universal soul without the premise of the organism.[85] This means that infinity can be visual-

---

[81] F. Hölderlin, "Empedokles," *Werke,* p. 372:

    So wagts! was ihr geerbt, was ihr erworben,
    Was euch der Väter Mund erzählt, gelehrt,
    Gesetz' und Bräuch', der alten Götter Namen,
    Vergeßt es kühn, und hebt, wie Neugeborne,
    Die Augen auf zur göttlichen Natur!
    Wenn dann der Geist sich an des Himmels Licht
    Entzündet, süßer Lebensothem euch
    Den Busen, wie zum erstenmale, tränkt,
    . . . wenn euch das Leben
    Der Welt ergreift, ihr Friedensgeist, und euchs
    Wie heilger Wiegensang die Seele stillet,
    Dann . . .

[82] F. Hölderlin, "Empedokles," *Werke,* p. 368:

    So mußt es geschehen.
    So will es der Geist
    Und die reifende Zeit,
    Denn *einmal* bedurften
    Wir Blinden des Wunders.

[83] A. W. Schlegel, *Vorlesungen über schöne Literatur und Kunst,* II, 291.

[84] *Novalis Schriften,* II, 407. Cf. also II, 340f., where a more detailed analysis derives the same thought from the problem of perception.

[85] Ricarda Huch, *Ausbreitung und Verfall der Romantik,* p. 48, proceeds in this latter order. She postulates: "Die Welt ist eine lebendige Einheit"; all the other romantic principles follow thereupon as plausible consequences.

ized in its finite symbolic or organic representation, but that the retracing of it in terms of its finite symbols remains an infinite task. We can "see a world in a grain of sand,"[86] but to build the world from grains of sand is not within human power; it is the infinite labor of cosmic growth. This is the reason why it had to become characteristic of romantic thought and romantic poetry that it could never complete the plans which it conceived. It kept "discoursing" from one finite representation of the infinite to the next and never succeeded in covering the whole. This has been strikingly expressed by Henrich Steffens: "Whenever I tried to write a poem," he confessed in his memoirs,[87] "a subject imposed itself upon me which was of so deep and infinite a kind, that it was impossible to master it. . . The poem which I had in mind, would have been a poem of the universe." Here, indeed, we have virtually a definition of all romantic poetry. "It is the quintessence of romantic poetry," said Friedrich Schlegel,[88] "that it must be eternally growing, that it can never be complete." Romantic poetry is by definition a poem of the universe. It embraces everything "from the vastest system of art which contains several other systems to the sigh and the kiss breathed out by a child as the poet of artless song." Indeed, the universal poem of romanticism is the universe itself. The spirit of the world, said Schelling,[89] is thinking of a great poem which will be finished in the indeterminate future when time and eternity coincide. Until then the relentless growth of all living existence is "discoursing" through parts of the whole poem. We must visualize the whole in each part, and every poet must endeavor to conceive each partial work which he can

[86] Cf. p. 138, n. 12.

[87] Henrich Steffens, *Was ich erlebte* (Breslau, 1840-1844), IV, 401. Cf. also F. Strich, *Klassik und Romantik*, pp. 138f., and Else Huesmann, *Henrich Steffens in seinen Beziehungen zur deutschen Frühromantik unter besonderer Berücksichtigung der Naturphilosophie* (Kiel, 1929), p. 49.

[88] F. Schlegel, "Athenäums-Fragmente," 116.

[89] F. W. Schelling, "Philosophie der Kunst," §42, *Kunstanschauung der Frühromantik*, edited by Andreas Müller, "Deutsche Literatur, Reihe Romantik," III: "Wir können . . . behaupten, daß bis zu dem in noch unbestimmbarer Ferne liegenden Punkt, wo der Weltgeist das große Gedicht, auf das er sinnt, selbst vollendet haben, und das Nacheinander der modernen Welt sich in ein Zumal verwandelt haben wird, jeder große Dichter berufen sei, von dieser noch im Werden begriffenen (mythologischen) Welt, von der ihm seine Zeit nur einen Teil offenbaren kann,—von dieser Welt, sage ich, diesen ihm offenbaren Teil zu einem Ganzen zu bilden und aus dem Stoff derselben sich seine Mythologie zu schaffen."

produce as a representation of the whole. Indeed, there cannot be a romantic world poem, but neither can there be a truly romantic poem which does not aim at being a finite representation of one.

The fate of Goethe's plan to write a universal epic is typical in many respects.

There prevailed," Steffens wrote in his memoirs,[90] "in the circle of Goethe, Fichte, Schelling, and Schlegel the conscious and passionate will to collaborate in the perfection of a philosophical view of the world and to secure for it not only an adequate poetic expression but also an adequate application to the concerns of practical life.

Steffens refers here to the summer of the year 1798, i.e., the period in which Goethe read Eschenmayer's essay *On the Deduction of the Laws of Magnetic Phenomena from the Principles of a Metaphysics of Nature.*[91] It was due to the impression of this book that Goethe conceived the plan to write a poem on magnetism which would have been a parallel to that on the metamorphosis of plants. In a letter to Knebel[92] Goethe explained the purpose which he had in mind: "It seems necessary," he wrote, "to achieve in individual bits (*einzeln*) what would probably prove impossible as a whole." Yet, Goethe apparently found it hard to accept this conclusion and to abandon the plan of a universal poem of closed Lucretian form. Early in 1799 he referred once more to it, again in a letter to Knebel whose interest in these matters was naturally intense, for he was then already engaged in his translation of Lucretius' *De rerum natura.* Finally, however, Goethe dropped the project definitely. Still, a variety of individual poems, especially those which were grouped under the title of "God and World," must be considered as "individual bits" of the universal poem of which Goethe saw more and more clearly that it could not be completed. However, these bits are no fragments. Each one is complete and perfect in itself. Each one is an organic repetition of the whole in which it could have functioned as a part.

The plan of a classically developed universal poem, which

[90] Cf. Margarethe Plath, "Der Goethe-Schellingsche Plan eines philosophischen Naturgedichts," *Preußische Jahrbücher,* CVI (1901), p. 45.
[91] Cf. p. 162, n. 13.
[92] Goethe to Knebel, letter of July 1798. Also quoted by F. Strich, *Mythologie,* I, 332.

Goethe had abandoned, was inherited, as it were, by Schelling. Lucretius, whom Goethe would have tried to equal, was replaced by Dante as the model. The significance of this change may be inferred from a remark which August Wilhelm Schlegel made in his Berlin lectures of 1801 to 1804. He distinguished two possible forms of a perfect philosophical poem: the mythical and the prophetic. It is Dante whom Schlegel considered as the greatest representative of the latter.[93] Schelling's prophetic poem would have conceived of nature as one living organism animated by a universal soul and represented in temporal deployment by an infinite number of parts, each one of which could be considered as a metamorphic repetition of all the others as also of the whole.[94] Yet this poem too had to be executed "in bits." Only a few fragments of it such as "Fate of the Earth" and "Animal and Plant" are extant. They do not, furthermore, succeed in suggesting the lacking whole as Goethe's *"Gottnatur,"* e.g., certainly does. In his system of identities Schelling thought later on to have supplied an adequate substitute for the universal poem which he too could not produce.[95]

The so-called younger Romanticists were no longer interested in the problem of a universal poem. In them the organism of German thought attained a new metamorphosis. Self-sufficient organic concepts like state, nation, folk, history took the place of world, globe, nature, etc., of which they had formerly been constituent parts. Yet as an undercurrent the longing for a universal poem might probably be traced all through the Nineteenth Century[96]

[93] Cf. R. Haym, *Romantische Schule,* p. 862.

[94] Cf. F. Strich, *Mythologie,* II, 29ff.: "§5. Schellings Naturepos und sein Weg zur neuen Mythologie."

[95] Cf. M. Plath, "Der Goethe-Schellingsche Plan eines philosophischen Naturgedichts," p. 48; also R. Haym, *Romantische Schule,* p. 722: "[Das Identitätssystem] war wie ein philosophischer Auszug . . . jener Universalpoesie, welche Friedrich Schlegel gefordert hatte."

[96] Schelling's poem seems to have been the model for Johann Jakob Wagner's epic on nature, which was published as an appendix to this author's *Dichterschule,* Ulm, 1840. Wagner's philosophy was tetradic. It conceived of the cross rather than of the trinity as the basic mystery of the Christian world. This peculiarity is essential for the structure of his cosmic poem, which is fully characterized by the following excerpts:

 1. Leben strömet von Gott in's All und wieder zurücke,
  Seiend und werdend zugleich, stets thätig, sei es im Geiste,
  Wo es Erkenntnisse strahlt, und sei es im ruhenden Steine,

and down to its rebirth in new forms and with new means in the generation of Mombert, with his *Creation* of 1897. In 1855 a certain Frauenstädt expressed his conviction that "Goethe *would* have been the man"[97] to function as the Lucretius and Dante of his age; as late as 1922[98] Aldous Huxley had to lament the fact that even "the Twentieth Century still awaits its Lucretius, its own philosophical Dante."

Yet, all these facts and observations do not warrant the conclusion that romantic universalism was a failure. They merely

---

Wo es geschlagen von dir helltönende Laute entsendet.
§1 der Dichterschule . . .

32. Nur der ewige Wechsel genügt dem Leben, unendlich
Selbst im Endlichen noch erfreut es seiner Natur sich,
Daß es werdend sei und seiend werde auf immer . . .

67. Viere sind drum der Worte, die alles sagen, wie immer
Sein mag oder geschehen, Form, Wesen, Streit und Vermittlung.
Immer eilt das Wesen zur Form, durch Streit und Vermittlung
Sich zum Dinge gestaltend, es geht die Form in das Wesen
Schwindend wieder zurück, wenn die vermittelnden Bande
Nicht mehr binden und einerlei wird, was entgegengesetzt war . . .
Erste Stufe: die Einzelheit.

136. Erster Stufe Gesetz verwandelt das Sein in ein Dasein . . .
Zweite Stufe: die Entwicklung.

245. Entwicklung endet, wo das Fundament,
An dem man Art und Stufe schon erkennt,
Zusammendrängt, was in dem Ding gelegen . . .
Dritte Stufe: Verdoppelung . . .

300. Als Eiland schwimmt es [das Leben] in dem All der Leben,
Von ihm berührt und überall umgeben.
Erregt von der Berührung giebt es sich
In ihre Form und eignet innerlich
Sie an, und das Berührende verschwindet,
Wo das Berührte sich in eigner Tiefe gründet . . .
Vierte Stufe: Ganzheit . . .

354. Wo sich noch Beseelung zu solcher Entwicklung gesellet,
Wird das große vollkommen vom kleinen Leben gespiegelt,
Zwar im Wesen beschränkt, doch in den Formen der Ganzheit
Jenem gleichgestellt, wie alle Kreise sich gleichen . . .

409. Alle doch hält sie [die Dinge] zusammen der Ring des Ganzen, von diesem
Prallen sie wieder zurück, wie an Meeres Ufer die Brandung
Auf sich selbst geworfen, und in sich wühlend, bis jedem
Form sich bildet und Kraft, die allen andern gemäß ist,
Und notwendig erscheint, was jedem einzeln zu Teil wird.

[97] Christian M. Julius Frauenstädt, *Die Naturwissenschaft in ihrem Einfluß auf Poesie, Religion, Moral und Philosophie* (Leipzig, 1855), p. 47.

[98] Aldous Huxley, "The Subject Matter of Poetry," *Chapbook*, London, March, 1920.

prove that the modern world escapes Lucretian comprehension.[99]
It is an infinite world, and a complete representation of it would
also have to be infinite. Further, however, it is an organic world,
and this means that all of its partial poetic representations must
be organic repetitions of the ideal, nonexistent whole. What Adam
Müller[100] said in his lectures of 1808 about the work of Hardenberg may well be repeated with regard to all romantic literature: It consists but of fragments; yet there is "in each fragment
—aside from its individual significance—a something which one
would like to call an organic longing to flow out into the others.
There is in each word an intangible urge to seize the others and to
form the new gospel which Lessing promised." However, one may
go one step farther. With regard to Hardenberg, the most romantic
of all romantics, it is necessary to speak of a conscious endeavor,
not merely, as Müller did, of an "intangible urge" and a vague
"longing" for a universal dissolution of all self-sufficiencies. Hardenberg's plan for a cosmic "encyclopedistic" can prove this
point. He himself characterized this enterprise as a "scientific
bible,"[101] explaining that "bible" meant the "real and ideal model"
of all books, the book of books, one might say the prototype of
all possible books. To write "the scientific bible"; to treat the
sciences according to Goethes' method;[102] to prepare for print a
manuscript of the "encyclopedic, systematic index of our mind,"
which we have before us in the totality of nature's phenomena:[103]
these are then but different ways of referring to the one great business of Hardenberg's life.[104] From this point of view it becomes

[99] Cf. G. Santayana, *Three Philosophical Poets*. The third of these essays, on
Goethe, develops the thought that modern knowledge is too complex for the realization of the ideal of an *uomo universale*.

[100] A. Müller, *Vorlesungen*, pp. 81f.

[101] *Novalis Schriften*, III, 208.

[102] *Novalis Schriften*, III, 251. Cf. p. 154, n. 78.

[103] *Novalis Schriften*, II, 369.

[104] Hardenberg's enclycopedic endeavors represent a typical trend of the age. Carl
Friedrich Burdach, *Propädeutik zum Studium der gesamten Heilkunst* (Leipzig,
1800), demanded a truly encyclopedic education for students of medicine. The ideal
physician is here described as a veritable universalist. This fact may serve to indicate
the broader psychic bases of the romantic version of encyclopedism. Cf. R. Haym,
Romantische Schule, p. 722: Schelling's system of identities was "die Verwirk-
lichung jener Enzyklopädie, welche . . . Hardenberg im Sinne lag"; p. 744 on Fried-

necessary to consider all his works, not only his fragments and certainly not only those which were written in conscious elaboration of his "encyclopedistic" plan, as fragments of it, i.e., as fragments of Hardenberg's bible. This is the task to which he devoted his entire life, for he felt that God had devoted His Life to it, too.

Hardenberg's method might be described as a rational imitation of the methods of nature. Its endeavor was to connect everything with everything; to permit no isolation; to discuss all phenomena in terms of all the others. On this basis it is not only possible but necessary to approach, e.g., the data of physiology from the standpoint of the chemistry, poetry, mathematics, etc. There is consequently in Hardenberg's "encyclopedistic" a place for "poetic physiology, for chemical, philosophical, and mathematical physiology."[105] Theological, grammatical, political, economic, and all the other possible physiologies are merely gaps which Hardenberg did not find time to fill out. He actually began, however, to collect material on "moral astronomy,"[106] "technical pedagogy," "physical history," "physical philosophy," "natural artistics," "physical artistics," "mental physics," "mystic philology," "mathematical philosophy," "literary politics," "physiological politics," "physical grammar," "logical dynamics," "philosophical physics," "pathological logic," "pathological philosophy," "physical psychology," etc.[107]

---

rich Schlegel; pp. 829 and 911 on August Wilhelm Schlegel's "Privatissimum über Enzyklopädie," 1803; p. 907 on Schelling's *Philosophie der Kunst;* pp. 907 and 927f. on Hegel. H. Cysarz, *Erfahrung und Idee,* p. 178, gives, finally, a brief survey of the entire trend by contrasting Kant and Hegel as its basis and fulfillment: "Kant läßt die Einzelwissenschaften unabhängig bestehen, der Romantiker unterwirft sie systematisch seiner Philosophie; so entsteht die Wissenschaftslehre und der Globus Schellings, so das plotinistische Ideengebäude des Novalis, die Ansätze zur Philosophie der Geisteswissenschaften bei Friedrich Schlegel, die Enzyklopädie Hegels. Kant ist von leuchtender Klarheit im Einzelnen, läßt aber hinsichtlich des Ganzen Zweifeln und Deutungen Raum; demgegenüber stellt ein Denker wie Hegel gerade das Ganze seines Gebäudes in lückenloser, prachtvoller Architektonik vor unser Auge, während umgekehrt die Einzelheiten der Gedankengänge Schwierigkeiten bereiten."

[105] *Novalis Schriften,* III, 88, 93, and 129.

[106] *Novalis Schriften,* IV, 232, letter to Friedrich Schlegel of July, 1798. It is Hardenberg himself who suggests that the roots of the idea of a "moral astronomy" should be sought in Hemsterhuis.

[107] *Novalis Schriften,* III, 65, 68, 73, 75, 82, 85, 98, 106, 114, 178, 223, 226, 243.

Neither the absurdity of some of these combinations nor the fertility of others is at present of importance. The question is rather how any one thinker could have the courage to embark upon a venture of this sort. Is it not obvious in advance that there can be no end to it? Every new phenomenon which came to Hardenberg's attention should, strictly speaking, have been treated under as many aspects as there were other problems previously discussed. Completion of this plan could be imagined only in infinity. Yet, it is unlikely that Hardenberg gave ever any thought to the possibility of completion. He was a "loom of ideas,"[108] and thus he wove as the loom of Creation is weaving, connecting each thread with all the others of an infinite texture. Hardenberg's "encyclopedistic" was as little capable of completion as life or nature or the universal poem of the spirit of the world.[109] Yet are not these, which never reach completion, complete in every single moment?[110] Indeed, this seems to be the final essence of the romantic world of thought and of its works: there are but fragments, yet each one tends to be the whole.

[108] *Novalis Schriften*, IV, letter to Karoline Just of March 28, 1797.

[109] Cf. p. 261, n. 89.

[110] A passage from F. Strich, *Klassik und Romantik*, pp. 132f., may, indeed, be adapted so that it becomes a characterization of the romantic ideal instead of being exclusively applicable to Goethe's classicism, with which it was originally concerned: "Was war es, das die Romantiker nicht zu einem kosmogonischen Epos kommen ließ, obwohl sie sich doch die ganze Natur mit dichterischer Anschauungskraft vor die Seele gestellt hatten? Der Grund war dieser: daß ihre Naturanschauung innerlich nicht kosmogonisch war. Ihr *romantisches* Auge sah die Natur in jedem Augenblick, in jedem Punkt am Ziel."

BIBLIOGRAPHY

Note: The following books and articles were of general importance in the progress of the foregoing analyses. Sources used for unessential quotations are fully identified in the notes. Obligations not explicitly acknowledged are unconscious but none the less real.

Abbreviations: ADB = Allgemeine Deutsche Biographie; DL = Deutsche Literatur in Entwicklungsreihen; DNL = Deutsche National-Literatur; OED = Oxford English Dictionary; PMLA = Publications of the Modern Language Association of America.

Abercrombie, Lascelles.   Romanticism. London, 1926.
Akenside, Mark.   "The Pleasures of Imagination." The Poems of the Pleasures. Philadelphia, 1870.
    Cf. G. R. Potter.
Alembert, Jean le Rond d'.   Traité de dynamique. Nouvelle édition, revue et fort augmentée par l'auteur. Paris, 1758.
Alexander, Samuel.   Space, Time, and Deity. The Gifford lectures at Glasgow 1916-1918. 2 vols. London (1920), 1927.
Allgemeine Deutsche Biographie. Various editors. 56 vols. Leipzig: Dunckor & Humblot, 1875-1912.
Arnim, Achim von.   Versuch einer Theorie der elektrischen Erscheinungen. Halle: Jacob Gebauer, 1799.
    Cf. H. Becker, E. Darmstädter, H. R. Liedke, O. Mallon, R. Steig.
Arnim, Sophie Gräfin von.   Carl Gustav Carus. Sein Leben und Wirken. Dresden, 1930.
Baader, Franz Xaver von.   Sämmtliche Werke. Edited by . . . Franz Hoffmann. 15 vols. Leipzig, 1850-1860.
    Cf. D. Baumgardt, F. Lieb, J. Nohl.
Barthels, Ernst.   Goethes Wissenschaftslehre in ihrer modernen Tragweite. Bonn, 1922.
Baumgardt, David.   Franz von Baader und die philosophische Romantik. "Deutsche Vierteljahresschrift für Literatur-Wissenschaft und Geistesgeschichte, Buchreihe." Vol. 10. Halle, 1927.
Becker, Herma.   Achim von Arnim in den wissenschaftlichen und politischen Strömungen seiner Zeit. "Abhandlungen zur mittleren und neueren Geschichte." Vol. 37. Berlin and Leipzig, 1912.
Beethoven, Ludwig van.   Beethovens Denkmal im Wort. Edited by Richard Benz. Offenbach-on-Main: Gerstung, 1924.
    Cf. F. Cassirer.

Benz, Richard. Märchendichtung der Romantiker. Gotha, 1908.
  Cf. L. v. Beethoven.
Bernoulli, Christoph and Kern, Hans (editors). Romantische Natur-
  philosophie. "Gott-Natur, Schriftenreihe zur Neubegründung der
  Naturphilosophie." Edited by Wilhelm Rößle. Jena: Eugen
  Diederichs, 1926.
Berthelot, René. Science et philosophie chez Goethe. Paris, 1932.
Beyersdorff, Robert. Giordano Bruno und Shakespeare. Wissenschaft-
  liche Beilage zum Programm des Großherzoglichen Gymnasiums in
  Oldenburg, 1889.
Biese, Alfred. Das Naturgefühl im Wandel der Zeiten. Leipzig: Quelle
  & Meyer, 1926.
Biot, Jean Baptiste. "De l'Influence des idées exactes dans les ouvrages
  littéraires" (Mercure de France, 1809). Mélanges scientifiques et
  littéraires. Vol. 2. Paris, 1858. Pp. 1-20.
Blake, William.
  Cf. C. Robinson, M. Wilson.
Bonnet, Charles. La Palingénésie philosophique ou idées sur l'état
  passé et sur l'état futur des êtres vivans. Vol. 1. Geneva, 1769.
Börne, Ludwig. Gesammelte Schriften. Vollständige Ausgabe in drei
  Bänden. Leipzig: Reclam, n.d.
Boucke, Ewald Augustus (editor). [Introduction to] Goethes Werke.
  Kleine Ausgabe. Vol. 1: Gedichte. Leipzig: Bibliograpisches In-
  stitut, n.d.
Braid, James. The Power of the Mind over the Body. An experimental
  inquiry into the nature and cause of the phenomena attributed by
  Baron Reichenbach and others to a new imponderable. London,
  1846.
Brecht, Walther. Heinse und der ästhetische Immoralismus. Zur
  Geschichte der italienischen Renaissance in Deutschland. Berlin,
  1911.
Brentano, Clemens Maria. Sämtliche Werke. Edited by Carl Schüdde-
  kopf. Munich and Leipzig, 1909-1917 (not completed).
Brentano, Clemens Maria. [Selections in] Märchen. Edited by Andreas
  Müller. "DL. Reihe Romantik." Vol. 14. Leipzig: Reclam, 1930.
  Cf. R. Steig.
Brockes, Barthold Heinrich. [Selections in] Gegner der zweiten schlesi-
  schen Schule. Edited by Ludwig Fulda. "DNL." Vol. 39. Berlin
  and Stuttgart, 1884. Pp. 275-382.
Brown, Junius Flagg. Psychology and the Social Order. New York and
  London: McGraw-Hill, 1936.
Brüggemann, Fritz. Die Ironie als entwicklungsgeschichtliches Mo-

ment. Beitrag zur Vorgeschichte der deutschen Romantik. Jena, 1909.

Brüggemann, Fritz (editor). [Introduction to] Das Weltbild der deutschen Aufklärung. "DL. Reihe Aufklärung." Vol. 2. Leipzig: Reclam, 1930.

Bruhns, Karl (editor). Alexander von Humboldt. Eine wissenschaftliche Biographie. Leipzig, 1872.

Bruno, Giordano. Le Opere italiane. Edited by Paul Lagarde. Vol. 1. Göttingen, 1888.
     Cf. R. Beyersdorff, W. Saenger, J. Sarauw.

Buchheim, Karl. Wahrheit und Geschichte. Leipzig: Hegner, 1935.

Buchner, Eberhard (editor). Ärzte und Kurpfuscher. Kulturhistorisch interessante Dokumente aus alten deutschen Zeitungen. Munich: Albert Langen, 1922.

Bulle, Ferdinand. Franziskus Hemsterhuis und der deutsche Irrationalismus des 18. Jahrhunderts. Jena, 1911.

Bulle, Ferdinand. "Zur Struktur des Pantheismus: Die Kategorie der Totalität in Goethes naturwissenschaftlichen Schriften." *Euphorion*, XXI (1914), 156-182.

Burdach, Karl Friedrich. Blicke ins Leben (4 vols. 1842-1848). [Extracts in] Romantische Naturphilosophie. Edited by Christoph Bernoulli and Hans Kern. Jena: Eugen Diederichs, 1926. Pp. 197-220.

Burdach, Karl Friedrich. Die Zeitrechnung des menschlichen Lebens (1829). [Essentially unabridged in] Romantische Naturphilosophie. Edited by Christoph Bernoulli and Hans Kern. Jena: Eugen Diederichs, 1926. Pp. 177-196.

Carrel, Alexis. Man the Unknown. New York: Harper, 1935.

Carus, Carl Gustav. Briefe über Goethes Faust. First series. Leipzig, 1835.

Carus, Carl Gustav. Denkschrift zum 100jährigen Geburtsfeste Goethes. Ueber ungleiche Befähigung der verschiedenen Menschheitsstämme für höhere geistige Entwicklung. Leipzig, 1849.

Carus, Carl Gustav. Goethe, zu dessen näherem Verständnis. Leipzig, 1843 (Vienna, 1863; Dresden, 1927; Leipzig, 1931).

Carus, Carl Gustav. Lebenserinnerungen und Denkwürdigkeiten. 4 vols. Leipzig, 1856-1866.

Carus, Carl Gustav. Mnemosyne. Blätter aus Gedenk- und Tagebüchern. Pforzheim, 1848.

Carus, Carl Gustav. Natur und Idee *oder* Das Werdende und sein Gesetz. Eine philosophische Grundlage für die specielle Naturwissenschaft. Vienna, 1861.

Carus, Carl Gustav. Organon der Erkenntnis der Natur und des Geistes. Leipzig, 1856.

Carus, Carl Gustav. Physis. Zur Geschichte des leiblichen Lebens. Stuttgart, 1851.

Carus, Carl Gustav. Psyche. Zur Entwicklungsgeschichte der Seele (Pforzheim, 1846). Stuttgart, 1851² (Abridged edition by Ludwig Klages. Jena, 1926).

Carus, Carl Gustav. Symbolik der menschlichen Gestalt. Ein Handbuch zur Menschenkenntnis. Leipzig, 1853.

Carus, Carl Gustav. Vergleichende Psychologie *oder* Geschichte der Seele in der Reihenfolge der Thierwelt. Vienna, 1866.

Carus, Carl Gustav. Zwölf Briefe über das Erdleben. Stuttgart, 1841.
  Cf. S. v. Arnim, H. Kern, E. Langewisch, A. Meyer, E. Wäsche.

Cassirer, Ernst. Idee und Gestalt. Fünf Aufsätze. Berlin, 1921.

Cassirer, Ernst. Individuum und Kosmos in der Philosophie der Renaissance. "Studien der Bibliothek Warburg." Edited by Fritz Saxl. Vol. 10. Leipzig and Berlin, 1927.

Cassirer, Fritz. Beethoven und die Gestalt. Stuttgart, Berlin, Leipzig, 1925.

Chénier, André. Poésies. Edited by L. Becq de Fouquières. Paris, 1862.

Corday, Michel. "L'Image scientifique en littérature." *La Revue de Paris,* V (1904), 837-853.

Creuzer, Friedrich.
  Cf. E. Howald.

Croce, Benedetto ([Articles published in 1912 and 1913. Collected as] Zur Theorie und Geschichte der Historiographie. Tübingen, 1915). Teoria e storia della storiografia. Bari, 1917.

Crum, Ralph Brinckerhoff. Scientific Thought in Poetry. New York, 1931.

Cusanus, Nikolaus Krebs.
  Cf. E. Cassirer (Individuum und Kosmos).

Cysarz, Herbert. Erfahrung und Idee. Probleme und Lebensformen in der deutschen Literatur von Hamann bis Hegel. Vienna and Leipzig, 1921.

Cysarz, Herbert. "Zur Zeit- und Wesensbestimmung des dichterischen Barockstils." *Forschungen und Fortschritte,* XI (1935), 409f.

Dacqué, Edgar. "Außen und Innen der organischen Entwicklung." *Corona,* VI (1936), 129-162.

Dacqué, Edgar. Urwelt, Sage und Menschheit. Munich (1924), 1925³.

Darmstädter, Ernst. "Achim von Arnim und die Naturwissenschaft." *Euphorion,* XXXII (1931), 454-475.

Darmstaedter, Ludwig. Handbuch zur Geschichte der Naturwissenschaften und der Technik. In chronologischer Darstellung. Unter Mitwirkung von Prof. Dr. R. Du Bois-Reymond und Oberst z.D. C. Schaefer. Berlin, 1908².

Dessoir, Max. Vom Jenseits der Seele. Die Geheimwissenschaften in kritischer Betrachtung. Stuttgart (1917), 1920⁴⁻⁵.

Deubel, Werner. "Goethe als Begründer eines neuen Weltbildes." *Jahrbuch der Goethe-Gesellschaft*, XVII (1931), 27-80.

Deubel, Werner. "Gräkogermanisch-Gräkojudaisch." *Völkische Kultur*, October, 1934.

Deubel, Werner. "Umrisse eines neuen Schillerbildes." *Jahrbuch der Goethe-Gesellschaft*, XX (1934), 1ff.

Deutsche Literatur. Sammlung literarischer Kunst- und Kulturdenkmäler in Entwicklungsreihen. Edited by . . . Prof. Dr. Heinz Kindermann. Leipzig: Reclam, 1928ff.

Deutsche National-Literatur. Historisch-kritische Ausgabe. Edited by . . . Joseph Kürschner. Berlin and Stuttgart, 1882-1897.

Diderot, Denis. Œuvres complètes. Edited by J. Assézat. Paris, 1875. Cf. E. Key.

Diepgen, Paul. Deutsche Medizin vor hundert Jahren. Ein Beitrag zur Geschichte der Romantik. [Publications of] "Freiburger wissenschaftliche Gesellschaft." Vol. 10. Freiburg i. Br., 1923.

Drachman, Julian M. Studies in the Literature of Natural Science. New York, 1930.

Draper, John William. History of the Conflict between Religion and Science (1875). Abridged by Charles T. Sprading. New York: Vanguard Press, 1926.

Drews, Arthur. Die Lehre von Raum und Zeit in der Nachkantischen Philosophie. Halle, 1889.

Du Bois-Reymond, Emil. Culturgeschichte und Naturwissenschaft (*Deutsche Rundschau*, November, 1877). Leipzig, 1878.

Durant, Will. The Story of Philosophy. New York, 1926.

Eichendorff, Joseph Freiherr von. [Selections in] Friedrich Baron de la Motte-Fouqué und Joseph Freiherr von Eichendorff. Edited by Max Koch. "DNL." Vol. 146, 2. Berlin and Stuttgart, 1893.

Eichendorff, Joseph Freiherr von. Geschichte der poetischen Literatur Deutschlands. 2 vols. Paderborn (1857), 1861.

Einstein, Albert. Cosmic Religion with Other Opinions and Aphorisms. New York: Covici-Friede, 1931.

Elkuß, Siegbert. Zur Beurteilung der Romantik und zur Kritik ihrer Erforschung. Munich, 1918.

Ellis, Oliver. Poetry and Science and Other Essays in Prose. Manchester: Sherratt, 1924.

Ennemoser, Joseph. "Beiträge zur Seelenkunde der Thiere." *Zeitschrift für psychische Aerzte*, III (1820f.), 49-100 and 679-708 (not completed).

Ennemoser, Joseph. Der Geist des Menschen in der Natur *oder* Die Psychologie in Übereinstimmung mit der Naturkunde. Stuttgart and Tübingen, 1849.

Erhard, Johann Benjamin. Denkwürdigkeiten des Philosophen und Arztes Johann Benjamin Erhard. Edited by Karl August Varnhagen von Ense. Stuttgart, 1830.

Erman, Wilhelm. Der tierische Magnetismus in Preußen vor und nach den Befreiungskriegen. "Beihefte der Historischen Zeitschrift." Vol. 4. Munich and Berlin, 1925.

Ermatinger, Emil. Die Weltanschauung des jungen Wieland. Frauenfeld, 1907.

Eschenmayer, Carl August. Psychologie in drei Theilen als empirische, reine und angewandte. Stuttgart and Tübingen, 1817.

Eucken, Rudolf (Grundbegriffe der Gegenwart. Leipzig, 1904). Geistige Strömungen der Gegenwart. Leipzig, 1916[5].

Feuchtersleben, Ernst Freiherr von.
    Cf. M. Neuburger.

Fichte, Johann Gottlieb. Werke. Auswahl in sechs Bänden. Edited by Fritz Medicus. "Philosophische Bibliothek." Vols. 127ff. Leipzig: Felix Meiner, 1908-1912.

Fichte, Johann Gottlieb. Die Schriften zu J. G. Fichtes Atheismus-Streit. Edited by Hans Lindau. "Bibliothek der Philosophen." Edited by Fritz Mauthner. Vol. 4. Munich: Georg Müller, 1912.

Fiesel, Eva Lehmann. Die Sprachphilosophie der deutschen Romantik 1801-1816. Tübingen, 1927.

Fischer, E. K. Deutsche Kunst und Art. Von den Künsten als Ausdruck der Zeiten. Dresden: Sibyllen-Verlag, 1924.

Fischer, Johann Carl. Geschichte der Physik seit der Wiederherstellung der Künste und Wissenschaften bis auf die neuesten Zeiten. 8 vols. "Geschichte der Naturwissenschaften." [Section 8 of] "Geschichte der Künste und Wissenschaften seit der Wiederherstellung derselben bis ans Ende des 18. Jahrhunderts. Von einer Gesellschaft gelehrter Männer ausgearbeitet." Göttingen, 1801-1808.

Fontenelle, Bernard le Bovier de. Entretiens sur la pluralité des mondes (1686). Augmentés des Dialogues des morts. Nouvelle édition. Marseilles, 1780.

Frauenstädt, Christian M. Julius. Die Naturwissenschaft in ihrem Einfluß auf Poesie, Religion, Moral und Philosophie. Leipzig, 1855.

Fusil, Casimir Alexandre. La Poésie scientifique de 1750 à nos jours. Paris, 1918.

Giersberg, Hermann. "Gehirnverpflanzungen bei Amphibien." *Forschungen und Fortschritte,* XII (1936), 326f.

Giese, Fritz. Der romantische Charakter. Vol. 1: Die Entwicklung des Androgynenproblems in der Frühromantik. Langensalza, 1919.

Girtanner, Christoph. Über das Kantische Prinzip für die Naturgeschichte. Göttingen, 1796.

Goedeke, Karl. Grundriß zur Geschichte der deutschen Dichtung aus den Quellen. Continued by Edmund Goetze. Dresden, 1907-1935³.
Cf. F. v. Schiller.

Goethe, Johann Wolfgang von. Sämmtliche Werke in vierzig Bänden. Stuttgart and Augsburg: Cotta, 1858.

Goethe, Johann Wolfgang von. Werke. Herausgegeben im Auftrage der Großherzogin Sophie von Sachsen. Weimar: Böhlau, 1887-1919.

Goethe, Johann Wolfgang von. Goethe und die Romantik. Briefe mit Erläuterungen. Edited by Oskar Walzel and Carl Schüddekopf. "Schriften der Goethe-Gesellschaft." Vols. 13-14. Weimar, 1898-1899.
Cf. E. Barthels, R. Berthelot, E. A. Boucke, F. Bulle, C. G. Carus, E. Cassirer ("Goethe und die mathematische Physik." Idee und Gestalt), W. Deubel, A. Hansen, H. v. Helmholtz, R. Hering, W. Jablonski, E. Key, C. v. Klinckowstroem, H. A. Korff, J. Körner, W. Lubosch, A. Meyer, R. M. Meyer, M. Plath, W. Saenger, G. Santayana, J. Schiff, O. Schmidt, R. Virchow, H. Wohlbold.

Görres, Joseph von. Gesammelte Schriften. Edited by Wilhelm Schellberg. Cologne, 1926ff. Vol. 2, 1: Naturwissenschaftliche, kunst- und naturphilosophische Schriften I (1800-1803). Edited by Robert Stein. With an introduction to Görres' "Aphorismen über die Kunst" by Adolf Dyroff. Cologne, 1932. Vol. 2, 2: Naturwissenschaftliche und naturphilosophische Schriften II (1793-1810). Edited by Robert Stein. Cologne, 1934.

Gray, George W. "Our Greater Galaxy." *Yale Review,* XXV (Autumn, 1935), 60-75.

Gruppe, Otto Friedrich. Antäus. Ein Briefwechsel über spekulative Philosophie in ihrem Konflikt mit Wissenschaft und Sprache (1831). Gruppes Philosophische Werke. Vol. 1. Edited by Fritz Mauthner. "Bibliothek der Philosophen." Edited by Fritz Mauthner. Vol. 12. Munich: Georg Müller, 1914.

Gundolf (Gundelfinger), Friedrich. Dichter und Helden. Heidelberg, 1921.

Gundolf (Gundelfinger), Friedrich. Paracelsus. Berlin: Bondi, 1928.

Hamburger, Käte. "Novalis und die Mathematik." Romantik-Forschungen. "Deutsche Vierteljahresschrift für Literatur-

Wissenschaft und Geistesgeschichte, Buchreihe." Vol. 16. Halle: Niemeyer, 1929. Pp. 113-184.

Hansen, Adolph. Goethes Morphologie (Metamorphose der Pflanzen und Osteologie). Ein Beitrag zum sachlichen und philosophischen Verständnis und zur Kritik der morphologischen Begriffsbildung. Gießen, 1919.

Hardenberg, Friedrich von. Novalis Schriften. 4 vols. Edited by Paul Kluckhohn. Leipzig: Bibliographisches Institut, n.d.
>   Cf. K. Hamburger, A. Huber, W. Olshausen, E. Spenlé, R. Unger ("Novalis' Hymnen an die Nacht." "Zur Datierung und Deutung der Hymnen an die Nacht." Herder, Novalis und Kleist).

Haym, Rudolf. Die romantische Schule. Ein Beitrag zur Geschichte des deutschen Geistes (1870). Edited by Oskar Walzel. Berlin, 1920[4].

Heinse, Wilhelm. Sämmtliche Werke. Edited by Carl Schüddekopf. Leipzig, 1903-1910.
>   Cf. W. Brecht.

Helmholtz, Hermann von. "Goethes Vorahnungen kommender naturwissenschaftlicher Ideen." Goethes naturwissenschaftliches Denken und Wirken. Published by the editorial board of Die Naturwissenschaften. Berlin, 1932.

Hemmeter, John C. "Mutationen in geschichtlichen Begriffen und der Zusammenhang medizinischer Ideen und Lehren." Festschrift zur Feier seines 60. Geburtstages Max Neuburger gewidmet. Vienna, 1928.

Hemsterhuis, Franziskus. Alexis oder Von dem goldenen Zeitalter. Translated by Friedrich Heinrich Jacobi. Riga: Johann Friedrich Hartknoch, 1787.

Hemsterhuis, Franziskus. Über den Menschen und die Beziehungen desselben. "Vermischte Philosophische Schriften des H. Hemsterhuis." Vol. 1. Leipzig, 1782.

Hemsterhuis, Franziskus (anon.). Lettre sur l'homme et ses rapports. Paris, 1772.
>   Cf. F. Bulle.

Herder, Johann Gottfried. Sämmtliche Werke. 32 vols. Edited by Bernhard Suphan. Berlin, 1877-1913.

Herder, Johann Gottfried. Philosophie. Ausgewählte Denkmäler aus der Werdezeit der neuen deutschen Bildung. Edited by Horst Stephan. "Philosophische Bibliothek." Vol. 112. Leipzig: Felix Meiner, 1906.
>   Cf. O. Loerke, R. Unger ("Herder und der Palingenesiegedanke." Herder, Novalis und Kleist).

Hering, Robert. "Der Prosahymnus 'Die Natur' und sein Verfasser." *Jahrbuch der Goethe-Gesellschaft*, XIII (1927), 138-156.

Hölderlin, Friedrich. Sämtliche Werke. Edited by Friedrich Michael. 1 vol. Leipzig: Insel-Verlag, n.d.
    Cf. E. Cassirer ("Hölderlin und der deutsche Idealismus." Idee und Gestalt), F. Gundolf ("Hölderlins Archipelagus." Dichter und Helden).

Hoppe, Edmund. Geschichte der Elektrizität. Leipzig: Johann Ambrosius Barth, 1884.

Hoppe, Edmund. Zur Geschichte der Fernwirkung. Beilage zum Jahresbericht des Wilhelm-Gymnasiums. Hamburg, 1901.

Howald, Ernst (editor). Der Kampf um Creuzers Symbolik. Eine Auswahl von Dokumenten. Tübingen: J. C. B. Mohr (Paul Siebeck), 1926.

Huber, A. "Studien zu Novalis mit besonderer Berücksichtigung der Naturphilosophie." *Euphorion*, VI (1899), Supplement 4. Pp. 90ff.

Huch, Ricarda. Die Blütezeit der Romantik. Leipzig (1899), 1920[11].

Huch, Ricarda. Ausbreitung und Verfall der Romantik. Leipzig (1902), 1920[9].

Huesmann, Else. Henrich Steffens in seinen Beziehungen zur deutschen Frühromantik unter besonderer Berücksichtigung der Naturphilosophie. Kiel, 1929.

Hufeland, Christoph Wilhelm. Art of Prolonging Life. Edited by Erasmus Wilson, F. R. S. ([Translation of] Makrobiotik *oder* Die Kunst, das menschliche Leben zu verlängern. 1796). Boston, 1854.

Hufeland, Friedrich. Über Sympathie (Weimar, 1811). [Extracts in] Romantische Naturphilosophie. Edited by Christoph Bernoulli and Hans Kern. Jena: Eugen Diederichs, 1926. Pp. 32-98.

Humboldt, Alexander von. Cosmos. A Sketch of a Physical Description of the Universe. Translated from the German by E. C. Otté. Vol. 3. New York: Harper, 1860.

Humboldt, Alexander von. "Die Lebenskraft *oder* Der Rhodische Genius." *Die Horen,* I, 5 (1795), 90-96.
    Cf. K. Bruhns.

Huschke, Aemilius. Mimische und Physiognomische Studien. Translated from the Latin by Dr. med. Will Rink. "Der Körper als Ausdruck. Schriftenreihe zur Gestaltenkunde." Edited by Theodor Lessing and Will Rink. Vol. 2. Dresden: Madaus, 1931.

Jablonski, Walter. "Die geistesgeschichtliche Stellung der Naturforschung Goethes." *Jahrbuch der Goethe-Gesellschaft,* XV (1929), 22-61.

Jespersen, Otto. Language. Its Nature, Development, and Origin. New York: Henry Holt, 1922.

Joël, Karl. Der Ursprung der Naturphilosophie aus dem Geiste der Mystik. With an appendix "Archaische Romantik." Jena, 1906.

Jung-Stilling, Heinrich. Sämmtliche Schriften. Vol. 6: Theorie der Geisterkunde. Stuttgart, 1837.

Kant, Immanuel. Gesammelte Schriften. Published by the Prussian Academy of Sciences. Berlin, 1900-1936.

Kant, Immanuel. Metaphysische Anfangsgründe der Naturwissenschaften. Riga: Johann Friedrich Hartknoch, 1786.

Kant, Immanuel. Versuch, den Begriff der negativen Größen in die Weltweisheit einzuführen. Grätz, 1797.
Cf. R. Unger.

Kaßner, Rudolf. Die Grundlagen der Physiognomik. Leipzig, 1922.

Kern, Hans. Die Philosophie des Carl Gustav Carus. Berlin, 1926.
Cf. Chr. Bernoulli.

Key, Ellen. "Der Diderot Goethes." Seelen und Werke. Berlin: Fischer, 1911. Pp. 1-60.

Kieser, Dietrich Georg von. System des Tellurismus oder tierischen Magnetismus (1822). [Extracts in] Romantische Naturphilosophie. Edited by Christoph Bernoulli and Hans Kern. Jena: Eugen Diederichs, 1926. Pp. 99-109.

Klages, Ludwig. Die Grundlagen der Charakterkunde. Leipzig: Johann Ambrosius Barth, 1928[6].

Kleist, Heinrich von.
Cf. E. Cassirer ("Heinrich von Kleist und die Kantische Philosophie." Idee und Gestalt), R. Unger ("Das Todesproblem bei Heinrich von Kleist." Herder, Novalis und Kleist).

Klinckowstroem, Carl Graf von. "Goethe und Ritter." Jahrbuch der Goethe-Gesellschaft, VIII (1921), 135-151.

Klinckowstroem, Carl Graf von. "Johann Wilhelm Ritter und der Elektromagnetismus." Archiv für die Geschichte der Naturwissenschaft und der Technik, IX (1922), 68ff.

Kluckhohn, Paul. Die Auffassung der Liebe in der Literatur des 18. Jahrhunderts und in der deutschen Romantik. Halle (1922), 1931.

Kluckhohn, Paul (editor). [Introduction to] Weltanschauung der Frühromantik. "DL. Reihe Romantik." Vol. 5. Leipzig: Reclam, 1932.
Cf. F. v. Hardenberg.

Koch, Willi August (editor). Briefe deutscher Romantiker. Leipzig: Dieterich, 1938.

Kolbe, Georg. "Zur Geschichte der Totenmaske." Das ewige Antlitz.

Edited by Ernst Benkard. Berlin: Frankfurter Verlags-Anstalt, 1926.

Koreff, David Ferdinand.
    Cf. F. v. Oppeln-Bronikowski.

Korff, Hermann August. Geist der Goethezeit. Versuch einer ideellen Entwicklung der klassisch-romantischen Literaturgeschichte. 2 vols. Leipzig: J. J. Weber, 1923 and 1930.

Körner, Josef. "Krisenjahre der Frühromantik." *Forschungen und Fortschritte*, XII (1936), 406f.

Körner, Josef (editor). Krisenjahre der Frühromantik. Briefe aus dem Schlegelkreis. Funde und Forschungen zum Geistesleben des 19. Jahrhunderts. Vol. 1. Brünn, 1936.

Körner, Josef. Romantiker und Klassiker. Die Brüder Schlegel in ihren Beziehungen zu Schiller und Goethe. Berlin, 1924.

Kossel, Walter. "Zu Philipp Lenards 50jährigem Doktorjubiläum." *Forschungen und Fortschritte*, XII (1936), 247f.

Kotzebue, August von. "Das neue Jahrhundert." Neue Schauspiele. Vol. 5. 1801.

Laiblin, Wilhelm. "Vom mythischen Gehalt unserer Märchen. Ihre kosmische und innerseelische Symbolik." Vom Sinn des Mythos. Essays by Wilhelm Schloz and Wilhelm Laiblin. "Schriften zur deutschen Glaubensbewegung." Vol. 7. Stuttgart: Karl Gutbrod, 1935. Pp. 76-164.

Langewisch, Eva. Das teleologische Prinzip bei Carl Gustav Carus. Würzburg, 1927.

Lavater, Johann Caspar. Physiognomische Fragmente. Zur Beförderung der Menschenkenntniß und Menschenliebe. 4 vols. Leipzig and Winterthur, 1775-1778.

Le Sage, Georges Louis. "Lucrèce Newtonien." Nouveaux mémoires de l'Académie de Berlin. Année 1782. Berlin, 1784. Pp. 404ff.

Lieb, Fritz. Franz Baaders Jugendgeschichte. Munich, 1926.

Liedke, Herbert R. Literary Criticism and Romantic Theory in the Work of Achim von Arnim. "Columbia University Germanic Studies, New Series," No. 6. New York: Columbia University Press, 1937.

Loerke, Oskar. "Herders Weltgebäude." *Die neue Rundschau*, XLVI (1935), 561-593.

Lovejoy, Arthur O. The Great Chain of Being. A Study of the History of an Idea. The William James Lectures delivered at Harvard University, 1933. Cambridge, Mass., 1936.

Lubosch, Wilhelm. "Was verdankt die vergleichend-anatomische Wissenschaft den Arbeiten Goethes?" *Jahrbuch der Goethe-Gesellschaft*, VI (1919), 157-191.

Lucretius. De rerum natura. Lateinisch und Deutsch von Hermann Diels. Vol. 1: T. LVCRETI CARI DE RERUM NATURA. Vol. 2: LUKREZ VON DER NATUR. Berlin: Weidmannsche Buchhandlung, 1923 and 1924.
  Cf. G. Santayana.

Mahrholz, Werner. Literargeschichte und Literarwissenschaft. "Kröners Taschenausgabe." Vol. 88. Leipzig, 1932².

Mallon, Otto. Arnim-Bibliographie. Berlin, 1925.

Matschow, Conrad. "Aus der Geschichte des technischen Vereinswesens." *Forschungen und Fortschritte,* XII (1936), 347f.

Meißner, Paul. "Die geistesgeschichtlichen Grundlagen des englischen Literaturbarocks." *Forschungen und Fortschritte,* XI (1935), 435f.

Meißner, Paul. Die geistesgeschichtlichen Grundlagen des englischen Literaturbarocks. Munich: Hueber, 1934.

Merkel, Franz Rudolf. Der Naturphilosoph Gotthilf Heinrich Schubert und die deutsche Romantik. Strasbourg, 1912 (Enlarged edition. Munich: Beck, 1913).

Metzger, Wilhelm. Gesellschaft, Recht und Staat in der Ethik des deutschen Idealismus. Heidelberg, 1917.

Meyer, Adolf. "Goethes Naturerkenntnis. Ihre Voraussetzung in der Antike. Ihre Krönung durch Carus." *Jahrbuch des Freien Deutschen Hochstifts,* 1929. Pp. 196ff.

Meyer, Richard M. "Goethe als Naturforscher." *Euphorion,* I (1894), 26ff.

Moritz, Karl Philipp (editor). ΓΝΩΘΙ ΣΑΥΤΟΝ *oder* Magazin zur Erfahrungsseelenkunde als ein Lesebuch für Gelehrte und Ungelehrte. Berlin: August Mylius (1783-1793), 1805².

Müller, Adam. Vorlesungen über deutsche Wissenschaft und Literatur (1808). Edited by Artur Salz. Munich, 1920.

Müller, Adam. Die Lehre vom Gegensatz. Erstes Buch (no more published). Berlin: Realschulbuchhandlung, 1804.

Musäus, Johann Karl August (anon.). Physiognomische Reisen. Voran ein physiognomisch Tagebuch heftweis' herausgegeben. 2 vols. Altenburg, 1778-1779.

Nadler, Josef. Die Berliner Romantik 1800-1814. Ein Beitrag zur gemeinvölkischen Frage: Renaissance, Romantik, Restauration. Berlin, 1921.

Nasse, Friedrich (editor). *Zeitschrift für psychische Aerzte.* [Since 1820] Mit besonderer Berücksichtigung des Magnetismus. 5 vols. Leipzig, 1818-1822 (Superseded by *Zeitschrift für die Anthropologie).*

Neuburger, Max. Der Arzt Ernst Freiherr von Feuchtersleben. Vienna, 1906.

Neuburger, Max. Johann Christian Reil, Stuttgart. 1913.

Neuburger, Max (Schillers Beziehungen zur Medizin. Vienna, 1905). "Schiller's Relation to Medicine." Translated by E. B. Krumbhaar. Essays in the History of Medicine. Edited by Fielding H. Garrison. New York: Medical Life Press, 1930. Pp. 147-186.

Neuburger, Max. Die Wiener medizinische Schule im Vormärz. Vienna, 1921.

Neuburger, Max. Festschrift zur Feier seines 60. Geburtstages am 8. Dezember 1928 Max Neuburger gewidmet von Freunden, Kollegen und Schülern. Internationale Beiträge zur Geschichte der Medizin. Vienna, 1928.

Niendorf, Klüd von. Weltkörper sind Lebewesen. 11 pp. Hamburg 20: Johann Lüdemann, n.d.

Nohl, Johannes. "Franz von Baader, der Philosoph der Romantik." *Euphorion*, XIX (1912), 612-633.

Nordenskiöld, Eric (Biologins Historia. 3 vols. Stockholm, 1920-1924). The History of Biology. New York: Alfred A. Knopf, 1928.

Novalis.
    Cf. F. v. Hardenberg.

Oken (Ockenfuß), Lorenz. Lehrbuch der Naturphilosophie (1809. Enlarged edition. 1830³). [Extracted paragraphs, consecutively numbered in] Romantische Naturphilosophie. Edited by Christoph Bernoulli and Hans Kern. Jena: Eugen Diederichs, 1926. Pp. 1-31.

Oken (Ockenfuß), Lorenz. Idee sulla classificazione filosofica dei tre regni della natura esposte dal Professore Oken alla riunione dei naturalisti in Pisa nell' Ottobre 1839. Milan, 1840.

Oken (Ockenfuß), Lorenz. Über das Universum als Fortsetzung des Sinnessystems. Ein Pythagoräisches Fragment. Jena, 1808.

Olshausen, Waldemar. Friedrich von Hardenbergs Beziehungen zur Naturwissenschaft seiner Zeit. Leipzig, 1905.

Oppeln-Bronikowski, Friedrich von. David Ferdinand Koreff. Serapionsbruder, Magnetiseur, Geheimrat und Dichter. Der Lebensroman eines Vergessenen aus Urkunden zusammengestellt. Berlin and Leipzig: Gebrüder Paetel, 1928.

Ostwald, Wilhelm. "Johann Wilhelm Ritter" (1894). Abhandlungen und Vorträge allgemeinen Inhalts. Leipzig, 1904.

Ostwald, Wilhelm. "Das Problem der Zeit" (1898). Abhandlungen und Vorträge allgemeinen Inhalts. Leipzig, 1904.

Owen, Sir Richard. On the Archetypes and Homologies of the Vertebrate Skeleton. London, 1848.

Paine, Thomas. Age of Reason. Being an Investigation of True and Fabulous Theology (1794). New York: Wiley, n.d.

Pallister, William. Poems of Science. New York, 1931.

Paracelsus Bombastus von Hohenheim, Philippus Aureolus Theophrastus.

    Cf. F. Gundolf.

Peter, Karl. "Erscheinungsformen der Zweckmäßigkeit in der Organismenwelt." *Forschungen und Fortschritte,* XII (1936), 174f.

Petersen, Julius. "Das goldene Zeitalter bei den deutschen Romantikern." Die Ernte. Abhandlungen zur Literatur-Wissenschaft Franz Muncker zu seinem 70. Geburtstag. Edited by Fritz Strich and Hans Heinrich Borchardt. Halle, 1926. Pp. 117-176.

Petersen, Julius. Die Wesensbestimmung der deutschen Romantik. Leipzig, 1926.

Peuten, Franz. Johann Gottfried Rademacher. Seine Erfahrungsheillehre und fünf vergessene Arzneipflanzen aus ihrem Heilmittelschatze. "Arbeiten der deutsch-nordischen Gesellschaft für Geschichte der Medizin." Edited by Fritz Lejeune. Vol. 10. Greifswald, 1933.

Plath, Margarete. "Der Goethe-Schellingsche Plan eines philosophischen Naturgedichts." *Preußische Jahrbücher,* CVI (1901), 44-74.

Plotinus.

    Cf. P. F. Reiff, J. Sarauw.

Poetzsch, Albert. Studien zur frühromantischen Geschichtsauffassung. Leipzig, 1907.

Pope, Alexander. "An Essay on Man. Address'd to a Friend." Epistles to a Friend. London, 1733-1734.

Potter, George Reuben. "Mark Akenside, Prophet of Evolution." *Modern Philology,* XXIV (1926), 55-64.

Rademacher, Johann Gottfried.

    Cf. F. Peuten.

Reichenbach, Karl Freiherr von.

    Cf. J. Braid.

Reiff, Paul Friedrich. "Plotin und die deutsche Romantik." *Euphorion,* XIX (1912), 591ff.

Reil, Johann Christian. "Von der Lebenskraft." *Archiv für die Physiologie,* I (1795), 8-162. Halle (Gesammelte kleine physiologische Schriften. Vol. 1. Vienna, 1811. Pp. 1-135). ("Klassiker der Medizin." Vol. 2. Edited by Karl Friedrich Jakob Sudhoff. Leipzig, 1910).

Reil, Johann Christian (editor). *Archiv für die Physiologie.* 12 vols. Halle. 1795-1815 (Continued as *Deutsches Archiv für die Physiologie* and later as *Archiv für Anatomie und Physiologie*).

    Cf. M. Neuburger.

Renard, Georges. La Méthode scientifique de l'histoire littéraire. Paris: Alcan, 1900.

Ritschl, Otto. Die Causalbetrachtung in den Geisteswissenschaften. Bonn, 1901.

Ritter, Johann Wilhelm. Die Physik als Kunst. Ein Versuch die Tendenz der Physik aus ihrer Geschichte zu deuten. Munich, 1806. Cf. C. v. Klinckowstroem, W. Ostwald, J. Schiff.

Robinson, Crabb (anon.). "William Blake. Künstler, Dichter und religiöser Schwärmer." Translated by Dr. Julius. *Vaterländisches Museum*, II, 1 (1810), 107-131 (Retranslated by Mrs. Esdaile. *The Library*, July, 1914).

Robinson, Victor. The Story of Medicine. New York: Boni, 1931.

Rosenberg, Alfred. Der Mythus des XX. Jahrhunderts. Munich: Hoheneichen-Verlag (1930), 1936.

Ross, Colonel Sir Ronald. "Address before the Royal Institution on June 4th, 1920." *Notices of the Proceedings*, XXIII (1920-1922), 206-227.

Saenger, Werner. Goethe und Giordano Bruno. Ein Beitrag zur Geschichte der Goethischen Weltanschauung. "Germanische Studien." Vol. 91. Berlin, 1930.

Santayana, George. Three Philosophical Poets. Lucretius, Dante, and Goethe. Cambridge, Mass., 1910.

Sarauw, Julie. Der Einfluß Plotins auf Giordano Brunos *Degli Eroici Furori*. Ein Beitrag zur Philosophie der Renaissance. Jena, 1916.

Schelling, Friedrich Wilhelm Joseph von. "Bruno *oder* Über das göttliche und natürliche Prinzip der Dinge." Werke. Edited by Otto Weiß. Vol. 2. Leipzig, 1907.

Schelling, Friedrich Wilhelm Joseph von. "Gedichte und metrische Übersetzungen. Zum Theil aus dem Nachlaß." Sämmtliche Werke. First series. Vol. 10. Stuttgart: Cotta, 1861. Pp. 429ff.

Schelling, Friedrich Wilhelm Joseph von. "Epikurisch Glaubensbekenntnis Heinz Widerporstens" (1799). Satiren und Parodien. Edited by Andreas Müller. "DL. Reihe Romantik." Vol. 9. Leipzig: Reclam, 1935.

Schelling, Friedrich Wilhelm Joseph von. Philosophie. Edited by Otto Braun. "Deutsche Bibliothek." Vol. 127. Berlin, 1918.

Schelling, Friedrich Wilhelm Joseph von. Von der Weltseele. Eine Hypothese der höhern Physik zur Erklärung des allgemeinen Organismus. Hamburg: Perthes, 1798. Cf. M. Plath, G. Stefansky.

Schiff, Julius. "Goethes chemische Berater und Freunde." *Deutsche Rundschau*, CLI (1912), 450-466.

Schiff, Julius. "Naturwissenschaftliche Gleichnisse in Goethes Dichtungen, Briefen und literarischen Schriften." Goethes naturwissenschaftliches Denken und Wirken. Published by the editorial board of *Die Naturwissenschaften*. Berlin, 1932.

Schiff, Julius. "Die romantischen Naturforscher Ritter und Schubert und ihre Beziehungen zu Goethe." *Nord und Süd*, CLXXIV (1920), 295-305.

Schiller, Friedrich von. Sämmtliche Schriften. 15 vols. Edited by Karl Goedeke. Stuttgart: Cotta, 1867-1876.

Schiller, Friedrich von. Werke. 15 vols. Edited by Ludwig Bellermann. Second edition. Leipzig: Bibliographisches Institut, n.d.
    Cf. E. Cassirer ("Die Methodik des Idealismus in Schillers philosophischen Schriften." Idee und Gestalt), W. Deubel, J. Körner, M. Neuburger, F. Strich.

Schlagdenhauffen, Alfred. Frédéric Schlegel et son groupe. La Doctrine de l'Athenaeum (1798-1800). Strasbourg, 1934.

Schlegel, August Wilhelm. Vorlesungen über schöne Literatur und Kunst (1801-1804). Edited by Jakob Minor. "Deutsche Literatur-Denkmale des 18. und 19. Jahrhunderts." Vols. 17-19. Heilbronn, 1884.
    Cf. J. Körner.

Schlegel, Friedrich. Seine prosaischen Jugendschriften. Edited by Jakob Minor. Vienna, 1906².
    Cf. J. Körner, A. Schlagdenhauffen.

Schleiden, Matthias Jacob. Poetry of the Vegetable World. An exposition of the Science of Botany and its relation to man. Translated by Alphonso Wood. Cincinnati, 1853.

Schloz, Wilhelm. "Die Weltanschauung des germanischen Mythos." Vom Sinn des Mythos. Essays by Wilhelm Schloz and Wilhelm Laiblin. "Schriften zur deutschen Glaubensbewegung." Vol. 7. Stuttgart: Karl Gutbrod, 1935. Pp. 1-75.

Schmidt, Oscar. Göthe's Verhältnis zu den organischen Naturwissenschaften. Berlin, 1853.

Schubert, Gotthilf Heinrich. Geschichte der Seele (1830; 1850⁴). [Extracts in] Romantische Naturphilosophie. Edited by Christoph Bernoulli and Hans Kern. Jena: Eugen Diederichs, 1926. Pp. 110ff.

Schubert, Gotthilf Heinrich. Die Symbolik des Traumes (Bamberg, 1814). [Extracts in] Romantische Naturphilosophie. Edited by Christoph Bernoulli and Hans Kern. Jena: Eugen Diederichs, 1926.
    Cf. F. R. Merkel, J. Schiff.

Schweitzer, Albert. Kultur und Ethik. Kulturphilosophie. Zweiter Teil. Munich: Beck, 1923.

Seligmann, Siegfried. Die magischen Heil- und Schutzmittel aus der unbelebten Natur. Stuttgart, 1927.

Shakespeare, William.
    Cf. R. Beyersdorff.

Sigerist, Ernst. "Kultur und Krankheit." *Kyklos*. Jahrbuch des Instituts für Geschichte der Medizin an der Universität Leipzig. Vol. 1. Leipzig, 1928.

Skibniewski, Stephan Leo von.   Theologie der Mechanik. Paderborn, 1928.

Söding, Hans.   "Wirkt der Wuchsstoff unspezifisch?" *Forschungen und Fortschritte*, XI (1935), 439f.

Sömmering, Samuel Thomas.   Über das Organ der Seele. Königsberg, 1796.

Spenlé, Édouard.   Novalis. Essai sur l'idéalisme romantique en Allemagne. Paris, 1904.

Staël-Holstein, Anne Louise Germaine Baronne de.   De l'Allemagne. 3 vols. Paris, 1818[5].

Stefansky, Georg.   Das Wesen der Romantik. Kritische Studien zu ihrer Geschichte. Stuttgart, 1923.

Stefansky, Georg.   Das hellenisch-deutsche Weltbild. Einleitung in die Lebensgeschichte Schellings. Bonn, 1925.

Steffens, Henrich.
    Cf. E. Huesmann.

Steig, Reinhold.   Achim von Arnim und die ihm nahe standen. 3 vols. I: Clemens Brentano. II: Bettina. III: Brüder Grimm. Stuttgart and Berlin: Cotta, 1894-1913.

Stephan, Horst (editor).   [Introduction to] Herders Philosophie. Ausgewählte Denkmäler aus der Werdezeit der neuen deutschen Bildung. "Philosophische Bibliothek." Vol. 112. Leipzig: Felix Meiner, 1906.

Stokoe, Frank Woodyer.   German Influence in the English Romantic Period (1788-1818). Cambridge, Engl., 1926.

Stolberg-Stolberg, Friedrich Leopold Graf zu.   [Selections in] Der Göttinger Dichterbund. Vol. 3. Edited by August Sauer. "DNL." Vol. 50. Berlin and Stuttgart, 1893.

Strich, Fritz.   Deutsche Klassik und Romantik *oder* Vollendung und Unendlichkeit. Munich, 1928[3].

Strich, Fritz.   Die Mythologie in der deutschen Literatur von Klopstock bis Wagner. 2 vols. Halle: Niemeyer, 1910.

Strich, Fritz.   Schiller. Sein Leben und sein Werk. Berlin, 1927.

Sudhoff, Karl Friedrich Jakob.   100 Jahre deutscher Naturforscher-Versammlungen. Leipzig, 1922.

Thomas, Calvin.   "Poetry and Science." *The Open Court*, III (1889), 1730ff.

Thorndike. Lynn.   Science and Thought in the Fifteenth Century. Studies in the History of Medicine and Surgery. New York, 1929.

Treviranus, Gottfried Reinhold.   Die Erscheinungen und Gesetze des organischen Lebens (1831-1833). [Extracts in] Romantische Naturphilosophie. Edited by Christoph Bernoulli and Hans Kern. Jena: Eugen Diederichs, 1926. Pp. 282-300.

Troeltsch, Ernst. Der Historismus und seine Probleme. Tübingen, 1922.

Trömmer, Ernst. Hypnotismus und Suggestion. "Aus Natur und Geisteswelt." Vol. 199. Leipzig: Teubner, 1922[4].

Troxler, Ignatius Paul Vitalis. Blicke in das Wesen des Menschen (1812). [Extracts in] Romantische Naturphilosophie. Edited by Christoph Bernoulli and Hans Kern. Jena: Eugen Diederichs, 1926. Pp. 239-257.

Troxler, Ignatius Paul Vitalis. Metaphysik *oder* Naturlehre des menschlichen Erkennens (1828). [Extracts in] Romantische Naturphilosophie. Edited by Christoph Bernoulli and Hans Kern. Jena: Eugen Diederichs, 1926. Pp. 257-281.

Troxler, Ignatius Paul Vitalis. Über das Leben und sein Problem (1806). [Extracts in] Romantische Naturphilosophie. Edited by Christoph Bernoulli and Hans Kern. Jena: Eugen Diederichs, 1926. Pp. 232-239.

Unger, Rudolf. " 'Der bestirnte Himmel über mir . . .' Zur geistesgeschichtlichen Deutung eines Kantwortes" (1924). Aufsätze zur Literatur- und Geistesgeschichte. Berlin, 1929. Pp. 40-66.

Unger, Rudolf. "Zur Geschichte des Palingenesiegedankens im 18ten Jahrhundert." *Deutsche Vierteljahresschrift für Literaturwissenschaft,* II, 2 (1924), 257-274.

Unger, Rudolf. Herder, Novalis und Kleist. Studien über die Entwicklung des Todesproblems in Denken und Dichten vom Sturm und Drang zur Romantik. "Deutsche Forschungen." Vol. 9. Frankfort-on-Main, 1922.

Varnhagen von Ense, Karl August (editor). [Epilogue to] Denkwürdigkeiten des Philosophen und Arztes Johann Benjamin Erhard. Stuttgart, 1830.

Verweyen, Johannes Maria. Naturphilosophie. "Aus Natur und Geisteswelt." Vol. 491. Leipzig: Teubner, 1919[2].

Virchow, Rudolf. Goethe als Naturforscher. Berlin, 1861.

Vogt, Carl. Köhlerglaube und Wissenschaft. Gießen, 1855.
Cf. A. Wagner.

Wagner, Andreas. Naturwissenschaft und Bibel. Im Gegensatz zu dem Köhlerglauben des Herrn Carl Vogt. Stuttgart: S. G. Liesching, 1855.

Wagner, Johann Jakob. Dichterschule. Ulm, 1840.

Wagner, Johann Jakob. Elementarlehre der Zeit und Raumgrößen (by Dr. Friedrich Buchwald. Erlangen, 1818). Ulm, 1851[2].

Wagner, Johann Jakob. Religion, Wissenschaft, Kunst und Staat in ihren gegenseitigen Verhältnissen betrachtet. Erlangen, 1819.

Wagner, Rudolph. Weten en Gelooven. Inzonderheid ten Opzigte van de Toekomst der Zielen. Translated from the German (Über Wissen und Glauben). Utrecht, 1855.

Walzel, Oskar. Deutsche Romantik. "Aus Natur und Geisteswelt." Vol. 232. Leipzig: Teubner, 1908.

Walzel, Oskar. Deutsche Romantik. II: Die Dichtung. "Aus Natur und Geisteswelt." Vol. 233. Leipzig: Teubner, 1918[4].

Walzel, Oskar. "Wesensfragen deutscher Romantik." *Jahrbuch des Freien Deutschen Hochstifts*, 1929. Pp. 253ff.

    Cf. J. G. v. Goethe.

Wäsche, Erwin. Carl Gustav Carus und die romantische Weltanschauung. Cologne, 1933.

Weinert, Hans. "Die neuesten Ergebnisse über die Abstammung des Menschen." *Forschungen und Fortschritte*, XII (1936), 401f.

Wenzl, Aloys. "Das Leib-Seeleproblem." *Forschungen und Fortschritte*, XII (1936), 393f.

Weygand, Conrad. "Gestalt und molekularer Aufbau der Kohlenstoff-Verbindungen." *Forschungen und Fortschritte*, XII (1936), 409f.

Wieland, Christoph Martin. Gesammelte Schriften. Erste Abteilung: Werke. Edited by the Prussian Academy of Sciences. Berlin, 1909ff.

Wieland, Christoph Martin. Sämmtliche Werke. Leipzig: Göschen, 1853-1858.

    Cf. E. Ermatinger.

Wilhelmsmeyer, Hans. "Der Totalitätsgedanke als Erkenntnisgrundsatz und als Menschheitsideal von Herder zu den Romantikern." *Euphorion*, XXXIV (1933), 211-243.

Wilson, Mona. The Life of William Blake. New York: Ballou, 1932.

Windelband, Wilhelm. Die Lehren vom Zufall. Berlin, 1870.

Wohlbold, Hans. "Die Naturerkenntnis im Weltbild Goethes." *Jahrbuch der Goethe-Gesellschaft*, XIII (1927), 1-46.

Ziegler, Theobald. Die geistigen und sozialen Strömungen Deutschlands im 19. und 20. Jahrhundert bis zum Beginn des Weltkrieges. Berlin (1916), 1921[7].

Zimmer, Heinrich. "Zur Symbolik der Hindutempel." *Forschungen und Fortschritte*, XIII (1937), 135f.

INDEX

INDEX